MACHINE LEARNING, NEURAL AND STATISTICAL CLASSIFICATION

ELLIS HORWOOD SERIES IN ARTIFICIAL INTELLIGENCE
Series Editor: Professor JOHN CAMPBELL, Department of Computer Science,
University College London

MACHINE LEARNING, NEURAL AND STATISTICAL CLASSIFICATION

Edited by

D. MICHIE, D.J. SPIEGELHALTER and C.C. TAYLOR

ELLIS HORWOOD

NEW YORK   LONDON   TORONTO   SYDNEY   TOKYO   SINGAPORE

First published 1994 by
Ellis Horwood Limited
Campus 400, Maylands Avenue
Hemel Hempstead
Hertfordshire, HP2 7EZ
and
Market Cross House, Cooper Street
Chichester
West Sussex, PO19 1EB, England
A division of
Simon & Schuster International Group

Printed and bound in Great Britain by
Bookcraft, Midsomer Norton

Library of Congress Cataloging-in-Publication Data

Machine learning, neural and statistical classification / editors, D.
  Michie, D.J. Spiegelhalter, C.C. Taylor.
      p.   cm.—(Artificial intelligence)
    Includes bibliographical references and index.
    ISBN 0-13-106360-X
    1. Machine learning.   2. Neural networks (Computer science)
  3. Classification—Statistical methods.   I. Michie, Donald.
  II. Spiegelhalter, D. J.   III. Taylor, C. C., 1959–   .   IV. Series:
  Artificial intelligence (Englewood Cliffs, N.J.)
  Q325.5.M324   1994
  001′.012—dc20   94–7096
                                                             CIP

British Library Cataloguing-in-Publication Data

A catalogue record for this book is available from
the British Library

ISBN 0-13-106360-X

  2   3   4   5   98   97   96   95

Contents

Preface

This volume is based on the "StatLog" project, funded in October, 1990 under the ESPRIT programme of the European Community, and concluded in June, 1993. A year or two earlier, Brian Ripley (then at Strathclyde University) had introduced a new topic to his Department by inviting one of us (D.M.) to give a course on "Artificial Intelligence Data Analysis". This set off the train of events which led to StatLog.

Reza Nakhaeizadeh, of Daimler-Benz, Germany, was overall Project Director, and Bob Henery, of Strathclyde University, U.K., was Technical Director. Together they co-ordinated the efforts of 6 academic and 6 industrial laboratories. Appendix C gives a full list of those who contributed. In addition to the experimental results, the project had the desirable effect of encouraging collaboration, overdue in this field, between workers in different disciplines. Statisticians, AI workers in machine learning, and neural net specialists came together in new patterns of interaction. We offer this book as a source of useful information for workers in medicine, agriculture, industry, finance and other applied studies. We also hope that it may contribute to the spread of similar collaborations in the scientific community at large.

As Editors, our task has been to create a unified volume from the work of many authors. Where gaps would otherwise have undermined the book's balance or completeness, we invited leading colleagues from outside StatLog's perimeter to contribute material specifically to bridge these gaps, notably in the reviews of new methods and issues contained in Chapters 12 and 13. Thematic unity and the avoidance of duplication occasioned much "cut-and-paste" across chapters as well as several iterations and revisions of the entire work. StatLog authors bore all this with exceptional patience and good cheer. We take this offer of expressing our appreciation.

It is also a pleasure to acknowledge the assistance of the publishers in the preparation of this volume. The text was typeset in LaTeX on a SUN Sparcstation IPC and printed on a SPARCprinter. Errors remain our responsibility, and we encourage readers to notify us of any they detect.

Donald Michie	David Spiegelhalter	Charles Taylor
Emeritus Professor	MRC Biostatistics Unit	Dept of Statistics
of Machine Intelligence	Institute of Public Health	University of Leeds
University of Edinburgh	Cambridge	

1

Introduction

D. Michie (1), D. J. Spiegelhalter (2) and C. C. Taylor (3)
(1) University of Strathclyde, (2) MRC Biostatistics Unit, Cambridge[1] and (3) University of Leeds

1.1 INTRODUCTION

The aim of this book is to provide an up-to-date review of different approaches to classification, compare their performance on a wide range of challenging data-sets, and draw conclusions on their applicability to realistic industrial problems.

Before describing the contents, we first need to define what we mean by classification, give some background to the different perspectives on the task, and introduce the European Community StatLog project whose results form the basis for this book.

1.2 CLASSIFICATION

The task of *classification* occurs in a wide range of human activity. At its broadest, the term could cover any context in which some decision or forecast is made on the basis of currently available information, and a *classification procedure* is then some formal method for repeatedly making such judgments in new situations. In this book we shall consider a more restricted interpretation. We shall assume that the problem concerns the construction of a procedure that will be applied to a continuing sequence of *cases*, in which each new case must be assigned to one of a set of pre-defined *classes* on the basis of observed *attributes* or *features*. The construction of a classification procedure from a set of data for which the true classes are known has also been variously termed *pattern recognition, discrimination,* or *supervised learning* (in order to distinguish it from *unsupervised* learning or *clustering* in which the classes are inferred from the data).

Contexts in which a classification task is fundamental include, for example, mechanical procedures for sorting letters on the basis of machine-read postcodes, assigning individuals to credit status on the basis of financial and other personal information, and the preliminary diagnosis of a patient's disease in order to select immediate treatment while awaiting definitive test results. In fact, some of the most urgent problems arising in science, industry

---

[1] *Address for correspondence*: MRC Biostatistics Unit, Institute of Public Health, University Forvie Site, Robinson Way, Cambridge CB2 2SR, U.K.

and commerce can be regarded as classification or decision problems using complex and often very extensive data.

We note that many other topics come under the broad heading of classification. These include problems of control, which is briefly covered in Chapter 13.

1.3   PERSPECTIVES ON CLASSIFICATION

As the book's title suggests, a wide variety of approaches has been taken towards this task. Three main historical strands of research can be identified: *statistical*, *machine learning* and *neural network*. These have largely involved different professional and academic groups, and emphasised different issues. All groups have, however, had some objectives in common. They have all attempted to derive procedures that would be able:

- to equal, if not exceed, a human decision-maker's behaviour, but have the advantage of consistency and, to a variable extent, explicitness,
- to handle a wide variety of problems and, given enough data, to be extremely general,
- to be used in practical settings with proven success.

1.3.1   Statistical approaches

Two main phases of work on classification can be identified within the statistical community. The first, "classical" phase concentrated on derivatives of Fisher's early work on linear discrimination. The second, "modern" phase exploits more flexible classes of models, many of which attempt to provide an estimate of the joint distribution of the features within each class, which can in turn provide a classification rule.

Statistical approaches are generally characterised by having an explicit underlying probability model, which provides a probability of being in each class rather than simply a classification. In addition, it is usually assumed that the techniques will be used by statisticians, and hence some human intervention is assumed with regard to variable selection and transformation, and overall structuring of the problem.

1.3.2   Machine learning

Machine Learning is generally taken to encompass automatic computing procedures based on logical or binary operations, that learn a task from a series of examples. Here we are just concerned with classification, and it is arguable what should come under the Machine Learning umbrella. Attention has focussed on decision-tree approaches, in which classification results from a sequence of logical steps. These are capable of representing the most complex problem given sufficient data (but this may mean an enormous amount!). Other techniques, such as genetic algorithms and inductive logic procedures (ILP), are currently under active development and in principle would allow us to deal with more general types of data, including cases where the number and type of attributes may vary, and where additional layers of learning are superimposed, with hierarchical structure of attributes and classes and so on.

Machine Learning aims to generate classifying expressions simple enough to be understood easily by the human. They must mimic human reasoning sufficiently to provide insight into the decision process. Like statistical approaches, background knowledge may be exploited in development, but operation is assumed without human intervention.

1.3.3 Neural networks

The field of Neural Networks has arisen from diverse sources, ranging from the fascination of mankind with understanding and emulating the human brain, to broader issues of copying human abilities such as speech and the use of language, to the practical commercial, scientific, and engineering disciplines of pattern recognition, modelling, and prediction. The pursuit of technology is a strong driving force for researchers, both in academia and industry, in many fields of science and engineering. In neural networks, as in Machine Learning, the excitement of technological progress is supplemented by the challenge of reproducing intelligence itself.

A broad class of techniques can come under this heading, but, generally, neural networks consist of layers of interconnected nodes, each node producing a non-linear function of its input. The input to a node may come from other nodes or directly from the input data. Also, some nodes are identified with the output of the network. The complete network therefore represents a very complex set of interdependencies which may incorporate any degree of nonlinearity, allowing very general functions to be modelled.

In the simplest networks, the output from one node is fed into another node in such a way as to propagate "messages" through layers of interconnecting nodes. More complex behaviour may be modelled by networks in which the final output nodes are connected with earlier nodes, and then the system has the characteristics of a highly nonlinear system with feedback. It has been argued that neural networks mirror to a certain extent the behaviour of networks of neurons in the brain.

Neural network approaches combine the complexity of some of the statistical techniques with the machine learning objective of imitating human intelligence: however, this is done at a more "unconscious" level and hence there is no accompanying ability to make learned concepts transparent to the user.

1.3.4 Conclusions

The three broad approaches outlined above form the basis of the grouping of procedures used in this book. The correspondence between type of technique and professional background is inexact: for example, techniques that use decision trees have been developed in parallel both within the machine learning community, motivated by psychological research or knowledge acquisition for expert systems, and within the statistical profession as a response to the perceived limitations of classical discrimination techniques based on linear functions. Similarly strong parallels may be drawn between advanced regression techniques developed in statistics, and neural network models with a background in psychology, computer science and artificial intelligence.

It is the aim of this book to put *all* methods to the test of experiment, and to give an objective assessment of their strengths and weaknesses. Techniques have been grouped according to the above categories. It is not always straightforward to select a group: for example some procedures can be considered as a development from linear regression, but have strong affinity to neural networks. When deciding on a group for a specific technique, we have attempted to ignore its professional pedigree and classify according to its essential nature.

1.4   THE STATLOG PROJECT

The fragmentation amongst different disciplines has almost certainly hindered communication and progress. The StatLog project [2] was designed to break down these divisions by selecting classification procedures regardless of historical pedigree, testing them on large-scale and commercially important problems, and hence to determine to what extent the various techniques met the needs of industry. This depends critically on a clear understanding of:

1. the aims of each classification/decision procedure;
2. the class of problems for which it is most suited;
3. measures of performance or benchmarks to monitor the success of the method in a particular application.

About 20 procedures were considered for about 20 datasets, so that results were obtained from around $20 \times 20 = 400$ large scale experiments. The set of methods to be considered was pruned after early experiments, using criteria developed for multi-input (problems), many treatments (algorithms) and multiple criteria experiments. A management hierarchy led by Daimler-Benz controlled the full project.

The objectives of the Project were threefold:

1. to provide critical performance measurements on available classification procedures;
2. to indicate the nature and scope of further development which particular methods require to meet the expectations of industrial users;
3. to indicate the most promising avenues of development for the commercially immature approaches.

1.4.1   Quality control

The Project laid down strict guidelines for the testing procedure. First an agreed data format was established, algorithms were "deposited" at one site, with appropriate instructions; this version would be used in the case of any future dispute. Each dataset was then divided into a training set and a testing set, and any parameters in an algorithm could be "tuned" or estimated **only** by reference to the training set. Once a rule had been determined, it was then applied to the test data. This procedure was validated at another site by another (more naïve) user for each dataset in the first phase of the Project. This ensured that the guidelines for parameter selection were not violated, and also gave some information on the ease-of-use for a non-expert in the domain. Unfortunately, these guidelines were not followed for the radial basis function (RBF) algorithm which for some datasets determined the number of centres and locations with reference to the test set, so these results should be viewed with some caution. However, it is thought that the conclusions will be unaffected.

1.4.2   Caution in the interpretations of comparisons

There are some strong caveats that must be made concerning comparisons between techniques in a project such as this.

First, the exercise is necessarily somewhat contrived. In any real application, there should be an iterative process in which the constructor of the classifier interacts with the

---

[2]ESPRIT project 5170. Comparative testing and evaluation of statistical and logical learning algorithms on large-scale applications to classification, prediction and control

expert in the domain, gaining understanding of the problem and any limitations in the data, and receiving feedback as to the quality of preliminary investigations. In contrast, StatLog datasets were simply distributed and used as test cases for a wide variety of techniques, each applied in a somewhat automatic fashion.

Second, the results obtained by applying a technique to a test problem depend on three factors:

1. the essential quality and appropriateness of the technique;
2. the actual implementation of the technique as a computer program ;
3. the skill of the user in coaxing the best out of the technique.

In Appendix B we have described the implementations used for each technique, and the availability of more advanced versions if appropriate. However, it is extremely difficult to control adequately the variations in the background and ability of all the experimenters in StatLog, particularly with regard to data analysis and facility in "tuning" procedures to give their best. Individual techniques may, therefore, have suffered from poor implementation and use, but we hope that there is no overall bias against whole classes of procedure.

1.5 THE STRUCTURE OF THIS VOLUME

The present text has been produced by a variety of authors, from widely differing backgrounds, but with the common aim of making the results of the StatLog project accessible to a wide range of workers in the fields of machine learning, statistics and neural networks, and to help the cross-fertilisation of ideas between these groups.

After discussing the general classification problem in Chapter 2, the next 4 chapters detail the methods that have been investigated, divided up according to broad headings of Classical statistics, modern statistical techniques, Decision Trees and Rules, and Neural Networks. The next part of the book concerns the evaluation experiments, and includes chapters on evaluation criteria, a survey of previous comparative studies, a description of the data-sets and the results for the different methods, and an analysis of the results which explores the characteristics of data-sets that make them suitable for particular approaches: we might call this "machine learning on machine learning". The conclusions concerning the experiments are summarised in Chapter 11.

The final chapters of the book broaden the interpretation of the basic classification problem. The fundamental theme of representing knowledge using different formalisms is discussed with relation to constructing classification techniques, followed by a summary of current approaches to dynamic control now arising from a rephrasing of the problem in terms of classification and learning.

2

Classification

R. J. Henery
University of Strathclyde[1]

2.1 DEFINITION OF CLASSIFICATION

Classification has two distinct meanings. We may be given a set of observations with the aim of establishing the existence of classes or clusters in the data. Or we may know for certain that there are so many classes, and the aim is to establish a rule whereby we can classify a new observation into one of the existing classes. The former type is known as Unsupervised Learning (or Clustering), the latter as Supervised Learning. In this book when we use the term classification, we are talking of Supervised Learning. In the statistical literature, Supervised Learning is usually, but not always, referred to as discrimination, by which is meant the establishing of the classification rule from given correctly classified data.

The existence of correctly classified data presupposes that someone (the Supervisor) is able to classify without error, so the question naturally arises: why is it necessary to replace this exact classification by some approximation?

2.1.1 Rationale

There are many reasons why we may wish to set up a classification procedure, and some of these are discussed later in relation to the actual datasets used in this book. Here we outline possible reasons for the examples in Section 1.2.

1. Mechanical classification procedures may be much faster: for example, postal code reading machines may be able to sort the majority of letters, leaving the difficult cases to human readers.

2. A mail order firm must take a decision on the granting of credit purely on the basis of information supplied in the application form: human operators may well have biases, *i.e.* may make decisions on irrelevant information and may turn away good customers.

---

[1]*Address for correspondence*: Department of Statistics and Modelling Science, University of Strathclyde, Glasgow G1 1XH, U.K.

3. In the medical field, we may wish to avoid the surgery that would be the only sure way of making an exact diagnosis, so we ask if a reliable diagnosis can be made on purely external symptoms.

4. The Supervisor (refered to above) may be the verdict of history, as in meteorology or stock-exchange transaction or investment and loan decisions. In this case the issue is one of forecasting.

2.1.2 Issues

There are also many issues of concern to the would-be classifier. We list below a few of these.

*   Accuracy. There is the reliability of the rule, usually represented by the proportion of correct classifications, although it may be that some errors are more serious than others, and it may be important to control the error rate for some key class.

*   Speed. In some circumstances, the speed of the classifier is a major issue. A classifier that is 90% accurate may be preferred over one that is 95% accurate if it is 100 times faster in testing (and such differences in time-scales are not uncommon in neural networks for example). Such considerations would be important for the automatic reading of postal codes, or automatic fault detection of items on a production line for example.

*   Comprehensibility. If it is a human operator that must apply the classification procedure, the procedure must be easily understood else mistakes will be made in applying the rule. It is important also, that human operators believe the system. An oft-quoted example is the Three-Mile Island case, where the automatic devices correctly recommended a shutdown, but this recommendation was not acted upon by the human operators who did not believe that the recommendation was well founded. A similar story applies to the Chernobyl disaster.

*   Time to Learn. Especially in a rapidly changing environment, it may be necessary to learn a classification rule quickly, or make adjustments to an existing rule in real time. "Quickly" might imply also that we need only a small number of observations to establish our rule.

At one extreme, consider the naïve 1-nearest neighbour rule, in which the training set is searched for the 'nearest' (in a defined sense) previous example, whose class is then assumed for the new case. This is very fast to learn (no time at all!), but is very slow in practice if all the data are used (although if you have a massively parallel computer you might speed up the method considerably). At the other extreme, there are cases where it is very useful to have a quick-and-dirty method, possibly for eyeball checking of data, or for providing a quick cross-checking on the results of another procedure. For example, a bank manager might know that the simple rule-of-thumb "only give credit to applicants who already have a bank account" is a fairly reliable rule. If she notices that the new assistant (or the new automated procedure) is mostly giving credit to customers who do **not** have a bank account, she would probably wish to check that the new assistant (or new procedure) was operating correctly.

2.1.3   Class definitions

An important question, that is improperly understood in many studies of classification, is the nature of the classes and the way that they are defined. We can distinguish three common cases, only the first leading to what statisticians would term classification:

1.   Classes correspond to labels for different populations: membership of the various populations is not in question. For example, dogs and cats form quite separate classes or populations, and it is known, with certainty, whether an animal is a dog or a cat (or neither). Membership of a class or population is determined by an independent authority (the *Supervisor*), the allocation to a class being determined independently of any particular attributes or variables.

2.   Classes result from a prediction problem. Here class is essentially an outcome that must be predicted from a knowledge of the attributes. In statistical terms, the class is a random variable. A typical example is in the prediction of interest rates. Frequently the question is put: will interest rates rise (class=1) or not (class=0).

3.   Classes are pre-defined by a partition of the sample space, *i.e.* of the attributes themselves. We may say that class is a function of the attributes. Thus a manufactured item may be classed as faulty if some attributes are outside predetermined limits, and not faulty otherwise. There is a rule that has already classified the data from the attributes: the problem is to create a rule that mimics the actual rule as closely as possible. Many credit datasets are of this type.

In practice, datasets may be mixtures of these types, or may be somewhere in between.

2.1.4   Accuracy

On the question of accuracy, we should always bear in mind that accuracy as measured on the training set and accuracy as measured on unseen data (the test set) are often very different. Indeed it is not uncommon, especially in Machine Learning applications, for the training set to be perfectly fitted, but performance on the test set to be very disappointing. Usually, it is the accuracy on the unseen data, when the true classification is unknown, that is of practical importance. The generally accepted method for estimating this is to use the given data, in which we assume that all class memberships are known, as follows. Firstly, we use a substantial proportion (the training set) of the given data to train the procedure. This rule is then tested on the remaining data (the test set), and the results compared with the known classifications. The proportion correct in the test set is an unbiased estimate of the accuracy of the rule provided that the training set is randomly sampled from the given data.

2.2   EXAMPLES OF CLASSIFIERS

To illustrate the basic types of classifiers, we will use the well-known Iris dataset, which is given, in full, in Kendall & Stuart (1983). There are three varieties of Iris: Setosa, Versicolor and Virginica. The length and breadth of both petal and sepal were measured on 50 flowers of each variety. The original problem is to classify a new Iris flower into one of these three types on the basis of the four attributes (petal and sepal length and width). To keep this example simple, however, we will look for a classification rule by which the varieties can be distinguished purely on the basis of the two measurements on Petal Length and Width. We have available fifty pairs of measurements of each variety from which to learn the classification rule.

2.2.1 Fisher's linear discriminants

This is one of the oldest classification procedures, and is the most commonly implemented in computer packages. The idea is to divide sample space by a series of lines in two dimensions, planes in 3-D and, generally hyperplanes in many dimensions. The line dividing two classes is drawn to bisect the line joining the centres of those classes, the direction of the line is determined by the shape of the clusters of points. For example, to differentiate between Versicolor and Virginica, the following rule is applied:

- If Petal Width $< 3.272 - 0.3254 \times$ Petal Length, then Versicolor.
- If Petal Width $> 3.272 - 0.3254 \times$ Petal Length, then Virginica.

Fisher's linear discriminants applied to the Iris data are shown in Figure 2.1. Six of the observations would be misclassified.

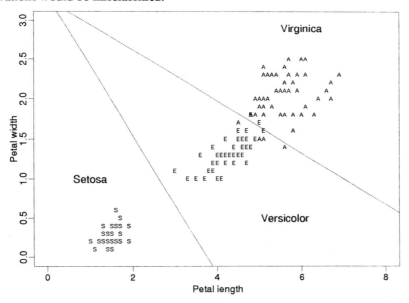

Fig. 2.1: Classification by linear discriminants: Iris data.

2.2.2 Decision tree and Rule-based methods

One class of classification procedures is based on recursive partitioning of the sample space. Space is divided into boxes, and at each stage in the procedure, each box is examined to see if it may be split into two boxes, the split usually being parallel to the coordinate axes. An example for the Iris data follows.

- If Petal Length < 2.65 then Setosa.
- If Petal Length > 4.95 then Virginica.

- If 2.65 < Petal Length < 4.95 then :

    if Petal Width < 1.65 then Versicolor;

    if Petal Width > 1.65 then Virginica.

The resulting partition is shown in Figure 2.2. Note that this classification rule has three mis-classifications.

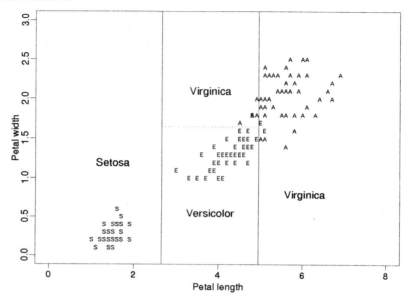

Fig. 2.2: Classification by decision tree: Iris data.

Weiss & Kapouleas (1989) give an alternative classification rule for the Iris data that is very directly related to Figure 2.2. Their rule can be obtained from Figure 2.2 by continuing the dotted line to the left, and can be stated thus:

- If Petal Length < 2.65 then Setosa.
- If Petal Length > 4.95 or Petal Width > 1.65 then Virginica.
- Otherwise Versicolor.

Notice that this rule, while equivalent to the rule illustrated in Figure 2.2, is stated more concisely, and this formulation may be preferred for this reason. Notice also that the rule is ambiguous if Petal Length < 2.65 and Petal Width > 1.65. The quoted rules may be made unambiguous by applying them in the given order, and they are then just a re-statement of the previous decision tree. The rule discussed here is an instance of a rule-based method: such methods have very close links with decision trees.

2.2.3   k-Nearest-Neighbour

We illustrate this technique on the Iris data. Suppose a new Iris is to be classified. The idea is that it is most likely to be near to observations from its own proper population. So we look at the five (say) nearest observations from all previously recorded Irises, and classify the observation according to the most frequent class among its neighbours. In Figure 2.3, the new observation is marked by a +, and the 5 nearest observations lie within the **circle** centred on the +. The apparent elliptical shape is due to the differing horizontal and vertical scales, but the proper scaling of the observations is a major difficulty of this method.

This is illustrated in Figure 2.3 , where an observation centred at + would be classified as Virginica since it has 4 Virginica among its 5 nearest neighbours.

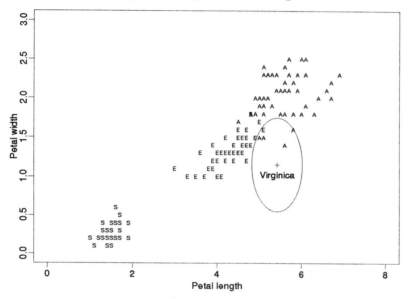

Fig. 2.3: Classification by 5-Nearest-Neighbours: Iris data.

2.3 CHOICE OF VARIABLES

As we have just pointed out in relation to k-nearest neighbour, it may be necessary to reduce the weight attached to some variables by suitable scaling. At one extreme, we might remove some variables altogether if they do not contribute usefully to the discrimination, although this is not always easy to decide. There are established procedures (for example, forward stepwise selection) for removing unnecessary variables in linear discriminants, but, for large datasets, the performance of linear discriminants is not seriously affected by including such unnecessary variables. In contrast, the presence of irrelevant variables is always a problem with k-nearest neighbour, regardless of dataset size.

2.3.1 Transformations and combinations of variables

Often problems can be simplified by a judicious transformation of variables. With statistical procedures, the aim is usually to transform the attributes so that their marginal density is approximately normal, usually by applying a monotonic transformation of the power law type. Monotonic transformations do not affect the Machine Learning methods, but they can benefit by combining variables, for example by taking ratios or differences of key variables. Background knowledge of the problem is of help in determining what transformation or combination to use. For example, in the Iris data, the product of the variables Petal Length and Petal Width gives a single attribute which has the dimensions of area, and might be labelled as Petal Area. It so happens that a decision rule based on the single variable Petal Area is a good classifier with only four errors:

- If Petal Area < 2.0 then Setosa.
- If 2.0 < Petal Area < 7.4 then Virginica.
- If Petal Area > 7.4 then Virginica.

This tree, while it has one more error than the decision tree quoted earlier, might be preferred on the grounds of conceptual simplicity as it involves only one "concept", namely Petal Area. Also, one less arbitrary constant need be remembered (*i.e.* there is one less node or cut-point in the decision trees).

2.4   CLASSIFICATION OF CLASSIFICATION PROCEDURES

The above three procedures (linear discrimination, decision-tree and rule-based, k-nearest neighbour) are prototypes for three types of classification procedure. Not surprisingly, they have been refined and extended, but they still represent the major strands in current classification practice and research. The 23 procedures investigated in this book can be directly linked to one or other of the above. However, within this book the methods have been grouped around the more traditional headings of classical statistics, modern statistical techniques, Machine Learning and neural networks. Chapters 3 – 6, respectively, are devoted to each of these. For some methods, the classification is rather abitrary.

2.4.1   Extensions to linear discrimination

We can include in this group those procedures that start from linear combinations of the measurements, even if these combinations are subsequently subjected to some non-linear transformation. There are 7 procedures of this type: Linear discriminants; logistic discriminants; quadratic discriminants; multi-layer perceptron (backprop and cascade); DIPOL92; and projection pursuit. Note that this group consists of statistical and neural network (specifically multilayer perceptron) methods only.

2.4.2   Decision trees and Rule-based methods

This is the most numerous group in the book with 9 procedures: NewID; AC^2; Cal5; CN2; C4.5; CART; IndCART; Bayes Tree; and ITrule (see Chapter 5).

2.4.3   Density estimates

This group is a little less homogeneous, but the 7 members have this in common: the procedure is intimately linked with the estimation of the local probability density at each point in sample space. The density estimate group contains: k-nearest neighbour; radial basis functions; Naive Bayes; Polytrees; Kohonen self-organising net; LVQ; and the kernel density method. This group also contains only statistical and neural net methods.

2.5   A GENERAL STRUCTURE FOR CLASSIFICATION PROBLEMS

There are three essential components to a classification problem.

1.   The relative frequency with which the classes occur in the population of interest, expressed formally as the *prior* probability distribution.

2. An implicit or explicit criterion for separating the classes: we may think of an underlying input/output relation that uses observed attributes to distinguish a random individual from each class.

3. The cost associated with making a wrong classification.

Most techniques implicitly confound components and, for example, produce a classification rule that is derived conditional on a particular prior distribution and cannot easily be adapted to a change in class frequency. However, in theory each of these components may be individually studied and then the results formally combined into a classification rule. We shall describe this development below.

2.5.1 Prior probabilities and the Default rule

We need to introduce some notation. Let the classes be denoted $A_i, i = 1, \ldots, q$, and let the prior probability π_i for the class A_i be:

$$\pi_i = p(A_i)$$

It is always possible to use the no-data rule: *classify any new observation as class A_k, irrespective of the attributes of the example.* This *no-data* or *default* rule may even be adopted in practice if the cost of gathering the data is too high. Thus, banks may give credit to all their established customers for the sake of good customer relations: here the cost of gathering the data is the risk of losing customers. The default rule relies only on knowledge of the prior probabilities, and clearly the decision rule that has the greatest chance of success is to allocate every new observation to the most frequent class. However, if some classification errors are more serious than others we adopt the minimum risk (least expected cost) rule, and the class k is that with the least expected cost (see below).

2.5.2 Separating classes

Suppose we are able to observe data x on an individual, and that we know the probability distribution of x within each class A_i to be $P(x|A_i)$. Then for any two classes A_i, A_j the *likelihood ratio* $P(x|A_i)/P(x|A_j)$ provides the theoretical optimal form for discriminating the classes on the basis of data x. The majority of techniques featured in this book can be thought of as implicitly or explicitly deriving an approximate form for this likelihood ratio.

2.5.3 Misclassification costs

Suppose the cost of misclassifying a class A_i object as class A_j is $c(i, j)$. Decisions should be based on the principle that the total cost of misclassifications should be minimised: for a new observation this means minimising the expected cost of misclassification.

Let us first consider the expected cost of applying the default decision rule: *allocate all new observations to the class A_d*, using suffix d as label for the decision class. When decision A_d is made for all new examples, a cost of $c(i, d)$ is incurred for class A_i examples and these occur with probability π_i. So the expected cost C_d of making decision A_d is:

$$C_d = \sum_i \pi_i c(i, d)$$

The Bayes minimum cost rule chooses that class that has the lowest expected cost. To see the relation between the minimum error and minimum cost rules, suppose the cost of misclassifications to be the same for all errors and zero when a class is correctly identified, *i.e.* suppose that $c(i, j) = c$ for $i \neq j$ and $c(i, j) = 0$ for $i = j$.

Then the expected cost is

$$C_d = \sum_i \pi_i c(i, d) = \sum_{i \neq d} \pi_i c = c \sum_{i \neq d} \pi_i = c(1 - \pi_d)$$

and the minimum cost rule is to allocate to the class with the greatest prior probability.

Misclassification costs are very difficult to obtain in practice. Even in situations where it is very clear that there are very great inequalities in the sizes of the possible penalties or rewards for making the wrong or right decision, it is often very difficult to quantify them. Typically they may vary from individual to individual, as in the case of applications for credit of varying amounts in widely differing circumstances. In one dataset we have assumed the misclassification costs to be the same for all individuals. (In practice, credit-granting companies must assess the potential costs for each applicant, and in this case the classification algorithm usually delivers an assessment of probabilities, and the decision is left to the human operator.)

2.6 BAYES RULE GIVEN DATA x

We can now see how the three components introduced above may be combined into a classification procedure.

When we are given information x about an individual, the situation is, in principle, unchanged from the no-data situation. The difference is that all probabilities must now be interpreted as conditional on the data x. Again, the decision rule with least probability of error is to allocate to the class with the highest probability of occurrence, but now the relevant probability is the conditional probability $p(A_i|x)$ of class A_i given the data x:

$$p(A_i|x) = \text{Prob}(\text{class} A_i \text{ given } x)$$

If we wish to use a minimum cost rule, we must first calculate the expected costs of the various decisions *conditional on the given information* x.

Now, when decision A_d is made for examples with attributes x, a cost of $c(i, d)$ is incurred for class A_i examples and these occur with probability $p(A_i|x)$. As the probabilities $p(A_i|x)$ depend on x, so too will the decision rule. So too will the expected cost $C_d(x)$ of making decision A_d:

$$C_d(x) = \sum_i p(A_i|x)c(i, d)$$

In the special case of equal misclassification costs, the minimum cost rule is to allocate to the class with the greatest *posterior probability*.

When Bayes theorem is used to calculate the conditional probabilities $p(A_i|x)$ for the classes, we refer to them as the *posterior probabilities* of the classes. Then the posterior probabilities $p(A_i|x)$ are calculated from a knowledge of the prior probabilities π_i and the conditional probabilities $P(x|A_i)$ of the data for each class A_i. Thus, for class A_i suppose that the probability of observing data x is $P(x|A_i)$. Bayes theorem gives the posterior probability $p(A_i|x)$ for class A_i as:

$$p(A_i|x) = \pi_i P(x|A_i) / \sum_j \pi_j P(x|A_j)$$

The divisor is common to all classes, so we may use the fact that $p(A_i|x)$ is proportional to $\pi_i P(x|A_i)$. The class A_d with minimum expected cost (minimum risk) is therefore that for which

$$\sum_i \pi_i c(i, d) P(x|A_i)$$

is a minimum.

Assuming now that the attributes have continuous distributions, the probabilities above become probability densities. Suppose that observations drawn from population A_i have probability density function $f_i(x) = f(x \mid A_i)$ and that the prior probability that an observation belongs to class A_i is π_i. Then Bayes' theorem computes the probability that an observation x belongs to class A_i as

$$p(A_i|x) = \pi_i f_i(x) / \sum_j \pi_j f_j(x)$$

A classification rule then assigns x to the class A_d with maximal *a posteriori* probability given x:

$$p(A_d|x) = \max_i p(A_i|x)$$

As before, the class A_d with minimum expected cost (minimum risk) is that for which

$$\sum_i \pi_i c(i, d) f_i(x)$$

is a minimum.

Consider the problem of discriminating between just two classes A_i and A_j. Then assuming as before that $c(i, i) = c(j, j) = 0$, we should allocate to class i if

$$\pi_j c(i, j) f_j(x) < \pi_i c(j, i) f_i(x)$$

or equivalently

$$\frac{f_i(x)}{f_j(x)} > \frac{\pi_j}{\pi_i} \frac{c(i, j)}{c(j, i)}$$

which shows the pivotal role of the likelihood ratio, which must be greater than the ratio of prior probabilities times the relative costs of the errors. We note the symmetry in the above expression: changes in costs can be compensated in changes in prior to keep constant the threshold that defines the classification rule - this facility is exploited in some techniques, although for more than two groups this property only exists under restrictive assumptions (see Breiman *et al.*, page 112).

2.6.1 Bayes rule in statistics

Rather than deriving $p(A_i|x)$ via Bayes theorem, we could also use the empirical frequency version of Bayes rule, which, in practice, would require prohibitively large amounts of data. However, in principle, the procedure is to gather together all examples in the training set that have the same attributes (exactly) as the given example, and to find class proportions $p(A_i|x)$ among these examples. The minimum error rule is to allocate to the class A_d with highest posterior probability.

Unless the number of attributes is very small and the training dataset very large, it will be necessary to use approximations to estimate the posterior class probabilities. For example, one way of finding an approximate Bayes rule would be to use not just examples with attributes matching exactly those of the given example, but to use examples that were near the given example in some sense. The minimum error decision rule would be to allocate to the most frequent class among these matching examples. Partitioning algorithms, and decision trees in particular, divide up attribute space into regions of self-similarity: all data within a given box are treated as similar, and posterior class probabilities are constant within the box.

Decision rules based on Bayes rules are optimal - no other rule has lower expected error rate, or lower expected misclassification costs. Although unattainable in practice, they provide the logical basis for all statistical algorithms. They are unattainable because they assume complete information is known about the statistical distributions in each class. Statistical procedures try to supply the missing distributional information in a variety of ways, but there are two main lines: *parametric* and *non-parametric*. Parametric methods make assumptions about the nature of the distributions (commonly it is assumed that the distributions are Gaussian), and the problem is reduced to estimating the parameters of the distributions (means and variances in the case of Gaussians). Non-parametric methods make no assumptions about the specific distributions involved, and are therefore described, perhaps more accurately, as *distribution-free*.

2.7   REFERENCE TEXTS

There are several good textbooks that we can recommend. Weiss & Kulikowski (1991) give an overall view of classification methods in a text that is probably the most accessible to the Machine Learning community. Hand (1981), Lachenbruch & Mickey (1975) and Kendall *et al.* (1983) give the statistical approach. Breiman *et al.* (1984) describe CART, which is a partitioning algorithm developed by statisticians, and Silverman (1986) discusses density estimation methods. For neural net approaches, the book by Hertz *et al.* (1991) is probably the most comprehensive and reliable. Two excellent texts on pattern recognition are those of Fukunaga (1990) , who gives a thorough treatment of classification problems, and Devijver & Kittler (1982) who concentrate on the k-nearest neighbour approach. A thorough treatment of statistical procedures is given in McLachlan (1992), who also mentions the more important alternative approaches. A recent text dealing with pattern recognition from a variety of perspectives is Schalkoff (1992).

3

Classical Statistical Methods

J. M. O. Mitchell
University of Strathclyde[1]

3.1 INTRODUCTION

This chapter provides an introduction to the classical statistical discrimination techniques and is intended for the non-statistical reader. It begins with Fisher's *linear discriminant*, which requires no probability assumptions, and then introduces methods based on maximum likelihood. These are linear discriminant, *quadratic discriminant* and *logistic discriminant*. Next there is a brief section on Bayes' rules, which indicates how each of the methods can be adapted to deal with unequal prior probabilities and unequal misclassification costs. Finally there is an illustrative example showing the result of applying all three methods to a two class and two attribute problem. For full details of the statistical theory involved the reader should consult a statistical text book, for example (Anderson, 1958).

The training set will consist of examples drawn from q known classes. (Often q will be 2.) The values of p numerically-valued attributes will be known for each of n examples, and these form the *attribute vector* $\mathbf{x} = (x_1, x_2, \ldots, x_p)$. It should be noted that these methods require numerical attribute vectors, and also require that none of the values is missing. Where an attribute is categorical with two values, an indicator is used, *i.e.* an attribute which takes the value 1 for one category, and 0 for the other. Where there are more than two categorical values, indicators are normally set up for each of the values. However there is then redundancy among these new attributes and the normal procedure is to drop one of them. In this way a single categorical attribute with j values is replaced by $j-1$ attributes whose values are 0 or 1. Where the attribute values are ordered, it may be acceptable to use a single numerical-valued attribute. Care has to be taken that the numbers used reflect the spacing of the categories in an appropriate fashion.

3.2 LINEAR DISCRIMINANTS

There are two quite different justifications for using Fisher's linear discriminant rule: the first, as given by Fisher (1936), is that it maximises the separation between the classes in

---

[1]*Address for correspondence*: Department of Statistics and Modelling Science, University of Strathclyde, Glasgow G1 1XH, U.K.

a least-squares sense; the second is by Maximum Likelihood (see Section 3.2.3). We will give a brief outline of these approaches. For a proof that they arrive at the same solution, we refer the reader to McLachlan (1992).

3.2.1 Linear discriminants by least squares

Fisher's linear discriminant (Fisher, 1936) is an empirical method for classification based purely on attribute vectors. A hyperplane (line in two dimensions, plane in three dimensions, etc.) in the p-dimensional attribute space is chosen to separate the known classes as well as possible. Points are classified according to the side of the hyperplane that they fall on. For example, see Figure 3.1, which illustrates discrimination between two "digits", with the continuous line as the discriminating hyperplane between the two populations.

This procedure is also equivalent to a t-test or F-test for a significant difference between the mean discriminants for the two samples, the t-statistic or F-statistic being constructed to have the largest possible value.

More precisely, in the case of two classes, let $\bar{x}$, $\bar{x}_1$, $\bar{x}_2$ be respectively the means of the attribute vectors overall and for the two classes. Suppose that we are given a set of coefficients $a_1, ..., a_p$ and let us call the particular linear combination of attributes

$$g(\mathbf{x}) = \sum a_j x_j$$

the *discriminant between the classes*. We wish the discriminants for the two classes to differ as much as possible, and one measure for this is the difference $g(\bar{x}_1) - g(\bar{x}_2)$ between the mean discriminants for the two classes divided by the standard deviation of the discriminants, s_g say, giving the following measure of discrimination:

$$\frac{g(\bar{x}_1) - g(\bar{x}_2)}{s_g}$$

This measure of discrimination is related to an estimate of misclassification error based on the assumption of a multivariate normal distribution for $g(\mathbf{x})$ (note that this is a weaker assumption than saying that $\mathbf{x}$ has a normal distribution). For the sake of argument, we set the dividing line between the two classes at the midpoint between the two class means. Then we may estimate the probability of misclassification for one class as the probability that the normal random variable $g(\mathbf{x})$ for that class is on the wrong side of the dividing line, *i.e.* the wrong side of

$$\frac{g(\bar{x}_1) + g(\bar{x}_2)}{2}$$

and this is easily seen to be

$$\Phi\left(\frac{g(\bar{x}_1) - g(\bar{x}_2)}{2s_g}\right)$$

where we assume, without loss of generality, that $g(\bar{x}_1) - g(\bar{x}_2)$ is negative. If the classes are not of equal sizes, or if, as is very frequently the case, the variance of $g(\mathbf{x})$ is not the same for the two classes, the dividing line is best drawn at some point other than the midpoint.

Rather than use the simple measure quoted above, it is more convenient algebraically to use an equivalent measure defined in terms of sums of squared deviations, as in analysis of variance. The *sum of squares* of $g(\mathbf{x})$ *within class* A_i is

$$\sum (g(\mathbf{x}) - g(\bar{\mathbf{x}}_i))^2,$$

the sum being over the examples in class A_i. The *pooled sum of squares within classes*, v say, is the sum of these quantities for the two classes (this is the quantity that would give us a standard deviation s_g). The *total sum of squares* of $g(\mathbf{x})$ is $\sum (g(\mathbf{x}) - g(\bar{\mathbf{x}}))^2 = t$ say, where this last sum is now over both classes. By subtraction, the *pooled sum of squares between classes* is $t - v$, and this last quantity is proportional to $(g(\bar{\mathbf{x}}_1) - g(\bar{\mathbf{x}}_2))^2$.

In terms of the F-test for the significance of the difference $g(\bar{\mathbf{x}}_1) - g(\bar{\mathbf{x}}_2)$, we would calculate the F-statistic

$$F = \frac{(t-v)/1}{v/(N-2)}$$

Clearly maximising the F-ratio statistic is equivalent to maximising the ratio t/v, so the coefficients a_j, $j = 1, \ldots, p$ may be chosen to maximise the ratio t/v. This maximisation problem may be solved analytically, giving an explicit solution for the coefficients a_i. There is however an arbitrary multiplicative constant in the solution, and the usual practice is to normalise the a_j in some way so that the solution is uniquely determined. Often one coefficient is taken to be unity (so avoiding a multiplication). However the detail of this need not concern us here.

To justify the "least squares" of the title for this section, note that we may choose the arbitrary multiplicative constant so that the separation $g(\bar{\mathbf{x}}_1) - g(\bar{\mathbf{x}}_2)$ between the class mean discriminants is equal to some predetermined value (say unity). Maximising the F-ratio is now equivalent to minimising the total sum of squares v. Put this way, the problem is identical to a regression of *class* (treated numerically) on the attributes, the dependent variable *class* being zero for one class and unity for the other.

The main point about this method is that it is a *linear* function of the attributes that is used to carry out the classification. This often works well, but it is easy to see that it may work badly if a linear separator is not appropriate. This could happen for example if the data for one class formed a tight cluster and the the values for the other class were widely spread around it. However the coordinate system used is of no importance. Equivalent results will be obtained after any linear transformation of the coordinates.

A practical complication is that for the algorithm to work the pooled sample covariance matrix must be invertible. The *covariance matrix* for a dataset with n_i examples from class A_i, is

$$S_i = \frac{1}{n_i - 1} X^T X - \bar{\mathbf{x}}^T \bar{x},$$

where X is the $n_i \times p$ matrix of attribute values, and $\bar{\mathbf{x}}$ is the p-dimensional row-vector of attribute means. The *pooled covariance matrix* S is $\sum (n_i - 1) S_i / (n - q)$ where the summation is over all the classes, and the divisor $n - q$ is chosen to make the pooled covariance matrix unbiased. For invertibility the attributes must be linearly independent, which means that no attribute may be an exact linear combination of other attributes. In order to achieve this, some attributes may have to be dropped. Moreover no attribute can be constant within each class. Of course an attribute which is constant within each class but not overall may be an excellent discriminator and is likely to be utilised in decision tree algorithms. However it will cause the linear discriminant algorithm to fail. This situation can be treated by adding a small positive constant to the corresponding diagonal element of the pooled covariance matrix, or by adding random noise to the attribute before applying the algorithm.

In order to deal with the case of more than two classes Fisher (1938) suggested the use of *canonical variates*. First a linear combination of the attributes is chosen to minimise the ratio of the pooled within class sum of squares to the total sum of squares. Then further linear functions are found to improve the discrimination. (The coefficients in these functions are the eigenvectors corresponding to the non-zero eigenvalues of a certain matrix.) In general there will be $\min(q-1, p)$ canonical variates. It may turn out that only a few of the canonical variates are important. Then an observation can be assigned to the class whose centroid is closest in the subspace defined by these variates. It is especially useful when the class means are ordered, or lie along a simple curve in attribute-space. In the simplest case, the class means lie along a straight line. This is the case for the head injury data (see Section 9.4.1), for example, and, in general, arises when the classes are ordered in some sense. In this book, this procedure was not used as a classifier, but rather in a qualitative sense to give some measure of reduced dimensionality in attribute space. Since this technique can also be used as a basis for explaining differences in mean vectors as in Analysis of Variance, the procedure may be called *manova*, standing for Multivariate Analysis of Variance.

3.2.2 Special case of two classes

The linear discriminant procedure is particularly easy to program when there are just two classes, for then the Fisher discriminant problem is equivalent to a multiple regression problem, with the attributes being used to predict the class value which is treated as a numerical-valued variable. The class values are converted to numerical values: for example, class A_1 is given the value 0 and class A_2 is given the value 1. A standard multiple regression package is then used to predict the class value. If the two classes are equiprobable, the discriminating hyperplane bisects the line joining the class centroids. Otherwise, the discriminating hyperplane is closer to the less frequent class. The formulae are most easily derived by considering the multiple regression predictor as a single attribute that is to be used as a one-dimensional discriminant, and then applying the formulae of the following section. The procedure is simple, but the details cannot be expressed simply. See Ripley (1993) for the explicit connection between discrimination and regression.

3.2.3 Linear discriminants by maximum likelihood

The justification of the other statistical algorithms depends on the consideration of probability distributions, and the linear discriminant procedure itself has a justification of this kind. It is assumed that the attribute vectors for examples of class A_i are independent and follow a certain probability distribution with probability density function (pdf) f_i. A new point with attribute vector $\mathbf{x}$ is then assigned to that class for which the probability density function $f_i(\mathbf{x})$ is greatest. This is a *maximum likelihood* method. A frequently made assumption is that the distributions are *normal* (or *Gaussian*) with different means but the same covariance matrix. The probability density function of the normal distribution is

$$\frac{1}{\sqrt{|2\pi\Sigma|}} \exp\left(-\frac{1}{2}(\mathbf{x}-\mu)^T \Sigma^{-1}(\mathbf{x}-\mu)\right), \tag{3.1}$$

where μ is a p-dimensional vector denoting the (theoretical) mean for a class and Σ, the (theoretical) covariance matrix, is a $p \times p$ (necessarily positive definite) matrix. The (sample) covariance matrix that we saw earlier is the sample analogue of this covariance matrix, which is best thought of as a set of coefficients in the pdf or a set of parameters for the distribution. This means that the points for the class are distributed in a cluster centered at μ of ellipsoidal shape described by Σ. Each cluster has the same orientation and spread though their means will of course be different. (It should be noted that there is in theory no absolute boundary for the clusters but the contours for the probability density function have ellipsoidal shape. In practice occurrences of examples outside a certain ellipsoid will be extremely rare.) In this case it can be shown that the boundary separating two classes, defined by equality of the two pdfs, is indeed a hyperplane and it passes through the mid-point of the two centres. Its equation is

$$\mathbf{x}^T \Sigma^{-1}(\mu_1 - \mu_2) - \frac{1}{2}(\mu_1 + \mu_2)^T \Sigma^{-1}(\mu_1 - \mu_2) = 0, \qquad (3.2)$$

where μ_i denotes the population mean for class A_i. However in classification the exact distribution is usually not known, and it becomes necessary to estimate the parameters for the distributions. With two classes, if the sample means are substituted for μ_i and the pooled sample covariance matrix for Σ, then Fisher's linear discriminant is obtained. With more than two classes, this method does not in general give the same results as Fisher's discriminant.

3.2.4   More than two classes

When there are more than two classes, it is no longer possible to use a single linear discriminant score to separate the classes. The simplest procedure is to calculate a linear discriminant for each class, this discriminant being just the logarithm of the estimated probability density function for the appropriate class, with constant terms dropped. Sample values are substituted for population values where these are unknown (this gives the "plug-in" estimates). Where the prior class proportions are unknown, they would be estimated by the relative frequencies in the training set. Similarly, the sample means and pooled covariance matrix are substituted for the population means and covariance matrix.

Suppose the prior probability of class A_i is π_i, and that $f_i(x)$ is the probability density of x in class A_i, and is the normal density given in Equation (3.1). The joint probability of observing class A_i and attribute x is $\pi_i f_i(x)$ and the logarithm of the probability of observing class A_i and attribute $\mathbf{x}$ is

$$\log \pi_i + \mathbf{x}^T \Sigma^{-1} \mu_i - \frac{1}{2}\mu_i^T \Sigma^{-1} \mu_i$$

to within an additive constant. So the coefficients β_i are given by the coefficients of $\mathbf{x}$

$$\beta_i = \Sigma^{-1}\mu_i$$

and the additive constant α_i by

$$\alpha_i = \log \pi_i - \frac{1}{2}\mu_i^T \Sigma^{-1} \mu_i$$

though these can be simplified by subtracting the coefficients for the last class.

The above formulae are stated in terms of the (generally unknown) population parameters Σ, μ_i and π_i. To obtain the corresponding "plug-in" formulae, substitute the corresponding sample estimators: S for Σ; $\bar{x}_i$ for μ_i; and p_i for π_i, where p_i is the sample proportion of class A_i examples.

3.3   QUADRATIC DISCRIMINANT

Quadratic discrimination is similar to linear discrimination, but the boundary between two discrimination regions is now allowed to be a quadratic surface. When the assumption of equal covariance matrices is dropped, then in the maximum likelihood argument with normal distributions a quadratic surface (for example, ellipsoid, hyperboloid, etc.) is obtained. This type of discrimination can deal with classifications where the set of attribute values for one class to some extent surrounds that for another. Clarke *et al.* (1979) find that the quadratic discriminant procedure is robust to small departures from normality and that heavy kurtosis (heavier tailed distributions than gaussian) does not substantially reduce accuracy. However, the number of parameters to be estimated becomes $qp(p+1)/2$, and the difference between the variances would need to be considerable to justify the use of this method, especially for small or moderate sized datasets (Marks & Dunn, 1974). Occasionally, differences in the covariances are of scale only and some simplification may occur (Kendall *et al.*, 1983) . Linear discriminant is thought to be still effective if the departure from equality of covariances is small (Gilbert, 1969). Some aspects of quadratic dependence may be included in the linear or logistic form (see below) by adjoining new attributes that are quadratic functions of the given attributes.

3.3.1   Quadratic discriminant - programming details

The quadratic discriminant function is most simply defined as the logarithm of the appropriate probability density function, so that one quadratic discriminant is calculated for each class. The procedure used is to take the logarithm of the probability density function and to substitute the sample means and covariance matrices in place of the population values, giving the so-called "plug-in" estimates. Taking the logarithm of Equation (3.1), and allowing for differing prior class probabilities π_i, we obtain

$$\log \pi_i f_i(x) = \log(\pi_i) - \frac{1}{2} \log(|\Sigma_i|) - \frac{1}{2}(\mathbf{x} - \mu_i)^T \Sigma_i^{-1}(\mathbf{x} - \mu_i)$$

as the quadratic discriminant for class A_i. Here it is understood that the suffix i refers to the sample of values from class A_i.

In classification, the quadratic discriminant is calculated for each class and the class with the largest discriminant is chosen. To find the a posteriori class probabilities explicitly, the exponential is taken of the discriminant and the resulting quantities normalised to sum to unity (see Section 2.6). Thus the posterior class probabilities $P(A_i|\mathbf{x})$ are given by

$$P(A_i|\mathbf{x}) = \exp[\log(\pi_i) - \frac{1}{2} \log(|\Sigma_i|) - \frac{1}{2}(\mathbf{x} - \mu_i)^T \Sigma_i^{-1}(\mathbf{x} - \mu_i)]$$

apart from a normalising factor.

If there is a cost matrix, then, no matter the number of classes, the simplest procedure is to calculate the class probabilities $P(A_i|\mathbf{x})$ and associated expected costs explicitly, using the formulae of Section 2.6. The most frequent problem with quadratic discriminants is caused when some attribute has zero variance in one class, for then the covariance matrix cannot be inverted. One way of avoiding this problem is to add a small positive constant term to the diagonal terms in the covariance matrix (this corresponds to adding random noise to the attributes). Another way, adopted in our own implementation, is to use some combination of the class covariance and the pooled covariance.

Once again, the above formulae are stated in terms of the unknown population parameters Σ_i, μ_i and π_i. To obtain the corresponding "plug-in" formulae, substitute the corresponding sample estimators: S_i for Σ_i; $\bar{x}_i$ for μ_i; and p_i for π_i, where p_i is the sample proportion of class A_i examples.

Many statistical packages allow for quadratic discrimination (for example, MINITAB has an option for quadratic discrimination, SAS also does quadratic discrimination).

3.3.2 Regularisation and smoothed estimates

The main problem with quadratic discriminants is the large number of parameters that need to be estimated and the resulting large variance of the estimated discriminants. A related problem is the presence of zero or near zero eigenvalues of the sample covariance matrices. Attempts to alleviate this problem are known as regularisation methods, and the most practically useful of these was put forward by Friedman (1989), who proposed a compromise between linear and quadratic discriminants via a two-parameter family of estimates. One parameter controls the smoothing of the class covariance matrix estimates. The smoothed estimate of the class i covariance matrix is

$$(1 - \delta_i)S_i + \delta_i S$$

where S_i is the class i sample covariance matrix and S is the pooled covariance matrix. When δ_i is zero, there is no smoothing and the estimated class i covariance matrix is just the i'th sample covariance matrix S_i. When the δ_i are unity, all classes have the same covariance matrix, namely the pooled covariance matrix S. Friedman (1989) makes the value of δ_i smaller for classes with larger numbers. For the i'th sample with n_i observations:

$$\delta_i = \delta(N - q)/\{\delta(N - q) + (1 - \delta)(n_i - 1)\}$$

where $N = n_1 + n_2 + .. + n_q$.

The other parameter λ is a (small) constant term that is added to the diagonals of the covariance matrices: this is done to make the covariance matrix non-singular, and also has the effect of smoothing out the covariance matrices. As we have already mentioned in connection with linear discriminants, any singularity of the covariance matrix will cause problems, and as there is now one covariance matrix for each class the likelihood of such a problem is much greater, especially for the classes with small sample sizes.

This two-parameter family of procedures is described by Friedman (1989) as "regularised discriminant analysis". Various simple procedures are included as special cases: ordinary linear discriminants ($\delta = 1, \lambda = 0$); quadratic discriminants ($\delta = 0, \lambda = 0$); and the values $\delta = 1, \lambda = 1$ correspond to a minimum Euclidean distance rule.

This type of regularisation has been incorporated in the Strathclyde version of *Quadisc*. Very little extra programming effort is required. However, it is up to the user, by trial and error, to choose the values of δ and λ. Friedman (1989) gives various shortcut methods for reducing the amount of computation.

3.3.3 Choice of regularisation parameters

The default values of $\delta = 0$ and $\lambda = 0$ were adopted for the majority of StatLog datasets, the philosophy being to keep the procedure "pure" quadratic.

The exceptions were those cases where a covariance matrix was not invertible. Non-default values were used for the head injury dataset (λ=0.05) and the DNA dataset (δ=0.3

approx.). In practice, great improvements in the performance of quadratic discriminants may result from the use of regularisation, especially in the smaller datasets.

3.4   LOGISTIC DISCRIMINANT

Exactly as in Section 3.2, logistic regression operates by choosing a hyperplane to separate the classes as well as possible, but the criterion for a good separation is changed. Fisher's linear discriminants optimises a quadratic cost function whereas in logistic discrimination it is a conditional likelihood that is maximised. However, in practice, there is often very little difference between the two, and the linear discriminants provide good starting values for the logistic. Logistic discrimination is identical, in theory, to linear discrimination for normal distributions with equal covariances, and also for independent binary attributes, so the greatest differences between the two are to be expected when we are far from these two cases, for example when the attributes have very non-normal distributions with very dissimilar covariances.

The method is only partially parametric, as the actual pdfs for the classes are not modelled, but rather the ratios between them.

Specifically, the logarithms of the prior odds π_1/π_2 times the ratios of the probability density functions for the classes are modelled as linear functions of the attributes. Thus, for two classes,

$$\log \frac{\pi_1 f_1(\mathbf{x})}{\pi_2 f_2(\mathbf{x})} = \alpha + \beta'\mathbf{x},$$

where α and the p-dimensional vector β are the parameters of the model that are to be estimated. The case of normal distributions with equal covariance is a special case of this, for which the parameters are functions of the prior probabilities, the class means and the common covariance matrix. However the model covers other cases too, such as that where the attributes are independent with values 0 or 1. One of the attractions is that the discriminant scale covers all real numbers. A large positive value indicates that class A_1 is likely, while a large negative value indicates that class A_2 is likely.

In practice the parameters are estimated by maximum *conditional* likelihood. The model implies that, given attribute values $\mathbf{x}$, the conditional class probabilities for classes A_1 and A_2 take the forms:

$$P(A_1|\mathbf{x}) = \frac{\exp(\alpha + \beta'\mathbf{x})}{1 + \exp(\alpha + \beta'\mathbf{x})}$$

$$P(A_2|\mathbf{x}) = \frac{1}{1 + \exp(\alpha + \beta'\mathbf{x})}$$

respectively.

Given independent samples from the two classes, the conditional likelihood for the parameters α and β is defined to be

$$L(\alpha,\beta) = \prod_{\{A_1 \text{sample}\}} P(A_1|\mathbf{x}) \prod_{\{A_2 \text{sample}\}} P(A_2|\mathbf{x})$$

and the parameter estimates are the values that maximise this likelihood. They are found by iterative methods, as proposed by Cox (1966) and Day & Kerridge (1967). Logistic models belong to the class of generalised linear models (GLMs), which generalise the use of linear regression models to deal with non-normal random variables, and in particular to deal with binomial variables. In this context, the binomial variable is an indicator variable that counts whether an example is class A_1 or not. When there are more than two classes, one class is taken as a reference class, and there are $q-1$ sets of parameters for the odds of each class relative to the reference class. To discuss this case, we abbreviate the notation for $\alpha + \beta'\mathbf{x}$ to the simpler $\beta'\mathbf{x}$. For the remainder of this section, therefore, $\mathbf{x}$ is a $(p+1)$-dimensional vector with leading term unity, and the leading term in β corresponds to the constant α.

Again, the parameters are estimated by maximum conditional likelihood. Given attribute values $\mathbf{x}$, the conditional class probability for class A_i, where $i \neq q$, and the conditional class probability for A_q take the forms:

$$P(A_i|\mathbf{x}) = \frac{\exp(\beta_i'\mathbf{x})}{\sum_{j=1,\ldots,q} \exp(\beta_j'\mathbf{x})}$$

$$P(A_q|\mathbf{x}) = \frac{1}{\sum_{j=1,\ldots,q} \exp(\beta_j'\mathbf{x})}$$

respectively. Given independent samples from the q classes, the conditional likelihood for the parameters β_i is defined to be

$$L(\beta_1, ..., \beta_{q-1}) = \prod_{\{A_1 \text{sample}\}} P(A_1|\mathbf{x}) \prod_{\{A_2 \text{sample}\}} P(A_2|\mathbf{x}) \ldots \prod_{\{A_q \text{sample}\}} P(A_q|\mathbf{x})$$

Once again, the parameter estimates are the values that maximise this likelihood.

In the basic form of the algorithm an example is assigned to the class for which the posterior is greatest if that is greater than 0, or to the reference class if all posteriors are negative.

More complicated models can be accommodated by adding transformations of the given attributes, for example products of pairs of attributes. As mentioned in Section 3.1, when categorical attributes with r (> 2) values occur, it will generally be necessary to convert them into $r-1$ binary attributes before using the algorithm, especially if the categories are not ordered. Anderson (1984) points out that it may be appropriate to include transformations or products of the attributes in the linear function, but for large datasets this may involve much computation. See McLachlan (1992) for useful hints. One way to increase complexity of model, without sacrificing intelligibility, is to add parameters in a *hierarchical* fashion, and there are then links with *graphical models* and *Polytrees*.

3.4.1 Logistic discriminant - programming details

Most statistics packages can deal with linear discriminant analysis for two classes. SYSTAT has, in addition, a version of logistic regression capable of handling problems with more than two classes. If a package has only binary logistic regression (*i.e.* can only deal with two classes), Begg & Gray (1984) suggest an approximate procedure whereby classes are all compared to a reference class by means of logistic regressions, and the results are then combined. The approximation is fairly good in practice according to Begg & Gray (1984).

Many statistical packages (GLIM, Splus, Genstat) now include a generalised linear model (GLM) function, enabling logistic regression to be programmed easily, in two or three lines of code.   The procedure is to define an indicator variable for class A_1 occurrences. The indicator variable is then declared to be a "binomial" variable with the "logit" link function, and generalised regression performed on the attributes. We used the package Splus for this purpose. This is fine for two classes, and has the merit of requiring little extra programming effort. For more than two classes, the complexity of the problem increases substantially, and, although it is technically still possible to use GLM procedures, the programming effort is substantially greater and much less efficient.

The maximum likelihood solution can be found via a Newton-Raphson iterative procedure, as it is quite easy to write down the necessary derivatives of the likelihood (or, equivalently, the log-likelihood). The simplest starting procedure is to set the β_i coefficients to zero except for the leading coefficients (α_i) which are set to the logarithms of the numbers in the various classes: *i.e.* $\alpha_i = \log n_i$, where n_i is the number of class A_i examples. This ensures that the values of β_i are those of the linear discriminant after the first iteration. Of course, an alternative would be to use the linear discriminant parameters as starting values.   In subsequent iterations, the step size may occasionally have to be reduced, but usually the procedure converges in about 10 iterations. This is the procedure we adopted where possible.

However, each iteration requires a separate calculation of the Hessian, and it is here that the bulk of the computational work is required. The Hessian is a square matrix with $(q-1)(p+1)$ rows, and each term requires a summation over all the observations in the whole dataset (although some saving can by achieved using the symmetries of the Hessian). Thus there are of order $q^2 p^2 N$ computations required to find the Hessian matrix at each iteration. In the KL digits dataset (see Section 9.3.2), for example, $q = 10$, $p = 40$, and $N = 9000$, so the number of operations is of order 10^9 in each iteration. In such cases, it is preferable to use a purely numerical search procedure, or, as we did when the Newton-Raphson procedure was too time-consuming, to use a method based on an approximate Hessian. The approximation uses the fact that the Hessian for the zero'th order iteration is simply a replicate of the design matrix (cf. covariance matrix) used by the linear discriminant rule. This zero-order Hessian is used for all iterations. In situations where there is little difference between the linear and logistic parameters, the approximation is very good and convergence is fairly fast (although a few more iterations are generally required).   However, in the more interesting case that the linear and logistic parameters are very different, convergence using this procedure is very slow, and it may still be quite far from convergence after, say, 100 iterations. We generally stopped after 50 iterations: although the parameter values were generally not stable, the predicted classes for the data were reasonably stable, so the predictive power of the resulting rule may not be seriously affected. This aspect of logistic regression has not been explored.

The final program used for the trials reported in this book was coded in Fortran, since the Splus procedure had prohibitive memory requirements.   Availablility of the Fortran code can be found in Appendix B.

3.5   BAYES' RULES

Methods based on likelihood ratios can be adapted to cover the case of unequal mis-classification costs and/or unequal prior probabilities. Let the prior probabilities be $\{\pi_i : i \in 1, \ldots, q\}$, and let $c(i, j)$ denote the cost incurred by classifying an example of Class A_i into class A_j.

As in Section 2.6, the minimum expected cost solution is to assign the data x to class A_d chosen to minimise $\sum_i \pi_i c(i, d) f(\mathbf{x}|A_i)$. In the case of two classes the hyperplane in linear discrimination has the equation

$$\mathbf{x}'\Sigma^{-1}(\mu_1 - \mu_2) - \frac{1}{2}(\mu_1 + \mu_2)'(\mu_1 - \mu_2) = \log\left(\frac{\pi_2}{\pi_1}\frac{c(2, 1)}{c(1, 2)}\right),$$

the right hand side replacing 0 that we had in Equation (3.2).

When there are more than two classes, the simplest procedure is to calculate the class probabilities $P(A_i|\mathbf{x})$ and associated expected costs explicitly, using the formulae of Section 2.6.

3.6   EXAMPLE

As illustration of the differences between the linear, quadratic and logistic discriminants, we consider a subset of the Karhunen-Loeve version of the digits data later studied in this book. For simplicity, we consider only the digits '1' and '2', and to differentiate between them we use only the first two attributes (40 are available, so this is a substantial reduction in potential information). The full sample of 900 points for each digit was used to estimate the parameters of the discriminants, although only a subset of 200 points for each digit is plotted in Figure 3.1 as much of the detail is obscured when the full set is plotted.

3.6.1   Linear discriminant

Also shown in Figure 3.1 are the sample centres of gravity (marked by a cross). Because there are equal numbers in the samples, the linear discriminant boundary (shown on the diagram by a full line) intersects the line joining the centres of gravity at its mid-point. Any new point is classified as a '1' if it lies below the line *i.e.* is on the same side as the centre of the '1's). In the diagram, there are 18 '2's below the line, so they would be misclassified.

3.6.2   Logistic discriminant

The logistic discriminant procedure usually starts with the linear discriminant line and then adjusts the slope and intersect to maximise the conditional likelihood, arriving at the dashed line of the diagram. Essentially, the line is shifted towards the centre of the '1's so as to reduce the number of misclassified '2's. This gives 7 fewer misclassified '2's (but 2 more misclassified '1's) in the diagram.

3.6.3   Quadratic discriminant

The quadratic discriminant starts by constructing, for each sample, an ellipse centred on the centre of gravity of the points. In Figure 3.1 it is clear that the distributions are of different shape and spread, with the distribution of '2's being roughly circular in shape and the '1's being more elliptical. The line of equal likelihood is now itself an ellipse (in general a conic section) as shown in the Figure. All points within the ellipse are classified as '1's. Relative to the logistic boundary, *i.e.* in the region between the dashed line and the ellipse, the quadratic rule misclassifies an extra 7 '1's (in the upper half of the diagram) but correctly classifies an extra 8 '2's (in the lower half of the diagram). So the performance of the quadratic classifier is about the same as the logistic discriminant in this case, probably due to the skewness of the '1' distribution.

Linear, Logistic and Quadratic discriminants

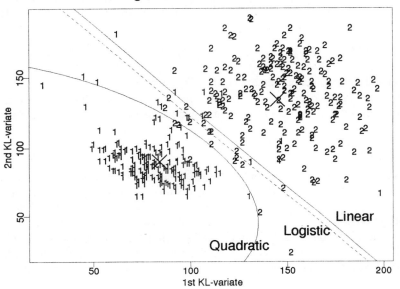

Fig. 3.1: Decision boundaries for the three discriminants: quadratic (curved); linear (full line); and logistic (dashed line). The data are the first two Karhunen-Loeve components for the digits '1' and '2'.

4

Modern Statistical Techniques

R. Molina (1), N. Pérez de la Blanca (1) and C. C. Taylor (2)
(1) University of Granada[1] and (2) University of Leeds

4.1 INTRODUCTION

In the previous chapter we studied the classification problem, from the statistical point of view, assuming that the form of the underlying density functions (or their ratio) was known. However, in most real problems this assumption does not necessarily hold. In this chapter we examine distribution-free (often called nonparametric) classification procedures that can be used without assuming that the form of the underlying densities are known.

Recall that q, n, p denote the number of classes, of examples and attributes, respectively. Classes will be denoted by $A_1, A_2, \ldots, A_q$ and attribute values for example i ($i = 1, 2, \ldots, n$) will be denoted by the p-dimensional vector $\mathbf{x}_i = (x_{1i}, x_{2i}, \ldots, x_{pi}) \in \mathcal{X}$. Elements in $\mathcal{X}$ will be denoted $\mathbf{x} = (x_1, x_2, \ldots, x_p)$.

The Bayesian approach for allocating observations to classes has already been outlined in Section 2.6. It is clear that to apply the Bayesian approach to classification we have to estimate $f(\mathbf{x} \mid A_j)$ and π_j or $p(A_j \mid \mathbf{x})$. Nonparametric methods to do this job will be discussed in this chapter. We begin in Section 4.2 with kernel density estimation; a close relative to this approach is the k-nearest neighbour (k-NN) which is outlined in Section 4.3. Bayesian methods which either allow for, or prohibit dependence between the variables are discussed in Sections 4.5 and 4.6. A final section deals with promising methods which have been developed recently, but, for various reasons, must be regarded as methods for the future. To a greater or lesser extent, these methods have been tried out in the project, but the results were disappointing. In some cases (ACE), this is due to limitations of size and memory as implemented in Splus. The pruned implementation of MARS in Splus (StatSci, 1991) also suffered in a similar way, but a standalone version which also does classification is expected shortly. We believe that these methods will have a place in classification practice, once some relatively minor technical problems have been resolved. As yet, however, we cannot recommend them on the basis of our empirical trials.

---

[1] *Address for correspondence*: Department of Computer Science and AI, Facultad de Ciencas, University of Granada, 18071 Granada, Spain

4.2 DENSITY ESTIMATION

A nonparametric approach, proposed in Fix & Hodges (1951), is to estimate the densities $f_j(\mathbf{x}), j = 1, 2, \ldots, q$ by nonparametric density estimation. Then once we have estimated $f_j(\mathbf{x})$ and the prior probabilities π_j we can use the formulae of Section 2.6 and the costs to classify $\mathbf{x}$ by minimum risk or minimum error.

To introduce the method, we assume that we have to estimate the $p-$dimensional density function $f(\mathbf{x})$ of an unknown distribution. Note that we will have to perform this process for each of the q densities $f_j(\mathbf{x}), j = 1, 2, \ldots, q$. Then, the probability, P, that a vector $\mathbf{x}$ will fall in a region $\mathcal{R}$ is given by

$$P = \int_{\mathcal{R}} f(\mathbf{x}')d\mathbf{x}'$$

Suppose that n observations are drawn independently according to $f(\mathbf{x})$. Then we can approach P by k/n where k is the number of these n observations falling in $\mathcal{R}$. Furthermore, if $f(\mathbf{x})$ does not vary appreciably within $\mathcal{R}$ we can write

$$P \approx f(\mathbf{x})V$$

where V is the volume enclosed by $\mathcal{R}$. This leads to the following procedure to estimate the density at $\mathbf{x}$. Let V_n be the volume of $\mathcal{R}_n$, k_n be the number of samples falling in $\mathcal{R}_n$ and $\hat{f}(\mathbf{x})$ the estimate of $f(\mathbf{x})$ based on a sample of size n, then

$$\hat{f}(\mathbf{x}) = \frac{k_n/n}{V_n} \qquad (4.1)$$

Equation (4.1) can be written in a much more suggestive way. If $\mathcal{R}_n$ is a $p-$dimensional hypercube and if λ_n is the length of the edge of the hypercube we have

$$\hat{f}(\mathbf{x}) = \frac{1}{n} \sum_{i=1}^{n} \frac{1}{V_n} \varphi\left(\frac{\mathbf{x} - \mathbf{x}_i}{\lambda_n} \right) \qquad (4.2)$$

where

$$\varphi(u) = \left\{ \begin{array}{ll} 1 & |u_j| \leq 1/2 \qquad j = 1, 2 \ldots, p \\ 0 & \text{otherwise} \end{array} \right.$$

Then (4.2) expresses our estimate for $f(\mathbf{x})$ as an average function of $\mathbf{x}$ and the samples $\mathbf{x}_i$. In general we could use

$$\hat{f}(\mathbf{x}) = \frac{1}{n} \sum_{i=1}^{n} K(\mathbf{x}, \mathbf{x}_i, \lambda_n)$$

where $K(\mathbf{x}, \mathbf{x}_i, \lambda_n)$ are kernel functions. For instance, we could use, instead of the Parzen window defined above,

$$K(\mathbf{x}, \mathbf{x}_i, \lambda_n) = \frac{1}{(\sqrt{2\pi}\lambda_n)^p} \exp\left\{ -\frac{1}{2} \sum_j \left(\frac{x_j - x_{ji}}{\lambda_n} \right)^2 \right\} \qquad (4.3)$$

The role played by λ_n is clear. For (4.3), if λ_n is very large $K(\mathbf{x}, \mathbf{x}_i, \lambda_n)$ changes very slowly with $\mathbf{x}$, resulting in a very smooth estimate for $f(\mathbf{x})$. On the other hand, if λ_n is small then $\hat{f}(\mathbf{x})$ is the superposition of n sharp normal distributions with small variances centered at the samples producing a very erratic estimate of $f(\mathbf{x})$. The analysis for the Parzen window is similar.

Before going into details about the kernel functions we use in the classification problem and about the estimation of the smoothing parameter λ_n, we briefly comment on the mean behaviour of $\hat{f}(\mathbf{x})$. We have

$$E[\hat{f}(\mathbf{x})] = \int K(\mathbf{x}, \mathbf{u}, \lambda_n) f(\mathbf{u}) d\mathbf{u}$$

and so the expected value of the estimate $\hat{f}(\mathbf{x})$ is an averaged value of the unknown density. By expanding $\hat{f}(\mathbf{x})$ in a Taylor series (in λ_n) about $\mathbf{x}$ one can derive asymptotic formulae for the mean and variance of the estimator. These can be used to derive plug-in estimates for λ_n which are well-suited to the goal of density estimation, see Silverman (1986) for further details.

We now consider our classification problem. Two choices have to be made in order to estimate the density, the specification of the kernel and the value of the smoothing parameter. It is fairly widely recognised that the choice of the smoothing parameter is much more important. With regard to the kernel function we will restrict our attention to kernels with p independent coordinates, *i.e.*

$$K(\mathbf{x}, \mathbf{x}_i, \lambda) = \prod_{j=1}^{p} K_{(j)}(x_j, x_{ji}, \lambda)$$

with $K_{(j)}$ indicating the kernel function component of the jth attribute and λ being not dependent on j. It is very important to note that as stressed by Aitchison & Aitken (1976), this factorisation does not imply the independence of the attributes for the density we are estimating.

It is clear that kernels could have a more complex form and that the smoothing parameter could be coordinate dependent. We will not discuss in detail that possibility here (see McLachlan, 1992 for details). Some comments will be made at the end of this section.

The kernels we use depend on the type of variable. For continuous variables

$$
\begin{aligned}
K_{(j)}(x_j, x_{ji}, \lambda) &= \frac{1}{\sqrt{-\pi/\log \lambda}} \exp\left\{ -\left(\frac{x_j - x_{ji}}{\sqrt{-1/\log \lambda}} \right)^2 \right\} \\
&= \frac{1}{\sqrt{-\pi/\log \lambda}} \lambda^{(x_j - x_{ji})^2}
\end{aligned}
$$

For binary variables

$$
\begin{aligned}
K_{(j)}(x_j, x_{ji}, \lambda) &= \left(\frac{\lambda}{1+\lambda} \right)^{(x_j - x_{ji})^2} \left(\frac{1}{1+\lambda} \right)^{1-(x_j - x_{ji})^2} \\
&= \frac{1}{1+\lambda} \lambda^{(x_j - x_{ji})^2}
\end{aligned}
$$

For nominal variables with T_j nominal values

$$
\begin{aligned}
K_{(j)}(x_j, x_{ji}, \lambda) &= \left(\frac{1}{1+(T_j-1)\lambda} \right)^{I(x_j, x_{ji})} \left(\frac{\lambda}{1+(T_j-1)\lambda} \right)^{1-I(x_j, x_{ji})} \\
&= \frac{1}{1+(T_j-1)\lambda} \lambda^{1-I(x_j, x_{ji})}
\end{aligned}
$$

where $I(x, y) = 1$ if $x = y$,   0 otherwise.

For ordinal variables with T_j nominal values

$$K_{(j)}(x_j, x_{ji}, \lambda) \quad = \quad \frac{\lambda^{(x_j - x_{ji})^2}}{\sum_{k=1}^{T_j} \lambda^{(x_k - x_{ji})^2}}$$

For the above expressions we can see that in all cases we can write

$$K_{(j)}(x_j, x_{ji}, \lambda) \quad = \quad \frac{1}{C(\lambda)} \lambda^{d^2(x_j, x_{ji})}$$

The problem is that since we want to use the same smoothing parameter, λ , for all the variables, we have to normalise them. To do so we substitute λ by λ^{1/s^2} where s^2 is defined, depending on the type of variable, by

continuous	binary
$\sum_{i=1}^{n}(x_{ji} - \bar{x}_j)^2$	$\sum_{i=1}^{n}(x_{ji} - \bar{x}_j)^2$
nominal	ordinal
$\dfrac{n^2 - \sum_{k=1}^{T_j} N_j^2(k)}{2n(n-1)}$	$\dfrac{1}{n-1}\sum_{i=1}^{n}(x_{ji} - \bar{x}_j)^2$

where $N_j(k)$ denotes the number of examples for which attribute j has the value k and $\bar{x}_j$ is the sample mean of the jth attribute.

With this selection of s^2 we have

$$\text{average}_{k \neq i} d^2(x_{jk}, x_{ji})/s^2 = 2 \qquad \forall j$$

So we can understand the above process as rescaling all the variables to the same scale.

For discrete variables the range of the smoothness parameter is the interval $(0, 1)$. One extreme leads to the uniform distribution and the other to a one-point distribution:

$$\lambda = 1 \qquad K(x_j, x_{ji}, 1) = 1/T_j$$
$$\lambda = 0 \qquad K(x_j, x_{ji}, 0) = 1 \quad \text{if} \quad x_j = x_{ji}, \qquad 0 \quad \text{if} \quad x_j \neq x_{ji}$$

For continuous variables the range is $0 < \lambda < 1$ and $\lambda = 1$ and $\lambda = 0$ have to be regarded as limiting cases. As $\lambda \to 1$ we get the "uniform distribution over the real line" and as $\lambda \to 0$ we get the Dirac spike function situated at the x_{ji}.

Having defined the kernels we will use, we need to choose λ. As $\lambda \to 0$ the estimated density approaches zero at all x except at the samples where it is $1/n$ times the Dirac delta function. This precludes choosing λ by maximizing the log likelihood with respect to λ. To estimate a good choice of smoothing parameter, a jackknife modification of the maximum likelihood method can be used. This was proposed by Habbema *et al.* (1974) and Duin (1976) and takes λ to maximise $\prod_{i=1}^{n} \hat{f}_i(\mathbf{x}_i)$ where

$$\hat{f}_i(\mathbf{x}_i) = \frac{1}{n-1} \sum_{\substack{k=1 \\ k \neq i}}^{n} K^{(p)}(\mathbf{x}_i, \mathbf{x}_k, \lambda)$$

This criterion makes the smoothness data dependent, leads to an algorithm for an arbitrary dimensionality of the data and possesses consistency requirements as discussed by Aitchison & Aitken (1976).

An extension of the above model for λ is to make λ_i dependent on the kth nearest neighbour distance to $\mathbf{x}_i$, so that we have a λ_i for each sample point. This gives rise to the so-called variable kernel model. An extensive description of this model was first given by Breiman *et al.* (1977). This method has promising results especially when lognormal or skewed distributions are estimated. The kernel width λ_i is thus proportional to the kth nearest neighbour distance in $\mathbf{x}_i$ denoted by d_{ik}, *i.e.* $\lambda_i = \alpha d_{ik}$. We take for d_{ik} the euclidean distance measured after standardisation of all variables. The proportionality factor α is (inversely) dependent on k. The smoothing value is now determined by two parameters, α and k; α can be though of as an overall smoothing parameter, while k defines the variation in smoothness of the estimated density over the different regions. If, for example $k = 1$, the smoothness will vary locally while for larger k values the smoothness tends to be constant over large regions, roughly approximating the fixed kernel model.

We use a Normal distribution for the component

$$ K_{(j)}(x_j, x_{ji}, \lambda_i) = \frac{1}{\alpha d_{ik} s_j \sqrt{2\pi}} \exp\left\{ -\frac{1}{2}\left(\frac{x_j - x_{ji}}{\alpha d_{ik} s_j}\right)^2 \right\} $$

To optimise for α and k the jackknife modification of the maximum likelihood method can again be applied . However, for the variable kernel this leads to a more difficult two-dimensional optimisation problem of the likelihood function $L(\alpha, k)$ with one continuous parameter (α) and one discrete parameter (k).

Silverman (1986, Sections 2.6 and 5.3) studies the advantages and disadvantages of this approach. He also proposes another method to estimate the smoothing parameters in a variable kernel model (see Silverman, 1986 and McLachlan, 1992 for details).

The algorithm we mainly used in our trials to classify by density estimation is ALLOC80 by Hermans *at al.* (1982) (see Appendix B for source).

4.2.1   Example

We illustrate the kernel classifier with some simulated data, which comprise 200 observations from a standard Normal distribution (class 1, say) and 100 (in total) values from an equal mixture of $N(\pm.8, 1)$ (class 2). The resulting estimates can then be used as a basis for classifying future observations to one or other class. Various scenarios are given in Figure 4.1 where a black segment indicates that observations will be allocated to class 2, and otherwise to class 1. In this example we have used equal priors for the 2 classes (although they are not equally represented), and hence allocations are based on maximum estimated likelihood. It is clear that the rule will depend on the smoothing parameters, and can result in very disconnected sets. In higher dimensions these segments will become regions, with potentially very nonlinear boundaries, and possibly disconnected, depending on the smoothing parameters used. For comparison we also draw the population probability densities, and the "true" decision regions in Figure 4.1 (top), which are still disconnected but very much smoother than some of those constructed from the kernels.

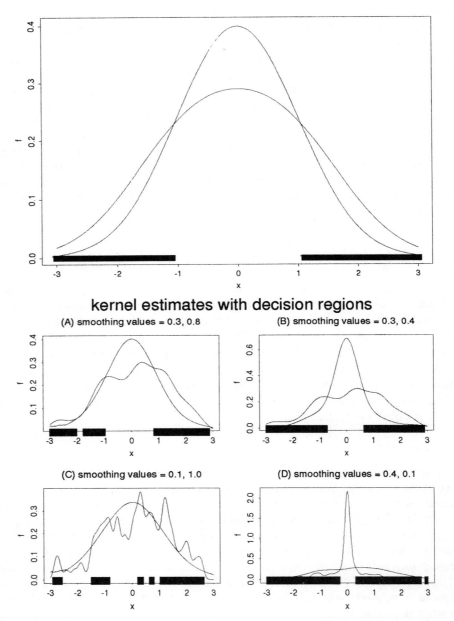

Fig. 4.1: Classification regions for kernel classifier (bottom) with true probability densities (top). The smoothing parameters quoted in (A) – (D) are the values of λ_n used in Equation (4.3) for class 1 and class 2, respectively.

4.3 K-NEAREST NEIGHBOUR

Suppose we consider estimating the quantities $f(x \mid A_h)$, $h = 1, \ldots, q$ by a nearest neighbour method. If we have training data in which there are n_h observations from class A_h with $n = \sum n_h$, and the hypersphere around x containing the k nearest observations has volume $v(x)$ and contains $k_1(x), \ldots, k_q(x)$ observations of classes $A_1, \ldots, A_q$ respectively, then π_h is estimated by n_h/n and $f(x \mid A_h)$ is estimated by $k_h(x)/(n_h v(x))$, which then gives an estimate of $p(A_h \mid x)$ by substitution as $\hat{p}(A_h \mid x) = k_h(x)/k$. This leads immediately to the classification rule: classify x as belonging to class A_c if $k_c = \max_h(k_h)$. This is known as the k-nearest neighbour (k-NN) classification rule. For the special case when $k = 1$, it is simply termed the nearest-neighbour (NN) classification rule.

There is a problem that is important to mention. In the above analysis it is assumed that π_h is estimated by n_h/n. However, it could be the case that our sample did not estimate properly the group-prior probabilities. This issue is studied in Davies (1988).

We study in some depth the NN rule. We first try to get a heuristic understanding of why the nearest-neighbour rule should work. To begin with, note that the class $\mathbf{A}_{NN}$ associated with the nearest neighbour is a random variable and the probability that $\mathbf{A}_{NN} = A_i$ is merely $p(A_i \mid x_{NN})$ where x_{NN} is the sample nearest to x. When the number of samples is very large, it is reasonable to assume that x_{NN} is sufficiently close to x so that $p(A_i \mid x) \approx p(A_i \mid x_{NN})$. In this case, we can view the nearest-neighbour rule as a randomised decision rule that classifies x by selecting the category A_i with probability $p(A_i \mid x)$. As a nonparametric density estimator the nearest neighbour approach yields a non-smooth curve which does not integrate to unity, and as a method of density estimation it is unlikely to be appropriate. However, these poor qualities need not extend to the domain of classification. Note also that the nearest neighbour method is equivalent to the kernel density estimate as the smoothing parameter tends to zero, when the Normal kernel function is used. See Scott (1992) for details.

It is obvious that the use of this rule involves choice of a suitable metric, *i.e.* how is the distance to the nearest points to be measured? In some datasets there is no problem, but for multivariate data, where the measurements are measured on different scales, some standardisation is usually required. This is usually taken to be either the standard deviation or the range of the variable. If there are indicator variables (as will occur for nominal data) then the data is usually transformed so that all observations lie in the unit hypercube. Note that the metric can also be class dependent, so that one obtains a distance conditional on the class. This will increase the processing and classification time, but may lead to a considerable increase in performance. For classes with few samples, a compromise is to use a regularised value, in which there is some trade-off between the within – class value, and the global value of the rescaling parameters. A study on the influence of data transformation and metrics on the k-NN rule can be found in Todeschini (1989).

To speed up the process of finding the nearest neighbours several approaches have been proposed. Fukunaka & Narendra (1975) used a branch and bound algorithm to increase the speed to compute the nearest neighbour, the idea is to divide the attribute space in regions and explore a region only when there are possibilities of finding there a nearest neighbour. The regions are hierarchically decomposed to subsets, sub-subsets and so on. Other ways to speed up the process are to use a condensed-nearest-neighbour rule (Hart,

1968), a reduced-nearest-neighbour-rule (Gates, 1972) or the edited-nearest-neighbour-rule (Hand & Batchelor, 1978). These methods all reduce the training set by retaining those observations which are used to correctly classify the discarded points, thus speeding up the classification process. However they have not been implemented in the k-NN programs used in this book.

The choice of k can be made by cross-validation methods whereby the training data is split, and the second part classified using a k-NN rule. However, in large datasets, this method can be prohibitive in CPU time. Indeed for large datasets, the method is very time consuming for $k > 1$ since all the training data must be stored and examined for each classification. Enas & Choi (1986), have looked at this problem in a simulation study and proposed rules for estimating k for the two classes problem. See McLachlan (1992) for details.

In the trials reported in this book, we used the nearest neighbour ($k = 1$) classifier with no condensing. (The exception to this was the satellite dataset - see Section 9.3.6 - in which k was chosen by cross-validation.) Distances were scaled using the standard deviation for each attribute, with the calculation conditional on the class. Ties were broken by a majority vote, or as a last resort, the default rule.

4.3.1 Example

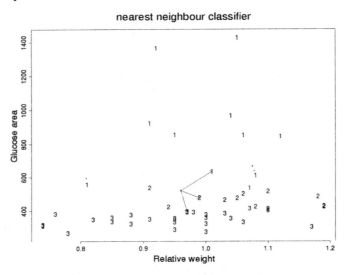

Fig. 4.2: Nearest neighbour classifier for one test example.

The following example shows how the nearest ($k = 1$) neighbour classifier works. The data are a random subset of dataset 36 in Andrews & Herzberg (1985) which examines the relationship between chemical subclinical and overt nonketotic diabetes in 145 patients (see above for more details). For ease of presentation, we have used only 50 patients and two of the six variables; Relative weight and Glucose area, and the data are shown in Figure 4.2 The classifications of 50 patients are one of overt diabetic (1), chemical diabetic (2) and normal(3) are labeled on the graph. In this example, it can be seen that Glucose Area (y-axis) is more useful in separating the three classes, and that class 3 is easier to distinguish than classes 1 and 2. A new patient, whose condition is supposed unknown is assigned the same classification as his nearest neighbour on the graph. The distance, as measured to each point, needs to be scaled in some way to take account for different variability in the different directions. In this case the patient is classified as being in class 2, and is classified correctly.

The decision regions for the nearest neighbour are composed of piecewise linear boundaries, which may be disconnected regions. These regions are the union of Dirichlet cells; each cell consists of points which are nearer (in an appropriate metric) to a given observation than to any other. For this data we have shaded each cell according to the class of its centre, and the resulting decision regions are shown in Figure 4.3

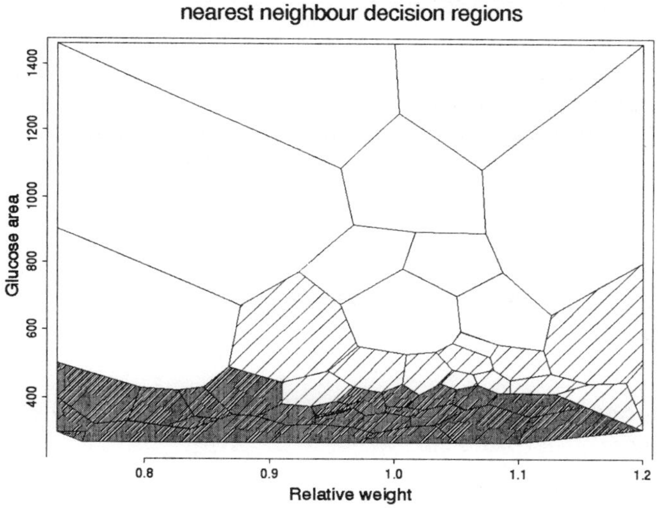

Fig. 4.3: Decision regions for nearest neighbour classifier.

4.4 PROJECTION PURSUIT CLASSIFICATION

As we have seen in the previous sections our goal has been to estimate $\{f(\mathbf{x} \mid A_j), \pi_j, j = 1, \ldots, q\}$ in order to assign $\mathbf{x}$ to class A_{i_0} when

$$\sum_j c(i_0, j)\hat{\pi}_j \hat{f}(\mathbf{x} \mid A_j) \leq \sum_j c(i, j)\hat{\pi}_j \hat{f}(\mathbf{x} \mid A_j) \qquad \forall i$$

We assume that we know $\pi_j, j = 1, \ldots, q$ and to simplify problems transform our minimum risk decision problem into a minimum error decision problem. To do so we simply alter $\{\pi_j\}$ and $\{c(i, j)\}$ to $\{\pi'_j\}$ and $\{c'(i, j)\}$ such that

$$c'(i, j)\pi'_j = c(i, j)\pi_j \quad \forall i, j$$

constraining $\{c'(i, j)\}$ to be of the form

$$c'(i, j) = \begin{cases} \text{constant} & \text{if } j \neq i \\ 0 & \text{otherwise} \end{cases}$$

Then an approximation to π'_j is

$$\pi_j' \propto \pi_j \sum_i c(i,j)$$

(see Breiman *et al.*, 1984 for details).

With these new prior and costs x is assigned to class A_{j_0} when

$$\hat{\pi}_{i_0}' \hat{f}(\mathbf{x} \mid A_{i_0}) \geq \hat{\pi}_j' \hat{f}(\mathbf{x} \mid A_j) \quad \forall j$$

or

$$\hat{p}(A_{i_0} \mid \mathbf{x}) \geq \hat{p}(A_j \mid \mathbf{x}) \quad \forall j$$

So our final goal is to build a good estimator $\{\hat{p}(A_j \mid \mathbf{x}), j = 1, \ldots, q\}$

To define the quality of an estimator $d(\mathbf{x}) = \{\hat{p}(A_j \mid \mathbf{x}), j = 1, \ldots, q\}$ we could use

$$E[\sum_j (p(A_j \mid \mathbf{x}) - \hat{p}(A_j \mid \mathbf{x}))^2] \tag{4.4}$$

Obviously the best estimator is $d_B(\mathbf{x}) = \{p(A_j \mid \mathbf{x}), j = 1, \ldots, q\}$, however, (4.4) is useless since it contains the unknown quantities $\{p(A_j \mid \mathbf{x}), j = 1, \ldots, q\}$ that we are trying to estimate. The problem can be put into a different setting that resolves the difficulty. Let Y, X a random vector on $\{A_1, \ldots, A_q\} \times \mathcal{X}$ with distribution $p(A_j, \mathbf{x})$ and define new variables $Z_j, j = 1, \ldots, q$ by

$$Z_j = \begin{cases} 1 & \text{if } Y = A_j \\ 0 & \text{otherwise} \end{cases}$$

then $E[Z_j \mid \mathbf{x}] = p(A_j \mid \mathbf{x})$. We then define the mean square error $R^*(d)$ by

$$E[\sum_j (Z_j - \hat{p}(A_j \mid \mathbf{x}))^2] \tag{4.5}$$

The very interesting point is that it can be easily shown that for any class probability estimator d we have

$$R^*(d) - R^*(d_B) = E[\sum_j (p(A_j \mid \mathbf{x}) - \hat{p}(A_j \mid \mathbf{x}))^2]$$

and so to compare two estimators $d_1(\mathbf{x}) = \{\hat{p}(A_j \mid \mathbf{x}), j = 1, \ldots, q\}$ and $d_2(\mathbf{x}) = \{p'(A_j \mid x), j = 1, \ldots, q\}$ we can compare the values of $R^*(d_1)$ and $R^*(d_2)$.

When projection pursuit techniques are used in classification problems $E[Z_k \mid \mathbf{x}]$ is modelled as

$$E[Z_k \mid \mathbf{x}] = \overline{Z}_k + \sum_{m=1}^{M} \beta_{km} \psi_m (\sum_{j=1}^{p} \alpha_{jm} x_j)$$

with $\overline{Z}_k = EZ_k$, $E\psi_m = 0$, $E\psi_m^2 = 1$ and $\sum_{j=1}^{p} \alpha_{jm}^2 = 1$. The coefficients β_{km}, α_{jm} and the functions ψ_m are parameters of the model and are estimated by least squares.

Equation (4.5) is approximated by

$$\sum_k \pi_k' \frac{n}{n_k} \sum_i [z_{ki} - \overline{z}_k - \sum_{m=1}^{M} \beta_{km} \psi_m (\sum_{j=1}^{p} \alpha_{jm} x_{ji})^2]/n \tag{4.6}$$

with

$$z_{ki} = \begin{cases} 1 & \text{if in observation } i, Y = A_i \\ 0 & \text{otherwise} \end{cases}$$

Then the above expression is minimised with respect to the parameters β_{km}, $\alpha_m^T = (\alpha_{1m}, \ldots, \alpha_{pm})$ and the functions ψ_m.

The "projection" part of the term projection pursuit indicates that the vector x is projected onto the direction vectors $\alpha_1, \alpha_2, \ldots, \alpha_M$ to get the lengths $\alpha_i x^t$, $i = 1, 2, \ldots, M$ of the projections, and the "pursuit" part indicates that the optimization technique is used to find "good direction" vectors $\alpha_1, \alpha_2, \ldots, \alpha_M$.

A few words on the ψ functions are in order. They are special scatterplot smoother designed to have the following features: they are very fast to compute and have a variable span. Aee StatSci (1991 for details.

It is the purpose of the projection pursuit algorithm to minimise (4.6) with respect to the parameters α_{jm}, β_{km} and functions ψ_m, $1 \le k \le q$, $1 \le j \le p$, $1 \le m \le M$, given the training data. The principal task of the user is to choose M, the number of predictive terms comprising the model. Increasing the number of terms decreases the bias (model specification error) at the expense of increasing the variance of the (model and parameter) estimates.

The strategy is to start with a relatively large value of M (say $M = M_L$) and find all models of size M_L and less. That is, solutions that minimise L_2 are found for $M = M_L, M_L - 1, M_L - 2, \ldots, 1$ in order of decreasing M. The starting parameter values for the numerical search in each M-term model are the solution values for the M most important (out of $M + 1$) terms of the previous model. The importance is measured as

$$I_m = \sum_{k=1}^{q} W_k |\beta_{km}| \qquad (1 \le m \le M)$$

normalised so that the most important term has unit importance. (Note that the variance of all the ψ_m is one.) The starting point for the minimisation of the largest model, $M = M_L$, is given by an M_L term stagewise model (Friedman & Stuetzle, 1981 and StatSci, 1991 for a very precise description of the process).

The sequence of solutions generated in this manner is then examined by the user and a final model is chosen according to the guidelines above.

The algorithm we used in the trials to classify by projection pursuit is SMART (see Friedman, 1984 for details, and Appendix B for availability)

4.4.1 Example

This method is illustrated using a 5-dimensional dataset with three classes relating to chemical and overt diabetes. The data can be found in dataset 36 of Andrews & Herzberg (1985) and were first published in Reaven & Miller (1979). The SMART model can be examined by plotting the smooth functions in the two projected data co-ordinates:

$$0.9998\,x_1 \quad + \quad 0.0045\,x_2 \quad - \quad 0.0213\,x_3 \quad + \quad 0.0010\,x_4 \quad - \quad 0.0044\,x_5$$
$$x_1 \quad - \quad 0.0065\,x_2 \quad - \quad 0.0001\,x_3 \quad + \quad 0.0005\,x_4 \quad - \quad 0.0008\,x_5$$

These are given in Figure 4.4 which also shows the class values given by the projected points of the selected training data (100 of the 145 patients). The remainder of the model chooses the values of β_{im} to obtain a linear combination of the functions which can then be used to model the conditional probabilities. In this example we get

$$\beta_{11} = -0.05 \qquad \beta_{12} = -0.33$$
$$\beta_{21} = -0.40 \qquad \beta_{22} = 0.34$$
$$\beta_{31} = 0.46 \qquad \beta_{32} = -0.01$$

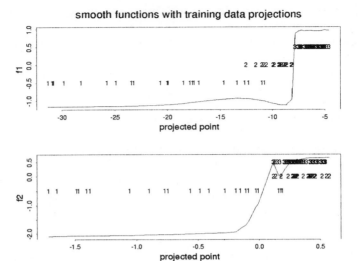

Fig. 4.4: Projected training data with smooth functions.

The remaining 45 patients were used as a test data set, and for each class the unscaled conditional probability can be obtained using the relevant coefficients for that class. These are shown in Figure 4.5, where we have plotted the predicted value against only one of the projected co-ordinate axes. It is clear that if we choose the model (and hence the class) to maximise this value, then we will choose the correct class each time.

4.5   NAIVE BAYES

All the nonparametric methods described so far in this chapter suffer from the requirements that all of the sample must be stored. Since a large number of observations is needed to obtain good estimates, the memory requirements can be severe.

In this section we will make independence assumptions, to be described later, among the variables involved in the classification problem. In the next section we will address the problem of estimating the relations between the variables involved in a problem and display such relations by mean of a directed acyclic graph.

The naïve Bayes classifier is obtained as follows. We assume that the joint distribution of classes and attributes can be written as

$$P(A_i, x_1, \ldots, x_n) = \pi_i \prod_{j=1}^{p} f(x_j \mid A_i)   \quad \forall i$$

the problem is then to obtain the probabilities $\{\pi_i, f(x_j \mid A_i), \quad \forall i, j\}$. The assumption of independence makes it much easier to estimate these probabilities since each attribute can be treated separately. If an attribute takes a continuous value, the usual procedure is to discretise the interval and to use the appropriate frequency of the interval, although there is an option to use the normal distribution to calculate probabilities.

The implementation used in our trials to obtain a naïve Bayes classifier comes from the IND package of machine learning algorithms IND 1.0 by Wray Buntine (see Appendix B for availability).

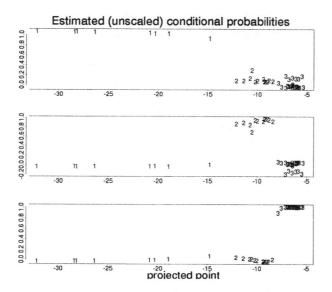

Fig. 4.5: Projected test data with conditional probablities for three classes. Class 1 (top), Class 2 (middle), Class 3 (bottom).

4.6 CAUSAL NETWORKS

We start this section by introducing the concept of causal network.

Let $G = (V, E)$ be a directed acyclic graph (DAG). With each node $v \in V$ a finite state space Ω_v is associated. The total set of configuration is the set

$$\Omega = \times_{v \in V} \Omega_v$$

Typical elements of Ω_v are denoted x_v and elements of Ω are $(x_v, v \in V)$. We assume that we have a probability distribution $P(V)$ over Ω, where we use the short notation

$$P(V) = P\{X_v = x_v, v \in V\}$$

Definition 1 *Let $G = (V, E)$ be a directed acyclic graph (DAG). For each $v \in V$ let $c(v) \subseteq V$ be the set of all parents of v and $d(v) \subseteq V$ be the set of all descendent of v. Furthermore for $v \in V$ let $a(v)$ be the set of variables in V excluding v and v's descendent. Then if for every subset $W \subseteq a(v)$, W and v are conditionally independent given $c(v)$, the $C = (V, E, P)$ is called a causal or Bayesian network.*

There are two key results establishing the relations between a causal network $C = (V, E, P)$ and $P(V)$. The proofs can be found in Neapolitan (1990).

The first theorem establishes that if $C = (V, E, P)$ is a causal network, then $P(V)$ can be written as

$$P(V) = \prod_{v \in V} P(v \mid c(v))$$

Thus, in a causal network, if one knows the conditional probability distribution of each variable given its parents, one can compute the joint probability distribution of all the variables in the network. This obviously can reduce the complexity of determining the distribution enormously. The theorem just established shows that if we know that a DAG and a probability distribution constitute a causal network, then the joint distribution can be retrieved from the conditional distribution of every variable given its parents. This does not imply, however, that if we arbitrarily specify a DAG and conditional probability distributions of every variables given its parents we will necessary have a causal network. This inverse result can be stated as follows.

Let V be a set of finite sets of alternatives (we are not yet calling the members of V variables since we do not yet have a probability distribution) and let $G = (V, E)$ be a DAG. In addition, for $v \in V$ let $c(v) \subseteq V$ be the set of all parents of v, and let a conditional probability distribution of v given $c(v)$ be specified for every event in $c(v)$, that is we have a probability distribution $\hat{P}(v \mid c(v))$. Then a joint probability distribution P of the vertices in V is uniquely determined by

$$P(V) = \prod_{v \in V} \hat{P}(v \mid c(v))$$

and $C = (V, E, P)$ constitutes a causal network.

We illustrate the notion of network with a simple example taken from Cooper (1984). Suppose that metastatic cancer is a cause of brain tumour and can also cause an increase in total serum calcium. Suppose further that either a brain tumor or an increase in total serum calcium could cause a patient to fall into a coma, and that a brain tumor could cause papilledema. Let

a_1 = metastatic cancer present a_2 = metastatic cancer not present
b_1 = serum calcium increased b_2 = serum calcium not increased
c_1 = brain tumor present c_2 = brain tumor not present
d_1 = coma present d_2 = coma not present
e_1 = papilledema present e_2 = papilledema not present

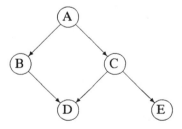

Fig. 4.6: DAG for the cancer problem.

Then, the structure of our knowledge-base is represented by the DAG in Figure 4.6. This structure together with quantitative knowledge of the conditional probability of every variable given all possible parent states define a causal network that can be used as device to perform efficient (probabilistic) inference, (absorb knowledge about variables as it arrives, be able to see the effect on the other variables of one variable taking a particular value and so on). See Pearl (1988) and Lauritzen & Spiegelhalter (1988).

So, once a causal network has been built, it constitutes an efficient device to perform probabilistic inference. However, there remains the previous problem of building such a network, that is, to provide the structure and conditional probabilities necessary for characterizing the network. A very interesting task is then to develop methods able to learn the net directly from raw data, as an alternative to the method of eliciting opinions from the experts.

In the problem of learning graphical representations, it could be said that the statistical community has mainly worked in the direction of building undirected representations: chapter 8 of Whittaker (1990) provides a good survey on selection of undirected graphical representations up to 1990 from the statistical point of view. The program BIFROST (Højsgaard et al., 1992) has been developed, very recently, to obtain causal models. A second literature on model selection devoted to the construction of directed graphs can be found in the social sciences (Glymour et al., 1987; Spirtes et al., 1991) and the artificial intelligence community (Pearl, 1988; Herkovsits & Cooper, 1990; Cooper & Herkovsits, 1991 and Fung & Crawford, 1991).

In this section we will concentrate on methods to build a simplified kind of causal structure, polytrees (singly connected networks); networks where no more than one path exists between any two nodes. Polytrees, are directed graphs which do not contain loops in the skeleton (the network without the arrows) that allow an extremely efficient local propagation procedure.

Before describing how to build polytrees from data, we comment on how to use a polytree in a classification problem. In any classification problem, we have a set of variables $W = \{X_i, i = 1, \ldots, p\}$ that (possibly) have influence on a distinguished classification variable A. The problem is, given a particular instantiation of these variables, to predict the value of A, that is, to classify this particular case in one of the possible categories of A. For this task, we need a set of examples and their correct classification, acting as a training sample. In this context, we first estimate from this training sample a network (polytree), structure displaying the causal relationships among the variables $V = \{X_i, i = 1, .., p\} \cup A$; next, in propagation mode, given a new case with unknown classification, we will instantiate and propagate the available information, showing the more likely value of the classification variable A.

It is important to note that this classifier can be used even when we do not know the value of all the variables in V. Moreover, the network shows the variables in V that directly have influence on A, in fact the parents of A, the children of A and the other parents of the children of A (the knowledge of these variables makes A independent of the rest of variables in V)(Pearl, 1988). So the rest of the network could be pruned, thus reducing the complexity and increasing the efficiency of the classifier. However, since the process of building the network does not take into account the fact that we are only interested in classifying, we should expect as a classifier a poorer performance than other classification oriented methods. However, the built networks are able to display insights into the classification problem that other methods lack. We now proceed to describe the theory to build polytree-based representations for a general set of variables $Y_1, \ldots, Y_m$.

Assume that the distribution $P(\mathbf{y})$ of m discrete-value variables (which we are trying to estimate) can be represented by some unknown polytree F_0, that is, $P(\mathbf{y})$ has the form

$$P(\mathbf{y}) = \prod_{i=1}^{m} P(y_i \mid y_{j_1(i)}, y_{j_2(i)}, \cdots, y_{j_i(i)})$$

where $\{y_{j_1(i)}, y_{j_2(i)}, \cdots, y_{j_i(i)}\}$ is the (possibly empty) set of direct parents of the variable X_i in F_0, and the parents of each variable are mutually independent. So we are aiming at simpler representations than the one displayed in Figure 4.6. The skeleton of the graph involved in that example is not a tree.

Then, according to key results seen at the beginning of this section, we have a causal network $C = (Y, E, P)$ and (Y, E) is a polytree. We will assume that $P(\mathbf{y})$ is nondegenerate, meaning that there exists a connected DAG that displays all the dependencies and independencies embedded in P.

It is important to keep in mind that a naïve Bayes classifier (Section 4.5) can be represented by a polytree, more precisely a tree in which each attribute node has the class variable C as a parent.

The first step in the process of building a polytree is to learn the skeleton. To build the skeleton we have the following theorem:

Theorem 1   *If a nondegenerate distribution $P(\mathbf{y})$ is representable by a polytree F_0, then any Maximum Weight Spanning Tree (MWST) where the weight of the branch connecting Y_i and Y_j is defined by*

$$I(Y_i, Y_j) = \sum_{y_i, y_j} P(y_i, y_j) \log \frac{P(y_i, y_j)}{P(y_i) P(y_j)}$$

will unambiguously recover the skeleton of F_0.

Having found the skeleton of the polytree we move on to find the directionality of the branches. To recover the directions of the branches we use the following facts: nondegeneracy implies that for any pairs of variables (Y_i, Y_j) that do not have a common descendent we have

$$I(Y_i, Y_j) > 0$$

Furthermore, for the pattern

$$Y_i \rightarrow Y_k \leftarrow Y_j \tag{4.7}$$

we have

$$I(Y_i, Y_j) = 0 \ \text{ and } \ I(Y_i, Y_j \mid Y_k) > 0$$

where

$$I(Y_i, Y_j \mid Y_k) = \sum_{y_i, y_j, y_k} P(y_i, y_j, y_k) \log \frac{P(y_i, y_j \mid y_k)}{P(y_i \mid y_k) P(y_j \mid y_k)}$$

and for any of the patterns

$$Y_i \leftarrow Y_k \leftarrow Y_j, \ \ Y_i \leftarrow Y_k \rightarrow Y_j \ and \ Y_i \rightarrow Y_k \rightarrow Y_j$$

we have

$$I(Y_i, Y_j) > 0 \ \text{ and } \ I(Y_i, Y_j \mid Y_k) = 0$$

Taking all these facts into account we can recover the head–to–head patterns, (4.7), which are the really important ones. The rest of the branches can be assigned any direction as long as we do not produce more head–to–head patterns. The algorithm to direct the skeleton can be found in Pearl (1988).

The program to estimate causal polytrees used in our trials is CASTLE, ($\mathcal{C}$ausal $\mathcal{S}$tructures From Inductive $\mathcal{L}$earning). It has been developed at the University of Granada for the ESPRIT project StatLog (Acid *et al.* (1991a); Acid *et al.* (1991b)). See Appendix B for availability.

4.6.1   Example

We now illustrate the use of the Bayesian learning methodology in a simple model, the *digit recognition in a calculator*.

Digits are ordinarily displayed on electronic watches and calculators using seven horizontal and vertical lights in on–off configurations (see Figure 4.7). We number the lights as shown in Figure 4.7.   We take $Z = (Cl, Z_1, Z_2, \ldots, Z_7)$ to be an eight–dimensional

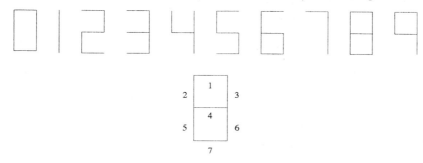

Fig. 4.7: Digits.

vector where $Cl = i$ denotes the ith digit, $i = 0, 1, 2, \ldots, 9$ and when fixing Cl to i the remaining $(Z_1, Z_2, \ldots, Z_7)$ is a seven dimensional vector of zeros and ones with $z_m = 1$ if the light in the m position is on for the ith digit and $z_m = 0$ otherwise.

We generate examples from a faulty calculator. The data consist of outcomes from the random vector $Cl, X_1, X_2, \ldots, X_7$ where Cl is the class label, the digit, and assumes the values in $0, 1, 2, \ldots, 9$ with equal probability and the $X_1, X_2, \ldots, X_7$ are zero-one variables. Given the value of Cl, the $X_1, X_2, \ldots, X_7$ are each independently equal to the value corresponding to the Z_i with probability 0.9 and are in error with probability 0.1. Our aim is to build up the polytree displaying the (in)dependencies in X.

We generate four hundred samples of this distribution and use them as a learning sample. After reading in the sample, estimating the skeleton and directing the skeleton the polytree estimated by CASTLE is the one shown in Figure 4.8. CASTLE then tells us what we had expected:

   Z_i and Z_j are conditionally independent given Cl, $i, j = 1, 2, \ldots, 7$

Finally, we examine the predictive power of this polytree. The posterior probabilities of each digit given some observed patterns are shown in Figure 4.9.

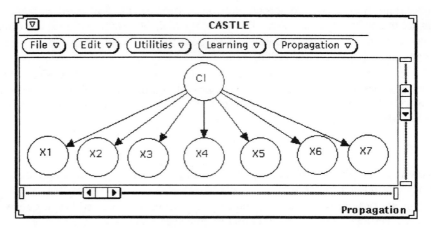

Fig. 4.8: Obtained polytree.

Digit	0	1	2	3	4	5	6	7	8	9
⌐	463	0	2	0	0	0	519	0	16	0
'	0	749	0	0	0	0	0	251	0	0
⌐┘	1	0	971	0	6	0	1	12	0	0
┐	1	0	0	280	0	699	19	2	0	0
└┐	0	21	0	0	913	0	0	1	2	63
⌐┘	290	0	0	0	0	644	51	5	10	0

Fig. 4.9: Probabilities × 1000 for some 'digits'.

4.7   OTHER RECENT APPROACHES

The methods discussed in this section are available via anonymous ftp from statlib, internet address 128.2.241.142. A version of ACE for nonlinear discriminant analysis is available as the S coded function $gdisc$. MARS is available in a FORTRAN version. Since these algorithms were not formally included in the StatLog trials (for various reasons), we give only a brief introduction.

4.7.1   ACE

Nonlinear transformation of variables is a commonly used practice in regression problems. The Alternating Conditional Expectation algorithm (Breiman & Friedman, 1985) is a simple iterative scheme using only bivariate conditional expectations, which finds those transformations that produce the best fitting additive model.

Suppose we have two random variables: the response, Y and the predictor, X, and we seek transformations $\theta(Y)$ and $f(X)$ so that $E\{\theta(Y)|X\} \approx f(X)$. The ACE algorithm approaches this problem by minimising the squared-error objective

$$E\{\theta(Y) - f(X)\}^2. \tag{4.8}$$

For fixed θ, the minimising f is $f(X) = E\{\theta(Y)|X\}$, and conversely, for fixed f the minimising θ is $\theta(Y) = E\{f(X)|Y\}$. The key idea in the ACE algorithm is to begin with some starting functions and alternate these two steps until convergence. With multiple predictors $X_1, \ldots, X_p$, ACE seeks to minimise

$$e^2 = E \left\{ \theta(Y) - \sum_{j=1}^{p} f_j(X_j) \right\}^2 \tag{4.9}$$

In practice, given a dataset, estimates of the conditional expectations are constructed using an automatic smoothing procedure. In order to stop the iterates from shrinking to zero functions, which trivially minimise the squared error criterion, $\theta(Y)$ is scaled to have unit variance in each iteration. Also, without loss of generality, the condition $E\theta = Ef_1 = \ldots = Ef_p = 0$ is imposed. The algorithm minimises Equation (4.9) through a series of single-function minimisations involving smoothed estimates of bivariate conditional expectations. For a given set of functions $f_1, \ldots, f_p$, minimising (4.9) with respect to $\theta(Y)$ yields a new $\theta(Y)$

$$\theta(Y) := \theta_{new}(Y) = \frac{E\left[\sum_{j=1}^{p} f_j(X_j)|Y\right]}{\left\|E\left[\sum_{j=1}^{p} f_j(X_j)|Y\right]\right\|} \tag{4.10}$$

with $\| \cdot \| = \left[E(\,\cdot\,)^2\right]^{1/2}$. Next e^2 is minimised for each f_i in turn with given $\theta(Y)$ and $f_{j \neq i}$ yielding the solution

$$f_i(X_i) := f_{i,new}(X_i) = E\left[\theta(Y) - \sum_{j \neq i} f_j(X_j) \,|\, X_i\right] \tag{4.11}$$

This constitutes one iteration of the algorithm which terminates when an iteration fails to decrease e^2.

ACE places no restriction on the type of each variable. The transformation functions $\theta(Y), f_1(X_1), \ldots, f_p(X_p)$ assume values on the real line but their arguments may assume values on any set so ordered real, ordered and unordered categorical and binary variables can all be incorporated in the same regression equation. For categorical variables, the procedure can be regarded as estimating optimal scores for each of their values.

For use in classification problems, the response is replaced by a categorical variable representing the class labels, A_j. ACE then finds the transformations that make the relationship of $\theta(A)$ to the $f_i(X_i)$ as linear as possible.

4.7.2 MARS

The MARS (Multivariate Adaptive Regression Spline) procedure (Friedman, 1991) is based on a generalisation of spline methods for function fitting. Consider the case of only one predictor variable, x. An approximating q^{th} order regression spline function $\hat{f}_q(x)$ is obtained by dividing the range of x values into $K + 1$ disjoint regions separated by K points called "knots". The approximation takes the form of a separate q^{th} degree polynomial in each region, constrained so that the function and its $q - 1$ derivatives are continuous. Each qth degree polynomial is defined by $q + 1$ parameters so there are a total of $(K + 1)(q + 1)$ parameters to be adjusted to best fit the data. Generally the order of the spline is taken to be low $(q \leq 3)$. Continuity requirements place q constraints at each knot location making a total of Kq constraints.

While regression spline fitting can be implemented by directly solving this constrained minimisation problem, it is more usual to convert the problem to an unconstrained optimisation by chosing a set of basis functions that span the space of all q^{th} order spline functions (given the chosen knot locations) and performing a linear least squares fit of the response on this basis function set. In this case the approximation takes the form

$$\hat{f}_q(x) = \sum_{k=0}^{K+q} a_k \, B_k^{(q)}(x) \tag{4.12}$$

where the values of the expansion coefficients $\{a_k\}_0^{K+q}$ are unconstrained and the continuity constraints are intrinsically embodied in the basis functions $\{B_k^{(q)}(x)\}_0^{K+q}$. One such basis, the "truncated power basis", is comprised of the functions

$$\{x^j\}_{j=0}^q, \ \{(x-t_k)_+^q\}_1^K \tag{4.13}$$

where $\{t_k\}_1^K$ are the knot locations defining the $K+1$ regions and the truncated power functions are defined

$$(x - t_k)_0^q = \begin{cases} 0 & x \le t_k \\ (x - t_k)^q & x > t_k \end{cases} \tag{4.14}$$

The flexibility of the regression spline approach can be enhanced by incorporating an automatic knot selection strategy as part of the data fitting process. A simple and effective strategy for automatically selecting both the number and locations for the knots was described by Smith(1982), who suggested using the truncated power basis in a numerical minimisation of the least squares criterion

$$\sum_{i=1}^N \left[y_i - \sum_{j=0}^q b_j x^j - \sum_{k=1}^K a_k (x - t_k)_+^q \right]^2 \tag{4.15}$$

Here the coefficients $\{b_j\}_0^q$, $\{a_k\}_1^K$ can be regarded as the parameters associated with a multiple linear least squares regression of the response y on the "variables" $\{x^j\}_0^q$ and $\{(x-t_k)_+^q\}_1^K$. Adding or deleting a knot is viewed as adding or deleting the corresponding variable $(x - t_k)_+^q$. The strategy involves starting with a very large number of eligible knot locations $\{t_1, \ldots, t_{K_{max}}\}$; we may choose one at every interior data point, and considering corresponding variables $\{(x - t_k)_+^q\}_1^{K_{max}}$ as candidates to be selected through a statistical variable subset selection procedure. This approach to knot selection is both elegant and powerful. It automatically selects the number of knots K and their locations $t_1, \ldots, t_K$ thereby estimating the global amount of smoothing to be applied as well as estimating the separate relative amount of smoothing to be applied locally at different locations.

The multivariate adaptive regression spline method (Friedman, 1991) can be viewed as a multivariate generalisation of this strategy. An approximating spline function $\hat{f}_q(\mathbf{x})$ of n variables is defined analogously to that for one variable. The n-dimensional space R^n is divided into a set of disjoint regions and within each one $\hat{f}_q(\mathbf{x})$ is taken to be a polynomial in n variables with the maximum degree of any single variable being q. The approximation and its derivatives are constrained to be everywhere continuous. This places constraints on the approximating polynomials in seperate regions along the $(n-1)$-dimensional region boundaries. As in the univariate case, $\hat{f}_q(\mathbf{x})$ is most easily constructed using a basis function set that spans the space of all q^{th} order n-dimensional spline functions.

MARS implements a forward/backward stepwise selection strategy. The forward selection begins with only the constant basis function $B_0(\mathbf{x}) = 1$ in the model. In each iteration we consider adding two terms to the model

$$
\begin{aligned}
&B_j(x - t)_+ \\
&B_j(t - x)_+
\end{aligned}
\qquad (4.16)
$$

where B_j is one of the basis functions already chosen, x is one of the predictor variables not represented in B_j and t is a knot location on that variable. The two terms of this form, which cause the greatest decrease in the residual sum of squares, are added to the model. The forward selection process continues until a relatively large number of basis functions is included in a deliberate attempt to overfit the data. The backward "pruning" procedure, standard stepwise linear regression, is then applied with the basis functions representing the stock of "variables". The best fitting model is chosen with the fit measured by a cross-validation criterion.

MARS is able to incorporate variables of different type; continuous, discrete and categorical.

5

Machine Learning of Rules and Trees

C. Feng (1) and D. Michie (2)
(1) The Turing Institute[1] and (2) University of Strathclyde

This chapter is arranged in three sections. Section 5.1 introduces the broad ideas underlying the main rule-learning and tree-learning methods. Section 5.2 summarises the specific characteristics of algorithms used for comparative trials in the StatLog project. Section 5.3 looks beyond the limitations of these particular trials to new approaches and emerging principles.

5.1 RULES AND TREES FROM DATA: FIRST PRINCIPLES

5.1.1 Data fit and mental fit of classifiers

In a 1943 lecture (for text see Carpenter & Doran, 1986) A.M.Turing identified Machine Learning (ML)[2] as a precondition for intelligent systems. A more specific engineering expression of the same idea was given by Claude Shannon in 1953, and that year also saw the first computational learning experiments, by Christopher Strachey (see Muggleton, 1993). After steady growth ML has reached practical maturity under two distinct headings: (a) as a means of engineering rule-based software (for example in "expert systems") from sample cases volunteered interactively and (b) as a method of data analysis whereby rule-structured classifiers for predicting the classes of newly sampled cases are obtained from a "training set" of pre-classified cases. We are here concerned with heading (b), exemplified by Michalski and Chilausky's (1980) landmark use of the AQ11 algorithm (Michalski & Larson, 1978) to generate automatically a rule-based classifier for crop farmers.

Rules for classifying soybean diseases were inductively derived from a training set of 290 records. Each comprised a description in the form of 35 attribute-values, together with a confirmed allocation to one or another of 15 main soybean diseases. When used to

---

[1] *Addresses for correspondence*: Cao Feng, Department of Computer Science, University of Ottowa, Ottowa, K1N 6N5, Canada; Donald Michie, Academic Research Associates, 6 Inveralmond Grove, Edinburgh EH4 6RA, U.K.

[2] This chapter confines itself to a subset of machine learning algorithms, *i.e.* those that output *propositional* classifiers. Inductive Logic Programming (ILP) uses the symbol system of *predicate* (as opposed to propositional) logic, and is described in Chapter 12

classify 340 or so new cases, machine-learned rules proved to be markedly more accurate than the best existing rules used by soybean experts.

As important as a good fit to the data, is a property that can be termed "mental fit". As statisticians, Breiman and colleagues (1984) see data-derived classifications as serving "two purposes: (1) to predict the response variable corresponding to future measurement vectors as accurately as possible; (2) to understand the structural relationships between the response and the measured variables." ML takes purpose (2) one step further. The soybean rules were sufficiently meaningful to the plant pathologist associated with the project that he eventually adopted them in place of his own previous reference set. ML requires that classifiers should not only classify but should also constitute explicit concepts, that is, expressions in symbolic form meaningful to humans and evaluable in the head.

We need to dispose of confusion between the *kinds* of computer-aided descriptions which form the ML practitioner's goal and those in view by statisticians. Knowledge-compilations, "meaningful to humans and evaluable in the head", are available in Michalski & Chilausky's paper (their Appendix 2), and in Shapiro & Michie (1986, their Appendix B) in Shapiro (1987, his Appendix A), and in Bratko, Mozetic & Lavrac (1989, their Appendix A), among other sources. A glance at any of these computer-authored constructions will suffice to show their remoteness from the main-stream of statistics and its goals. Yet ML practitioners increasingly need to assimilate and use statistical techniques.

Once they are ready to go it alone, machine learned bodies of knowledge typically need little further human intervention. But a substantial synthesis may require months or years of prior interactive work, first to shape and test the overall logic, then to develop suitable sets of attributes and definitions, and finally to select or synthesize voluminous data files as training material. This contrast has engendered confusion as to the role of human interaction. Like music teachers, ML engineers abstain from interaction only when their pupil reaches the concert hall. Thereafter abstention is total, clearing the way for new forms of interaction intrinsic to the pupil's delivery of what has been acquired. But during the process of extracting descriptions from data the working method of ML engineers resemble that of any other data analyst, being essentially iterative and interactive.

In ML the "knowledge" orientation is so important that data-derived classifiers, however accurate, are not ordinarily acceptable in the absence of mental fit. The reader should bear this point in mind when evaluating empirical studies reported elsewhere in this book. StatLog's use of ML algorithms has not always conformed to purpose (2) above. Hence the reader is warned that the book's use of the phrase "machine learning" in such contexts is by courtesy and convenience only.

The Michalski-Chilausky soybean experiment exemplifies supervised learning,

given: a sample of input-output pairs of an unknown class-membership function,

required: a conjectured reconstruction of the function in the form of a rule-based expression human-evaluable over the domain.

Note that the function's output-set is unordered (*i.e.* consisting of categoric rather than numerical values) and its outputs are taken to be names of classes. The derived function-expression is then a classifier. In contrast to the prediction of numerical quantities, this book confines itself to the classification problem and follows a scheme depicted in Figure 5.1.

Constructing ML-type expressions from sample data is known as "concept learning".

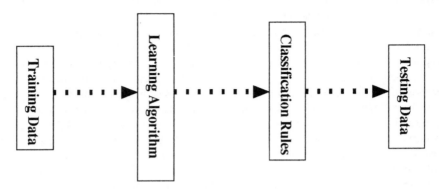

Fig. 5.1: Classification process from training to testing.

The first such learner was described by Earl Hunt (1962). This was followed by Hunt, Marin & Stone's (1966) CLS. The acronym stands for "Concept Learning System". In ML, the requirement for user-transparency imparts a bias towards logical, in preference to arithmetical, combinations of attributes. Connectives such as "and", "or", and "if-then" supply the glue for building rule-structured classifiers, as in the following englished form of a rule from Michalski and Chilausky's soybean study.

if   leaf malformation is absent and stem is abnormal and internal discoloration
              is black

then   Diagnosis is CHARCOAL ROT

Example cases (the "training set" or "learning sample") are represented as vectors of attribute-values paired with class names. The generic problem is to find an expression that predicts the classes of new cases (the "test set") taken at random from the same population. Goodness of agreement between the true classes and the classes picked by the classifier is then used to measure accuracy. An underlying assumption is that *either* training and test sets are randomly sampled from the same data source, *or* full statistical allowance can be made for departures from such a regime.

Symbolic learning is used for the computer-based construction of bodies of articulate expertise in domains which lie partly at least beyond the introspective reach of domain experts. Thus the above rule *was not of human expert authorship*, although an expert can assimilate it and pass it on. To ascend an order of magnitude in scale, KARDIO's comprehensive treatise on ECG interpretation (Bratko *et al.*, 1989) does not contain a single rule of human authorship. Above the level of primitive descriptors, every formulation was data-derived, and every data item was generated from a computable logic of heart/electrocardiograph interaction. Independently constructed statistical diagnosis systems are commercially available in computer-driven ECG kits, and exhibit accuracies in the 80% – 90% range. Here the ML product scores higher, being subject to error only if the initial logical model contained flaws. None have yet come to light. But the difference that illuminates the distinctive nature of symbolic ML concerns mental fit. Because of its mode of construction, KARDIO is able to support its decisions with insight into causes. Statistically derived systems do not. However, developments of Bayesian treatments initiated by ML-leaning statisticians (see Spiegelhalter, 1986) and statistically inclined ML theorists (see Pearl, 1988) may change this.

Although marching to a different drum, ML people have for some time been seen as a possibly useful source of algorithms for certain data-analyses required in industry. There are two broad circumstances that might favour applicability:

1. categorical rather than numerical attributes;
2. strong and pervasive conditional dependencies among attributes.

As an example of what is meant by a conditional dependency, let us take the classification of vertebrates and consider two variables, namely "breeding-ground" (values: sea, fresh-water, land) and "skin-covering" (values: scales, feathers, hair, none). As a value for the first, "sea" votes overwhelmingly for FISH. If the second attribute has the value "none", then on its own this would virtually clinch the case for AMPHIBIAN. But in combination with "breeding-ground = sea" it switches identification decisively to MAMMAL. Whales and some other sea mammals now remain the only possibility. "Breeding-ground" and "skin-covering" are said to exhibit strong conditional dependency. Problems characterised by violent attribute-interactions of this kind can sometimes be important in industry. In predicting automobile accident risks, for example, information that a driver is in the age-group 17 – 23 acquires great significance if and only if sex = male.

To examine the "horses for courses" aspect of comparisons between ML, neural-net and statistical algorithms, a reasonable principle might be to select datasets approximately evenly among four main categories as shown in Figure 5.2.

	conditional dependencies	
	strong and pervasive	weak or absent
attributes — all or mainly categorical	+	(+)
all or mainly numerical	+	(−)

Key: +   ML expected to do well
     (+)   ML expected to do well, marginally
     (−)   ML expected to do poorly, marginally

Fig. 5.2: Relative performance of ML algorithms.

In StatLog, collection of datasets necessarily followed opportunity rather than design, so that for light upon these particular contrasts the reader will find much that is suggestive, but less that is clear-cut. Attention is, however, called to the Appendices which contain additional information for readers interested in following up particular algorithms and datasets for themselves.

Classification learning is characterised by (i) the data-description language, (ii) the language for expressing the classifier, – *i.e.* as formulae, rules, *etc.* and (iii) the learning algorithm itself. Of these, (i) and (ii) correspond to the "observation language" and "hypothesis language" respectively of Section 12.2. Under (ii) we consider in the present chapter the machine learning of if-then rule-sets and of decision trees. The two kinds of language are interconvertible, and group themselves around two broad inductive inference strategies, namely specific-to-general and general-to-specific

5.1.2   Specific-to-general: a paradigm for rule-learning

Michalski's AQ11 and related algorithms were inspired by methods used by electrical engineers for simplifying Boolean circuits (see, for example, Higonnet & Grea, 1958). They exemplify the specific-to-general, and typically start with a maximally specific rule for assigning cases to a given class, - for example to the class MAMMAL in a taxonomy of vertebrates. Such a "seed", as the starting rule is called, specifies a value for every member of the set of attributes characterizing the problem, for example

Rule 1.123456789   **if** skin-covering = hair, breathing = lungs, tail = none, can-fly = y, reproduction = viviparous, legs = y, warm-blooded = y, diet = carnivorous, activity = nocturnal
then MAMMAL.

We now take the reader through the basics of specific-to-general rule learning. As a minimalist tutorial exercise we shall build a MAMMAL-recogniser.

The initial rule, numbered 1.123456789 in the above, is so specific as probably to be capable only of recognising bats. Specificity is relaxed by dropping attributes one at a time, thus:

Rule 1.23456789   **if** breathing = lungs, tail = none, can-fly = y, reproduction = viviparous, legs = y, warm-blooded = y, diet = carnivorous, activity = nocturnal
then MAMMAL;

Rule 1.13456789   **if** skin-covering = hair, tail = none, can-fly = y, reproduction = viviparous, legs = y, warm-blooded = y, diet = carnivorous, activity = nocturnal
then MAMMAL;

Rule 1.12456789   **if** skin-covering = hair, breathing = lungs, can-fly = y, reproduction = viviparous, legs = y, warm-blooded = y, diet = carnivorous, activity = nocturnal
then MAMMAL;

Rule 1.12356789   **if** skin-covering = hair, breathing = lungs, tail = none, reproduction = viviparous, legs = y, warm-blooded = y, diet = carnivorous, activity = nocturnal
thenMAMMAL;

Rule 1.12346789   **if** skin-covering = hair, breathing = lungs, tail = none, can-fly = y, legs = y, warm-blooded = y, diet = carnivorous, activity = nocturnal
bf then MAMMAL;

and so on for all the ways of dropping a single attribute, followed by all the ways of dropping two attributes, three attributes etc. Any rule which includes in its cover a "negative example", *i.e.* a non-mammal, is *incorrect* and is discarded during the process. The cycle terminates by saving a set of shortest rules covering only mammals. As a classifier, such a set is guaranteed *correct*, but cannot be guaranteed *complete*, as we shall see later.

In the present case the terminating set has the single-attribute description:

Rule 1.1   **if** skin-covering = hair
                       then MAMMAL;

The process now iterates using a new "seed" for each iteration, for example:

Rule 2.123456789   **if** skin-covering = none, breathing = lungs, tail = none, can-fly =
                       n, reproduction = viviparous, legs = n, warm-blooded = y, diet =
                       mixed, activity = diurnal
                       then MAMMAL;

leading to the following set of shortest rules:

Rule 2.15   **if** skin-covering = none, reproduction = viviparous
                       then MAMMAL;

Rule 2.17   **if** skin-covering = none, warm-blooded = y
                       then MAMMAL;

Rule 2.67   **if** legs = n, warm-blooded = y
                       then MAMMAL;

Rule 2.57   **if** reproduction = viviparous, warm-blooded = y
                       then MAMMAL;

Of these, the first covers naked mammals. Amphibians, although uniformly naked, are oviparous. The second has the same cover, since amphibians are not warm-blooded, and birds, although warm-blooded, are not naked (we assume that classification is done on adult forms). The third covers various naked marine mammals. So far, these rules collectively contribute little information, merely covering a few overlapping pieces of a large patchwork. But the last rule at a stroke covers almost the whole class of mammals. Every attempt at further generalisation now encounters negative examples. Dropping "warm-blooded" causes the rule to cover viviparous groups of fish and of reptiles. Dropping "viviparous" causes the rule to cover birds, unacceptable in a mammal-recogniser. But it also has the effect of including the egg-laying mammals "Monotremes", consisting of the duck-billed platypus and two species of spiny ant-eaters. Rule 2.57 fails to cover these, and is thus an instance of the earlier-mentioned kind of classifier that can be guaranteed *correct*, but cannot be guaranteed *complete*. Conversion into a *complete and correct* classifier is not an option for this purely specific-to-general process, since we have run out of permissible generalisations. The construction of Rule 2.57 has thus stalled in sight of the finishing line. But linking two or more rules together, each correct but not complete, can effect the desired result. Below we combine the rule yielded by the first iteration with, in turn, the first and the second rule obtained from the second iteration:

Rule 1.1   **if** skin-covering = hair
                       then MAMMAL;

Rule 2.15   **if** skin-covering = none, reproduction = viviparous
                       then MAMMAL;

Rule 1.1   **if** skin-covering = hair
                       then MAMMAL;

Rule 2.17   **if** skin-covering = none, warm-blooded = y
                       then MAMMAL;

These can equivalently be written as disjunctive rules:

if	skin-covering = hair
or	skin-covering = none, reproduction = viviparous
then	MAMMAL;

and

if	skin-covering = hair
or	skin-covering = none, warm-blooded = y
then	MAMMAL;

In rule induction, following Michalski, an attribute-test is called a *selector*, a conjunction of selectors is a *complex*, and a disjunction of complexes is called a *cover*. If a rule is true of an example we say that it *covers* the example. Rule learning systems in practical use qualify and elaborate the above simple scheme, including by assigning a prominent role to general-to-specific processes. In the StatLog experiment such algorithms are exemplified by CN2 (Clarke & Niblett, 1989) and ITrule. Both generate decision rules for each class in turn, for each class starting with a *universal rule* which assigns all examples to the current class. This rule ought to cover at least one of the examples belonging to that class. Specialisations are then repeatedly generated and explored until all rules consistent with the data are found. Each rule must correctly classify at least a prespecified percentage of the examples belonging to the current class. As few as possible *negative* examples, *i.e.* examples in other classes, should be covered. Specialisations are obtained by adding a condition to the left-hand side of the rule.

CN2 is an extension of Michalski's (1969) algorithm AQ with several techniques to process noise in the data. The main technique for reducing error is to minimise $(k + 1)/(k + n + c)$ (Laplacian function) where k is the number of examples classified correctly by a rule, n is the number classified incorrectly, and c is the total number of classes.

ITrule produces rules of the form "if ... then ... with probability ...". This algorithm contains probabilistic inference through the J-measure, which evaluates its candidate rules. J-measure is a product of prior probabilities for each class and the cross-entropy of class values conditional on the attribute values. ITrule cannot deal with continuous numeric values. It needs accurate evaluation of prior and posterior probabilities. So when such information is not present it is prone to misuse. Detailed accounts of these and other algorithms are given in Section 5.2.

5.1.3   Decision trees

Reformulation of the MAMMAL-recogniser as a completed decision tree would require the implicit "else NOT-MAMMAL" to be made explicit, as in Figure 5.3. Construction of the complete outline taxonomy as a set of descriptive concepts, whether in rule-structured or tree-structured form, would entail repetition of the induction process for BIRD, REPTILE, AMPHIBIAN and FISH.

In order to be meaningful to the user (*i.e.* to satisfy the "mental fit" criterion) it has been found empirically that trees should be as *small* and as *linear* as possible. In fully linear trees, such as that of Figure 5.3, an internal node (*i.e.* attribute test) can be the parent of at most one internal node. All its other children must be end-node or "leaves" (outcomes). Quantitative measures of linearity are discussed by Arbab & Michie (1988), who present an algorithm, RG, for building trees biased towards linearity. They also compare RG with Bratko's (1983) AOCDL directed towards the same end. We now consider the general

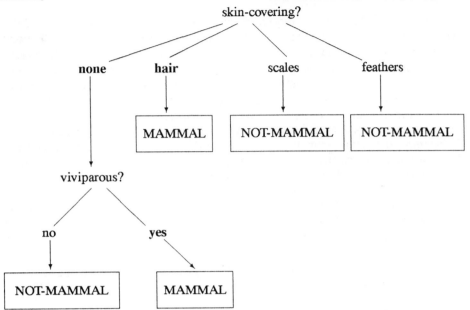

Fig. 5.3: Translation of a mammal-recognising rule (Rule 2.15, see text) into tree form. The attribute-values that figured in the rule-sets built earlier are here set larger in bold type. The rest are tagged with NOT-MAMMAL labels.

properties of algorithms that grow trees from data.

5.1.4 General-to-specific: top-down induction of trees

In common with CN2 and ITrule but in contrast to the specific-to-general earlier style of Michalski's AQ family of rule learning, decision-tree learning is general-to-specific. In illustrating with the vertebrate taxonomy example we will assume that the set of nine attributes are sufficient to classify *without error* all vertebrate species into one of MAMMAL, BIRD, AMPHIBIAN, REPTILE, FISH. Later we will consider elaborations necessary in underspecified or in inherently "noisy" domains, where methods from statistical data analysis enter the picture.

As shown in Figure 5.4, the starting point is a tree of only one node that allocates all cases in the training set to a single class. In the case that a mammal-recogniser is required, this default class could be NOT-MAMMAL. The presumption here is that in the population there are more of these than there are mammals.

Unless *all* vertebrates in the training set are non-mammals, some of the training set of cases associated with this single node will be correctly classified and others incorrectly, – in the terminology of Breiman and colleagues (1984), such a node is "impure". Each available attribute is now used on a trial basis to split the set into subsets. Whichever split minimises the estimated "impurity" of the subsets which it generates is retained, and the cycle is repeated on each of the augmented tree's end-nodes.

Numerical measures of impurity are many and various. They all aim to capture the degree to which expected frequencies of belonging to given classes (possibly estimated, for example, in the two-class mammal/not-mammal problem of Figure 5.4 as $M/(M + M')$) are affected by knowledge of attribute values. In general the goodness of a split into subsets (for example by skin-covering, by breathing organs, by tail-type, etc.) is the weighted mean decrease in impurity, weights being proportional to the subset sizes. Let us see how these ideas work out in a specimen development of a mammal-recognising tree. To facilitate comparison with the specific-to-general induction shown earlier, the tree is represented in Figure 5.5 as an if-then-else expression. We underline class names that label temporary leaves. These are nodes that need further splitting to remove or diminish impurity.

This simple taxonomic example lacks many of the complicating factors encountered in classification generally, and lends itself to this simplest form of decision tree learning. Complications arise from the use of numerical attributes in addition to categorical, from the occurrence of error, and from the occurrence of unequal misclassification costs. Error can inhere in the values of attributes or classes ("noise"), or the domain may be deterministic, yet the supplied set of attributes may not support error-free classification. But to round off the taxonomy example, the following from Quinlan (1993) gives the simple essence of tree learning:

To construct a decision tree from a set T of training cases, let the classes be denoted $C_1, C_2, \ldots, C_j$. There are three possibilities:

- T contains one or more cases, all belonging to a single class C_j;
  The decision tree for T is a leaf identifying class C_j.
- T contains no cases:
  The decision tree is again a leaf, but the class to be associated with the leaf must be determined from information other than T. For example, the leaf might be chosen in accordance with some background knowledge of the domain, such as the overall majority class.
- T contains cases that belong to a mixture of classes:
  In this situation, the idea is to refine T into subsets of cases that are, or seem to be heading towards, single-class collections of cases. A test is chosen based on a single attribute, that has two or more mutually exclusive outcomes $O_1, O_2, \ldots, O_n$. T is partitioned into subsets $T_1, T_2, \ldots, T_n$, where T_i contains all the cases in T that have outcome Oi of the chosen test. The decision tree for T consists of a decision node identifying the test and one branch for each possible outcome. The same tree-building machinery is applied recursively to each subset of training cases, so that the ith branch leads to the decision tree constructed from the subset T_i of training cases.

Note that this schema is general enough to include multi-class trees, raising a tactical problem in approaching the taxonomic material. Should we build in turn a set of yes/no recognizers, one for mammals, one for birds, one for reptiles, etc., and then daisy-chain them into a tree? Or should we apply the full multi-class procedure to the data wholesale, risking a disorderly scattering of different class labels along the resulting tree's perimeter? If the entire tree-building process is automated, as for the later standardised comparisons, the second regime is mandatory. But in interactive decision-tree building there is no generally "correct" answer. The analyst must be guided by context, by user-requirements and by intermediate results.

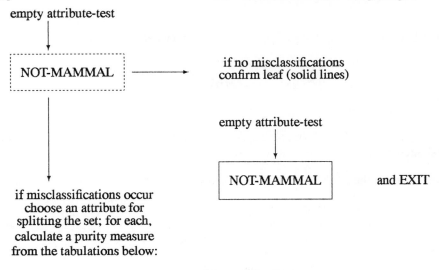

empty attribute-test

NOT-MAMMAL ─────────▶ if no misclassifications
confirm leaf (solid lines)

empty attribute-test

NOT-MAMMAL   and EXIT

if misclassifications occur
choose an attribute for
splitting the set; for each,
calculate a purity measure
from the tabulations below:

skin-covering?

	feathers	none	hair	scales	TOTAL
number of MAMMALs in set:	m_{fe}	m_{no}	m_{ha}	m_{sc}	M
number of NOT-MAMMALs:	m'_{fe}	m'_{no}	m'_{ha}	m'_{sc}	M'

breathing?

	lungs	gills	
number of MAMMALs in subset	m_{lu}	m_{gi}	M
number of NOT-MAMMALs	m'_{lu}	m'_{gi}	M'

tail?

	long	short	none	
number of MAMMALs in set	m_{lo}	m_{sh}	m_{no}	M
number of NOT-MAMMALs	m'_{lo}	m'_{sh}	m'_{no}	M'

and so on

Fig. 5.4: First stage in growing a decision tree from a training set. The single end-node is a candidate to be a leaf, and is here drawn with broken lines. It classifies all cases to NOT-MAMMAL. If correctly, the candidate is confirmed as a leaf. Otherwise available attribute-applications are tried for their abilities to split the set, saving for incorporation into the tree whichever maximises some chosen purity measure. Each saved subset now serves as a candidate for recursive application of the same split-and-test cycle.

Step 1: construct a single-leaf tree rooted in the empty attribute test:

> if ()
> then <u>NOT-MAMMAL</u>

Step2: if no impure nodes then EXIT

Step 3: construct from the training set all single-attribute trees and, for each, calculate the weighted mean impurity over its leaves;

Step 4: retain the attribute giving least impurity. Assume this to be skin-covering:

> if (skin-covering = hair)
> then MAMMAL
> if (skin-covering = feathers)
> then NOT-MAMMAL
> if (skin-covering = scales)
> then NOT-MAMMAL
> if (skin-covering = none)
> then <u>NOT-MAMMAL</u>

Step 5: if no impure nodes then EXIT

Otherwise apply Steps 3, and 4 and 5 recursively to each impure node, thus

Step 3: construct from the <u>NOT-MAMMAL</u> subset of Step 4 all single-attribute trees and, for each, calculate the weighted mean impurity over its leaves;

Step 4: retain the attribute giving least impurity. Perfect scores are achieved by "viviparous" and by "warm-blooded", giving:

if (skin-covering = hair)	and	if (skin-covering = hair)
then MAMMAL		then MAMMAL
if (skin-covering = feathers)		if (skin-covering = feathers)
then NOT-MAMMAL		then NOT-MAMMAL
if (skin-covering = scales)		if (skin-covering = scales)
then NOT-MAMMAL		then NOT-MAMMAL
if (skin-covering = none)		if (skin-covering = none)
then if (reproduction = viviparous)		then if (warm-blooded = y)
then MAMMAL		then MAMMAL
else NOT-MAMMAL		else NOT-MAMMAL

Step 5: EXIT

Fig. 5.5: Illustration, using the MAMMAL problem, of the basic idea of decision-tree induction.

Either way, the crux is the idea of refining T "into subsets of cases that are, or seem to be heading towards, single-class collections of cases." This is the same as the earlier described search for purity. Departure from purity is used as the "splitting criterion", *i.e.* as the basis on which to select an attribute to apply to the members of a less pure node for partitioning it into purer sub-nodes. But how to measure departure from purity? In practice, as noted by Breiman *et al.*, "overall misclassification rate is not sensitive to the choice of a splitting rule, as long as it is within a reasonable class of rules." For a more general consideration of splitting criteria, we first introduce the case where total purity of nodes is not attainable: *i.e.* some or all of the leaves necessarily end up mixed with respect to class membership. In these circumstances the term "noisy data" is often applied. But we must remember that "noise" (*i.e.* irreducible measurement error) merely characterises one particular form of inadequate information. Imagine the multi-class taxonomy problem under the condition that "skin-covering", "tail", and "viviparous" are omitted from the attribute set. Owls and bats, for example, cannot now be discriminated. Stopping rules based on complete purity have then to be replaced by something less stringent.

5.1.5 Stopping rules and class probability trees

One method, not necessarily recommended, is to stop when the purity measure exceeds some threshold. The trees that result are no longer strictly "decision trees" (although for brevity we continue to use this generic term), since a leaf is no longer guaranteed to contain a single-class collection, but instead a frequency distribution over classes. Such trees are known as "class probability trees". Conversion into classifiers requires a separate mapping from distributions to class labels. One popular but simplistic procedure says "pick the candidate with the most votes". Whether or not such a "plurality rule" makes sense depends in each case on (1) the distribution over the classes in the population from which the training set was drawn, *i.e.* on the priors, and (2) differential misclassification costs. Consider two errors: classifying the shuttle main engine as "ok to fly" when it is not, and classifying it as "not ok" when it is. Obviously the two costs are unequal.

Use of purity measures for stopping, sometimes called "forward pruning", has had mixed results. The authors of two of the leading decision tree algorithms, CART (Breiman *et al.*, 1984) and C4.5 (Quinlan 1993), independently arrived at the opposite philosophy, summarised by Breiman and colleagues as "Prune instead of stopping. Grow a tree that is much too large and prune it upward ..." This is sometimes called "backward pruning". These authors' definition of "much too large" requires that we continue splitting until each terminal node

either	is pure,
or	contains only identical attribute-vectors (in which case splitting is impossible),
or	has fewer than a pre-specified number of distinct attribute-vectors.

Approaches to the backward pruning of these "much too large" trees form the topic of a later section. We first return to the concept of a node's purity in the context of selecting one attribute in preference to another for splitting a given node.

5.1.6 Splitting criteria

Readers accustomed to working with categorical data will recognise in Figure 5.4 cross-tabulations reminiscent of the "contingency tables" of statistics. For example it only requires completion of the column totals of the second tabulation to create the standard input to a "two-by-two" χ_1^2. The hypothesis under test is that the distribution of cases between MAMMALs and NOT-MAMMALs is independent of the distribution between the two breathing modes. A possible rule says that the smaller the probability obtained by applying a χ^2 test to this hypothesis then the stronger the splitting credentials of the attribute "breathing". Turning to the construction of multi-class trees rather than yes/no concept-recognisers, an adequate number of fishes in the training sample would, under almost any purity criterion, ensure early selection of "breathing". Similarly, given adequate representation of reptiles, "tail=long" would score highly, since lizards and snakes account for 95% of living reptiles. The corresponding 5 x 3 contingency table would have the form given in Table 5.1. On the hypothesis of no association, the expected numbers in the $i \times j$ cells can be got from the marginal totals. Thus expected $e_{11} = N_M \times N_{\text{long}}/N$, where N is the total in the training set. Then $\sum[(\text{observed} - \text{expected})^2/\text{expected}]$ is distributed as χ^2, with degrees of freedom equal to $(i - 1) \times (j - 1)$, *i.e.* 8 in this case.

Table 5.1: Cross-tabulation of classes and "tail" attribute-values

	tail?			
	long	short	none	Totals
number in MAMMAL	n_{11}	n_{21}	n_{31}	N_M
number in BIRD	n_{12}	n_{22}	n_{32}	N_B
number in REPTILE	n_{13}	n_{23}	n_{33}	N_R
number in AMPHIBIAN	n_{14}	n_{24}	n_{34}	N_A
number in FISH	n_{15}	n_{25}	n_{35}	N_F
Total	N_{long}	N_{short}	N_{none}	N

Suppose, however, that the "tail" variable were not presented in the form of a categorical attribute with three unordered values, but rather as a number, – as the ratio, for example, of the length of the tail to that of the combined body and head. Sometimes the first step is to apply some form of clustering method or other approximation. But virtually every algorithm then selects, from all the dichotomous segmentations of the numerical scale meaningful for a given node, that segmentation that maximises the chosen purity measure over classes.

With suitable refinements, the CHAID decision-tree algorithm (CHi-squared Automatic Interaction Detection) uses a splitting criterion such as that illustrated with the foregoing contingency table (Kass, 1980). Although not included in the present trials, CHAID enjoys widespread commercial availability through its inclusion as an optional module in the SPSS statistical analysis package.

Other approaches to such tabulations as the above use information theory. We then enquire "what is the expected gain in information about a case's row-membership from knowledge of its column-membership?". Methods and difficulties are discussed by Quinlan (1993). The reader is also referred to the discussion in Section 7.3.3, with particular reference to "mutual information".

A related, but more direct, criterion applies Bayesian probability theory to the weighing of evidence (see Good, 1950, for the classical treatment) in a sequential testing framework (Wald, 1947). Logarithmic measure is again used, namely log-odds or "plausibilities" of hypotheses concerning class-membership. The plausibility-shift occasioned by each observation is interpreted as the weight of the evidence contributed by that observation. We ask: "what expected total weight of evidence, bearing on the j class-membership hypotheses, is obtainable from knowledge of an attribute's values over the $i \times j$ cells?". Preference goes to that attribute contributing the greatest expected total (Michie, 1990; Michie & Al Attar, 1991). The sequential Bayes criterion has the merit, once the tree is grown, of facilitating the recalculation of probability estimates at the leaves in the light of revised knowledge of the priors.

In their CART work Breiman and colleagues initially used an information-theoretic criterion, but subsequently adopted their "Gini" index. For a given node, and classes with estimated probabilities $p(j)$, $j = 1, \ldots, J$, the index can be written $1 - \sum p^2(j)$. The authors note a number of interesting interpretations of this expression. But they also remark that "... within a wide range of splitting criteria the properties of the final tree selected are surprisingly insensitive to the choice of splitting rule. The criterion used to prune or recombine upward is much more important."

5.1.7 Getting a "right-sized tree"

CART's, and C4.5's, pruning starts with growing "a tree that is much too large". How large is "too large"? As tree-growth continues and end-nodes multiply, the sizes of their associated samples shrink. Probability estimates formed from the empirical class-frequencies at the leaves accordingly suffer escalating estimation errors. Yet this only says that overgrown trees make unreliable probability estimators. Given an unbiased mapping from probability estimates to decisions, why should their performance *as classifiers* suffer?

Performance is indeed impaired by overfitting, typically more severely in tree-learning than in some other multi-variate methods. Figure 5.6 typifies a universally observed relationship between the number of terminal nodes (x-axis) and misclassification rates (y-axis). Breiman *et al.*, from whose book the figure has been taken, describe this relationship as "a fairly rapid initial decrease followed by a long, flat valley and then a gradual increase ..." In this long, flat valley, the minimum "is almost constant except for up-down changes well within the ± 1 SE range." Meanwhile the performance of the tree on the training sample (not shown in the Figure) continues to improve, with an increasingly over-optimistic error rate usually referred to as the "resubstitution" error. An important lesson that can be drawn from inspection of the diagram is that large simplifications of the tree can be purchased at the expense of rather small reductions of estimated accuracy.

Overfitting is the process of inferring more structure from the training sample than is justified by the population from which it was drawn. Quinlan (1993) illustrates the seeming paradox that an overfitted tree can be a worse classifier than one that has no information at all beyond the name of the dataset's most numerous class.

This effect is readily seen in the extreme example of random data in which the class of each case is quite unrelated to its attribute values. I constructed an artificial dataset of this kind with ten attributes, each of which took the value 0 or 1 with equal probability. The class was also binary, **yes** with probability 0.25 and **no** with probability 0.75. One thousand randomly generated cases were split intp a training set of 500 and a test set of 500. From this data, C4.5's initial tree-building routine

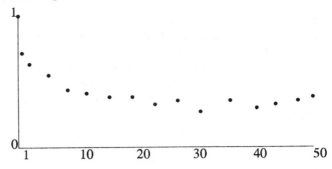

Fig. 5.6: A typical plot of misclassification rate against different levels of growth of a fitted tree. Horizontal axis: no. of terminal nodes. Vertical axis: misclassification rate measured on test data.

produces a nonsensical tree of 119 nodes that has an error rate of more than 35% on the test cases

....For the random data above, a tree consisting of just the leaf no would have an expected error rate of 25% on unseen cases, yet the elaborate tree is noticeably less accurate. While the complexity comes as no surprise, the increased error attributable to overfitting is not intuitively obvious. To explain this, suppose we have a two-class task in which a case's class is inherently indeterminate, with proportion $p \geq 0.5$ of the cases belonging to the majority class (here no). If a classifier assigns all such cases to this majority class, its expected error rate is clearly $1 - p$. If, on the other hand, the classifier assigns a case to the majority class with probability p and to the other class with probability $1 - p$, its expected error rate is the sum of

- the probability that a case belonging to the majority class is assigned to the other class, $p \times (1 - p)$, and
- the probability that a case belonging to the other class is assigned to the majority class, $(1 - p) \times p$ which comes to $2 \times p \times (1 - p)$. Since p is at least 0.5, this is generally greater than $1 - p$, so the second classifier will have a higher error rate. Now, the complex decision tree bears a close resemblance to this second type of classifier. The tests are unrelated to class so, like a symbolic pachinko machine, the tree sends each case randomly to one of the leaves. ...

Quinlan points out that the probability of reaching a leaf labelled with class C is the same as the relative frequency of C in the training data, and concludes that the tree's expected error rate for the random data above is $2 \times 0.25 \times 0.75$ or 37.5%, quite close to the observed value.

Given the acknowledged perils of overfitting, how should backward pruning be applied to a too-large tree? The methods adopted for CART and C4.5 follow different philosophies, and other decision-tree algorithms have adopted their own variants. We have now reached the level of detail appropriate to Section 5.2 , in which specific features of the various tree and rule learning algorithms, including their methods of pruning, are examined. Before proceeding to these candidates for trial, it should be emphasized that their selection was necessarily to a large extent arbitrary, having more to do with the practical logic of co-ordinating a complex and geographically distributed project than with judgements of merit or importance. Apart from the omission of entire categories of ML (as with the genetic and ILP algorithms discussed in Chapter 12) particular contributions to decision-tree learning should be acknowledged that would otherwise lack mention.

First a major historical role, which continues today, belongs to the Assistant algorithm developed by Ivan Bratko's group in Slovenia (Cestnik, Kononenko and Bratko, 1987). Assistant introduced many improvements for dealing with missing values, attribute splitting and pruning, and has also recently incorporated the m-estimate method (Cestnik and Bratko, 1991; see also Dzeroski, Cesnik and Petrovski, 1993) of handling prior probability assumptions.

Second, an important niche is occupied in the commercial sector of ML by the XpertRule family of packages developed by Attar Software Ltd. Facilities for large-scale data analysis are integrated with sophisticated support for structured induction (see for example Attar, 1991). These and other features make this suite currently the most powerful and versatile facility available for industrial ML.

5.2 STATLOG'S ML ALGORITHMS

5.2.1 Tree-learning: further features of C4.5

The reader should be aware that the two versions of C4.5 used in the StatLog trials differ in certain respects from the present version which was recently presented in Quinlan (1993). The version on which accounts in Section 5.1 are based is that of the radical upgrade, described in Quinlan (1993).

5.2.2 NewID

NewID is a similar decision tree algorithm to C4.5. Similar to C4.5, NewID inputs a set of examples E, a set of attributes a_i and a class c. Its output is a decision tree, which performs (probabilistic) classification. Unlike C4.5, NewID does not perform windowing. Thus its core procedure is simpler:

1. Set the current examples C to E.
2. If C satisfies the termination condition, then output the current tree and halt.
3. For each attribute a_i, determine the value of the evaluation function. With the attribute a_j that has the largest value of this function, divide the set C into subsets by attribute values. For each such subset of examples E_k, recursively re-enter at step (i) with E set to E_k. Set the subtrees of the current node to be the subtrees thus produced.

The termination condition is simpler than C4.5, *i.e.* it terminates when the node contains all examples in the same class. This simple-minded strategy tries to overfit the training data and will produce a complete tree from the training data. NewID deals with empty leaf nodes as C4.5 does, but it also considers the possibility of clashing examples. If the set of (untested) attributes is empty it labels the leaf node as CLASH, meaning that it is impossible to distinguish between the examples. In most situations the attribute set will not be empty. So NewID discards attributes that have been used, as they can contribute no more information to the tree.

For classification problems, where the class values are categorical, the evaluation function of NewID is the information gain function $gain(c, a)$. It does a similar 1-level lookahead to determine the best attribute to split on using a greedy search. It also handles numeric attributes in the same way as C4.5 does using the attribute subsetting method.

Numeric class values

NewID allows numeric class values and can produce a regression tree. For each split, it aims to reduce the spread of class values in the subsets introduced by the split, instead of trying to gain the most information. Formally, for each ordered categorical attribute with values in the set $\{v_j | j = 1, ..., m\}$, it chooses the one that minimises the value of:

$$\sum_{j=1}^{m} variance(\{\text{class of } e\} \mid \text{attribute value of } e = v_j\})$$

For numeric attributes, the attribute subsetting method is used instead.

When the class value is numeric, the termination function of the algorithm will also be different. The criterion that all examples share the same class value is no longer appropriate, and the following criterion is used instead: the algorithm terminates at a node N with examples S when

$$\sigma(S) \leq 1/k \, \sigma(E)$$

where $\sigma(S)$ is the standard deviation, E is the original example set, and the constant k is a user-tunable parameter.

Missing values

There are two types of missing values in NewID: unknown values and "don't-care" values. During the training phase, if an example of class c has an unknown attribute value, it is split into "fractional examples" for each possible value of that attribute. The fractions of the different values sum to 1. They are estimated from the numbers of examples of the same class with a known value of that attribute.

Consider attribute a with values yes and no. There are 9 examples at the current node in class c with values for a: 6 yes, 2 no and 1 missing ('?'). Naively, we would split the '?' in the ratio 6 to 2 (*i.e.* 75% yes and 25% no). However, the Laplace criterion gives a better estimate of the expected ratio of yes to no using the formula:

$$
\begin{aligned}
fraction(yes) &= (n_{c,yes} + 1)/(n_c + n_a) \\
&= (6 + 1)/(8 + 2),
\end{aligned}
$$

where

$n_{c,yes}$ is the no. examples in class c with attribute $a = yes$

n_c is the total no. examples in class c

n_a is the total no. examples in with a

and similarly for $fraction(no)$. This latter Laplace estimate is used in NewID.

"Don't-care"s ('*') are intended as a short-hand to cover all the possible values of the don't-care attribute. They are handled in a similar way to unknowns, except the example is simply duplicated, not fractionalised, for each value of the attribute when being inspected.

Thus, in a similar case with 6 *yes*'s, 2 *no*'s and 1 '*', the '*' example would be considered as 2 examples, one with value *yes* and one with value *no*. This duplication only occurs when inspecting the split caused by attribute a. If a different attribute b is being considered, the example with $a = *$ and a known value for b is only considered as 1 example. Note this is an ad hoc method because the duplication of examples may cause the total number of examples at the leaves to add up to more than the total number of examples originally in the training set.

When a tree is executed, and the testing example has an unknown value for the attribute being tested on, the example is again split fractionally using the Laplace estimate for the ratio – but as the testing example's class value is unknown, *all* the training examples at the node (rather than just those of class c) are used to estimate the appropriate fractions to split the testing example into. The numbers of training examples at the node are found by back-propagating the example counts recorded at the leaves of the subtree beneath the node back to that node. The class predicted at a node is the majority class there (if a tie with more than one majority class, select the first). The example may thus be classified, say, f_1 as c_1 and f_2 as c_2, where c_1 and c_2 are the majority classes at the two leaves where the fractional examples arrive.

Rather than predicting the majority class, a probabilistic classification is made, for example, a leaf with [6, 2] for classes c_1 and c_2 classifies an example 75% as c_1 and 25% as c_2 (rather than simply as c_1). For fractional examples, the distributions would be weighted and summed, for example, 10% arrives at leaf [6,2], 90% at leaf [1,3] $\Rightarrow$ class ratios are $10\% \times [6,2] + 90\% \times [1,3] = [1.5,2.9]$, thus the example is 34% c_1 and 66% c_2.

A testing example tested on an attribute with a don't-care value is simply duplicated for each outgoing branch, *i.e.* a whole example is sent down every outgoing branch, thus counting it as several examples.

Tree pruning

The pruning algorithm works as follows. Given a tree T induced from a set of learning examples, a further pruning set of examples, and a threshold value R: Then for each internal node N of the T, if the subtree of T lying below N provides $R\%$ better accuracy for the pruning examples than node N does (if labelled by the majority class for the learning examples at that node), then leave the subtree unpruned; otherwise, prune it (*i.e.* delete the sub-tree and make node N a leaf-node). By default, R is set to 10%, but one can modify it to suit different tasks.

Apart from the features described above (which are more relevant to the version of NewID used for StatLog), NewID has a number of other features. NewID can have binary splits for each attribute at a node of a tree using the subsetting principle. It can deal with ordered sequential attributes (*i.e.* attributes whose values are ordered). NewID can also accept a pre-specified ordering of attributes so the more important ones will be considered first, and the user can force NewID to choose a particular attribute for splitting at a node. It can also deal with structured attributes.

5.2.3 AC^2

AC^2 is not a single algorithm, it is a knowledge acquisition environment for expert systems which enables its user to build a knowledge base or an expert system from the analysis of examples provided by the human expert. Thus it placed considerable emphasis on the dialog and interaction of the system with the user. The user interacts with AC^2 via a graphical interface. This interface is consisting of graphical editors, which enable the user to define the domain, to interactively build the data base, and to go through the hierarchy of classes and the decision tree.

AC^2 can be viewed as an extension of a tree induction algorithm that is essentially the same as NewID. Because of its user interface, it allows a more natural manner of interaction with a domain expert, the validation of the trees produced, and the test of its accuracy and reliability. It also provides a simple, fast and cheap method to update the rule and data bases. It produces, from data and known rules (trees) of the domain, either a decision tree or a set of rules designed to be used by expert system.

5.2.4   Further features of CART

CART, *Classification and Regression Tree*, is a binary decision tree algorithm (Breiman *et al.*, 1984), which has exactly two branches at each internal node. We have used two different implementations of CART: the commercial version of CART and IndCART, which is part of the Ind package (also see Naive Bayes, Section 4.5). IndCART differs from CART as described in Breiman *et al.* (1984) in using a different (probably better) way of handling missing values, in not implementing the regression part of CART, and in the different pruning settings.

Evaluation function for splitting

The evaluation function used by CART is different from that in the ID3 family of algorithms. Consider the case of a problem with two classes, and a node has 100 examples, 50 from each class, the node has maximum impurity. If a split could be found that split the data into one subgroup of 40:5 and another of 10:45, then intuitively the impurity has been reduced. The impurity would be completely removed if a split could be found that produced sub-groups 50:0 and 0:50. In CART this intuitive idea of impurity is formalised in the *GINI* index for the current node c:

$$Gini(c) = 1 - \sum_j p_j^2$$

where p_j is the probability of class j in c. For each possible split the impurity of the subgroups is summed and the split with the maximum reduction in impurity chosen.

For ordered and numeric attributes, CART considers all possible splits in the sequence. For n values of the attribute, there are $n-1$ splits. For categorical attributes CART examines all possible binary splits, which is the same as attribute subsetting used for C4.5. For n values of the attribute, there are $2^{n-1} - 1$ splits. At each node CART searches through the attributes one by one. For each attribute it finds the best split. Then it compares the best single splits and selects the best attribute of the best splits.

Minimal cost complexity tree pruning

Apart from the evaluation function CART's most crucial difference from the other machine learning algorithms is its sophisticated pruning mechanism. CART treats pruning as a tradeoff between two issues: getting the right size of a tree and getting accurate estimates of the true probabilities of misclassification. This process is known as minimal cost-complexity pruning.

It is a two stage method. Considering the first stage, let T be a decision tree used to classify n examples in the training set C. Let E be the misclassified set of size m. If $l(T)$ is the number of leaves in T the *cost complexity* of T for some parameter α is:

$$R_\alpha = R(T) + \alpha \cdot l(T),$$

where $R(T) = m/n$ is the error estimate of T. If we regard α as the cost for each leaf, R_α is a linear combination of its error estimate and a penalty for its complexity. If α is small the penalty for having a large number of leaves is small and T will be large. As α increases, the minimising subtree will decrease in size. Now if we convert some subtree S to a leaf. The new tree T_α would misclassify k more examples but would contain $l(S) - 1$ fewer leaves. The cost complexity of T_α is the same as that of T if

$$\alpha = \frac{k}{n \cdot (l(S) - 1)}.$$

It can be shown that there is a unique subtree T_α which minimises $R_\alpha(T)$ for any value of α such that all other subtrees have higher cost complexities or have the same cost complexity and have T_α as a pruned subtree.

For $T_0 = T$, we can find the subtree such that α is as above. Let this tree be T_1. There is then a minimising sequence of trees $T_1 \supset T_2 \supset ...$, where each subtree is produced by pruning upward from the previous subtree. To produce T_{i+1} from T_i we examine each non-leaf subtree of T_i and find the minimum value of α. The one or more subtrees with that value of α will be replaced by leaves. The best tree is selected from this series of trees with the classification error not exceeding an expected error rate on some test set, which is done at the second stage.

This latter stage selects a single tree based on its reliability, *i.e.* classification error. The problem of pruning is now reduced to finding which tree in the sequence is the optimally sized one. If the error estimate $R(T_0)$ was unbiased then the largest tree T_1 would be chosen. However this is not the case and it tends to underestimate the number of errors. A more honest estimate is therefore needed. In CART this is produced by using cross-validation. The idea is that, instead of using one sample (training data) to build a tree and another sample (pruning data) to test the tree, you can form several pseudo-independent samples from the original sample and use these to form a more accurate estimate of the error. The general method is:

1. Randomly split the original sample E into n equal subsamples $S_1, ..., S_n$.
2. For $i = 1$ to n:
   a) Build a tree on the training set $S - S_i$; and
   b) Determine the error estimate R_i using the pruning set S_i.
3. Form the cross-validation error estimate as

$$\sum_{i=1}^{n} \frac{|S_i|}{|S|} R_i$$

Cross-validation and cost complexity pruning is combined to select the value of α. The method is to estimate the expected error rates of estimates obtained with T_α for all values of α using cross-validation. From these estimates, it is then possible to estimate an optimal value α_{opt} of α for which the estimated true error rate of $T_{\alpha_{opt}}$ for all the data is the minimum for all values of α. The value α_{opt} is that value of a which minimises the mean cross-validation error estimate. Once $T_{\alpha_{opt}}$ has been determined, the tree that is finally suggested for use is that which minimises the cost-complexity using α_{opt} and all the data.

The CART methodology therefore involves two quite separate calculations. First the value of α_{opt} is determined using cross-validation. Ten fold cross-validation is recommended. The second step is using this value of α_{opt} to grow the final tree.

Missing values

Missing attribute values in the training and test data are dealt with in CART by using surrogate splits. The idea is this: Define a measure of similarity between any two splits s and s' of a node N. If the best split of N is the split s on the attribute a, find the split s' on the attributes other than a that is most similar to s. If an example has the value of a missing, decide whether it goes to the left or right sub-tree by using the best surrogate split. If it is missing the variable containing the best surrogate split, then the second best is used, and so on.

5.2.5   Cal5

Cal5 is especially designed for continuous and ordered discrete valued attributes, though an added sub-algorithm is able to handle unordered discrete valued attributes as well.

Let the examples E be sampled from the examples expressed with n attributes. CAL5 separates the examples from the n dimensions into areas represented by subsets $E_i \in E$ $(i = 1, ..., n)$ of samples, where the class c_i $(j = 1, ..., m)$ exists with a probability

$$p(c_j) > \beta$$

where $\beta \leq 1$ is a decision threshold. Similar to other decision tree methods, only class areas bounded by hyperplanes parallel to the axes of the feature space are possible.

Evaluation function for splitting

The tree will be constructed sequentially starting with one attribute and branching with other attributes recursively, if no sufficient discrimination of classes can be achieved. That is, if at a node no decision for a class c_i according to the above formula can be made, a branch formed with a new attribute is appended to the tree. If this attribute is continuous, a discretisation, *i.e.* intervals corresponding to qualitative values has to be used.

Let N be a certain non-leaf node in the tree construction process. At first the attribute with the best local discrimination measure at this node has to be determined. For that two different methods can be used (controlled by an option): a statistical and an entropy measure, respectively. The statistical approach is working without any knowledge about the result of the desired discretisation. For continuous attributes the quotient (see Meyer-Brötz & Schürmann, 1970):

$$quotient(N) = \frac{A^2}{A^2 + D^2}$$

is a discrimination measure for a single attribute, where A is the standard deviation of examples in N from the centroid of the attribute value and D is the mean value of the square of distances between the classes. This measure has to be computed for each attribute. The attribute with the least value of $quotient(N)$ is chosen as the best one for splitting at this node. The entropy measure provided as an evaluation function requires an intermediate discretisation at N for each attribute a_i using the splitting procedure described below. Then the gain $g(N, a_i)$ of information will be computed for $a_i, i \in 1, ..., n$ by the well known ID3 entropy measure (Quinlan, 1986). The attribute with the largest value of the gain is chosen as the best one for splitting at that node. Note that at each node N all available attributes $a_1, a_2, ..., a_n$ will be considered again. If a_i is selected and occurs already in the path to N, than the discretisation procedure (see below) leads to a refinement of an already existing interval.

Discretisation

All examples $m_l \in E$ reaching the current node N are ordered along the axis of the selected new attribute a_i according to increasing values. *Intervals*, which contain an ordered set of values of the attribute, are formed recursively on the a_i-axis collecting examples from left to right until a class decision can be made on a given level of confidence α.

Let I be a current interval containing n examples of different classes and n_i the number of examples belonging to class c_i. Then n_i/n can be used to obtain an estimate of the probability $p(c_i|N)$ on the current node N. The hypothesis:

H1: There exists a class c_i occurring in I with $p(c_i|N) > \beta$,

will be tested against:

H2: For all classes c_j occurring in I the inequality $p(c_j|N) < \beta$ holds on a certain level of confidence $1 - \alpha$ (for a given α).

An estimation on the level $1 - \alpha$ yields a confidence interval $d(c_i)$ for $p(c_i|N)$ and in a long sequence of examples the true value of probability lies within $d(c_i)$ with probability $1 - \alpha$. The formula for computing this confidence interval:

$$d(c_i) = \frac{2\alpha c_i}{2\alpha n + 2} \mp \frac{1}{2\alpha n + 2} \sqrt{4\alpha c_i (1 - \frac{c_i}{n}) + 1}$$

is derived from the Tchebyschev inequality by supposing a Bernoulli distribution of class labels for each class c_i; see Unger & Wysotski (1981)).

Taking into account this confidence interval the hypotheses *H1* and *H2* are tested by:

H1: $d(c_i) > \beta$,

i.e. H1 is true, if the complete confidence interval lies above the predefined threshold, and

H2: $d(c_j) < \beta \ (j = 1, ...)$

i.e. this hypothesis is true, if for each class c_i the complete confidence interval is less than the threshold.

Now the following "meta-decision" on the dominance of a class in I can be defined as:

1. If there exists a class c_i, where *H1* is true then c_i dominates in I. The interval I is closed. The corresponding path of the tree is terminated.
2. If for all classes appearing in I the hypothesis *H2* is true, then no class dominates in I. In this case the interval will be closed, too. A new test with another attribute is necessary.
3. If neither 1. nor 2. occurs, the interval I has to be extended by the next example of the order of the current attribute. If there are no more examples for a further extension of I a majority decision will be made.

Merging

Adjacent intervals I_l, I_{l+1} with the same class label can be merged. The resultant intervals yield the leaf nodes of the decision tree. The same rule is applied for adjacent intervals where no class dominates and which contain identical remaining classes due to the following elimination procedure. A class within an interval I is removed, if the inequality:

$$d(c_i) > 1/n_I$$

is satisfied, where n_I is the total number of different class labels occurring in I (*i.e.* a class will be omitted, if its probability in I is less than the value of an assumed constant distribution of all classes occurring in I). These resultant intervals yield the intermediate nodes in the construction of the decision tree, for which further branching will be performed.

Every intermediate node becomes the start node for a further iteration step repeating the steps from sections 5.2.5 to 5.2.5. The algorithm stops when all intermediate nodes are all terminated. Note that a majority decision is made at a node if, because of a too small α, no estimation of probability can be done.

Discrete unordered attributes

To distinguish between the different types of attributes the program needs a special input vector. The algorithm for handling unordered discrete valued attributes is similar to that described in sections 5.2.5 to 5.2.5 apart from interval construction. Instead of intervals discrete points on the axis of the current attribute have to be considered. All examples with the same value of the current discrete attribute are related to one point on the axis. For each point the hypotheses *H1* and *H2* will be tested and the corresponding actions (a) and (b) performed, respectively. If neither *H1* nor *H2* is true, a majority decision will be made. This approach also allows handling mixed (discrete and continuous) valued attributes.

Probability threshold and confidence

As can be seen from the above two parameters affect the tree construction process: the first is a predefined threshold β for accept a node and the second is a predefined confidence level α. If the conditional probability of a class exceeds the threshold β the tree is pre-pruned at that node. The choice of β should depend on the training (or pruning) set and determines the accuracy of the approximation of the class hyperplane, *i.e.* the admissible error rate. The higher the degree of overlapping of class regions in the feature space the less the threshold has to be for getting a reasonable classification result.

Therefore by selecting the value of β the accuracy of the approximation and simultaneously the complexity of the resulting tree can be controlled by the user. In addition to a constant β the algorithm allows to choose the threshold β in a class dependent manner, taking into account different costs for misclassification of different classes. With other words the influence of a given cost matrix can be taken into account during training, if the different costs for misclassification can be reflected by a class dependent threshold vector. One approach has been adopted by CAL5:

1. every column i $(i = 1, ..., m)$ of the cost matrix will be summed up (S_i);
2. the threshold of that class relating to the column i, for which S_i is a maximum (S_{max}) has to be chosen by the user like in the case of a constant threshold (β_{max});
3. the other thresholds β_i will be computed by the formula

$$\beta_i = \delta(S_i/S_{max}) \cdot \beta_{max} \ (i = 1, ..., m).$$

From experience δ should be set to one. Thus all values of the class dependent thresholds are proportional to their corresponding column sums of the cost matrix, which can be interpreted as a penalty measure for misclassification into those classes.

Compared with the threshold the confidence level α for estimating the appropriate class probability has an inversely proportional effect. The less the value of α the better the demanded quality of estimation and the worse the ability to separate intervals, since the algorithm is enforced to construct large intervals in order to get sufficient statistics.

A suitable approach for the automatically choosing the parameters α and β is not available. Therefore a program for varying the parameter α between, by default, 0.15 and 0.6 and β between, by default, 0.4 and 0.9 in steps of 0.05 is used to predefine the best parameter combination, *i.e.* that which gives the minimum cost (or error rate, respectively) on a test set. However, this procedure may be computationally expensive in relation to the number of attributes and the size of data set.

5.2.6   Bayes tree

This is a Bayesian approach to decision trees that is described by Buntine (1992), and is available in the IND package. It is based on a full Bayesian approach: as such it requires the specification of prior class probabilities (usually based on empirical class proportions), and a probability model for the decision tree. A multiplicative probability model for the probability of a tree is adopted. Using this form simplifies the problem of computing tree probabilities, and the decision to grow a tree from a particular node may then be based on the increase in probability of the resulting tree, thus using only information local to that node. Of all potential splits at that node, that split is chosen which increases the posterior probability of the tree by the greatest amount.

Post-pruning is done by using the same principle, *i.e.* choosing the cut that maximises the posterior probability of the resulting tree. Of all those tree structures resulting from pruning a node from the given tree, choose that which has maximum posterior probability.

An alternative to post-pruning is to smooth class probabilities. As an example is dropped down the tree, it goes through various nodes. The class probabilities of each node visited contribute to the final class probabilities (by a weighted sum), so that the final class probabilities inherit probabilities evaluated higher up the tree. This stabilises the class probability estimates (*i.e.* reduces their variance) at the expense of introducing bias.

Costs may be included in learning and testing via a utility function for each class (the utility is the negative of the cost for the two-class case).

5.2.7   Rule-learning algorithms: CN2

This algorithm of Clark and Niblett's was sketched earlier. It aims to modify the basic AQ algorithm of Michalski in such a way as to equip it to cope with noise and other complications in the data. In particular during its search for good complexes CN2 does not automatically remove from consideration a candidate that is found to include one or more negative example. Rather it retains a set of complexes in its search that is evaluated statistically as covering a large number of examples of a given class and few of other classes. Moreover, the manner in which the search is conducted is general-to-specific. Each trial specialisation step takes the form of either adding a new conjunctive term or removing a disjunctive one. Having found a good complex, the algorithm removes those examples it covers from the training set and adds the rule "if <complex> then predict <class>" to the end of the rule list. The process terminates for each given class when no more acceptable complexes can be found.

Clark & Niblett's (1989) CN2 algorithm has the following main features: 1) the dependence on specific training examples during search (a feature of the AQ algorithm) is removed; 2) it combines the efficiency and ability to cope with noisy data of decision-tree learning with the if-then rule form and flexible search strategy of the AQ family; 3) it contrasts with other approaches to modify AQ to handle noise in that the basic AQ algorithm itself is generalised rather than "patched" with additional pre- and post-processing techniques; and 4) it produces both ordered and unordered rules.

CN2 inputs a set of training examples E and output a set of rules called **rule_list**. The core of CN2 is the procedure as follows, but it needs to use a sub-procedure to return the value of **best_cpx**:

1. Let **rule_list** be the empty list;
2. Let **best_cpx** be the best complex found from E;
3. If **best_cpx** or E is empty then stop and return **rule_list**;
4. Remove the examples covered by **best_cpx** from E and add the rule "**if best_cpx then** class=c" to the end of **rule_list** where c is the most common class of examples covered by **best_cpx**; re-enter at step (2).

This subprocedure is used for producing ordered rules. CN2 also produces a set of unordered rules, which uses a slightly different procedure. To produce unordered rules, the above procedure is repeated for each class in turn. In addition, in step 4 only the positive examples should be removed.

The procedure for finding the best complex is as follows:

1. Let the set **star** contain only the empty complex and **best_cpx** be nil;
2. Let **selectors** be the set of all possible selectors;
3. If **star** is empty, then return the current **best_cpx**;
4. Specialise all complexes in **star** as **newstar**, which is the set $\{x \wedge y | x \in \textbf{star}, \mathbf{y} \in \textbf{selectors}\}$ and remove all complexes in **newstar** that are either in **star** (*i.e.* the unspecialised ones) or are null (*i.e.* $big = yes \wedge big = no$);
5. For every complex C_i in **newstar**, if C_i is statistically significant (in significance) when tested on E and better than (in goodness) **best_cpx** according to user-defined criteria when tested on E, then replace the current value of **best_cpx** by C_i; remove all worst complexes from **newstar** until the size of **newstar** is below the user-defined maximum; set **star** to **newstar** and re-enter at step (3).

As can be seen from the algorithm, the basic operation of CN2 is that of generating a *complex* (*i.e.* a conjunct of attribute tests) which *covers* (*i.e.* is satisfied by) a subset of the training examples. This complex forms the *condition* part of a production rule "if condition **then** class =c", where *class* is the most common class in the (training) examples which satisfy the condition. The condition is a conjunction of selectors, each of which represents a test on the values of an attribute such as "weather=wet". The search proceeds in both AQ and CN2 by repeatedly specialising candidate complexes until one which covers a large number of examples of a single class and few of other classes is located. Details of each search are outlined below.

The search for specialisations

The CN2 algorithm works in an iterative fashion, each iteration searching for a complex covering a large number of examples of a single class c and few of other classes. (The examples of the current class are called "positive" examples and the other examples are called "negative" examples.) The complex must be both predictive and reliable, as determined by CN2's evaluation functions. Having found a good complex, those examples it covers are removed from the training set and the rule "**if** <complex> *then* class=c" is added to the end of the rule list. This greedy process iterates until no more satisfactory complexes can be found.

To generate a single rule, CN2 first starts with the most general rule "**if** true **then** class=c" (*i.e.* all examples are class c), where c is the current class. Then CN2 searches for complexes by carrying out a general-to-specific *beam* search. The extent of the beam search for a complex can be regulated by controlling the width (*i.e.* number of complexes explored in parallel) of the beam. At each stage in the search, CN2 retains a size-limited set or *star S* of "complexes explored so far". The system examines only specialisations of this set, carrying out a beam search of the space of complexes. A complex is specialised by adding a new conjunctive term in one of its selector. Each complex can be specialised in several ways, and CN2 generates and evaluates all such specialisations. The star is trimmed after completion of this step by removing its lowest ranking elements as measured by an evaluation function that we will describe shortly.

The implementation of the specialisation step in CN2 is to repeatedly *intersect*[3] the set of all possible selectors with the current star, eliminating all the null and unchanged elements in the resulting set of complexes. (A null complex is one that contains a pair of incompatible selectors, for example, $\text{big} = y \wedge \text{big} = n$).

Search heuristics

There are two *heuristics* used in the search for the best complexes and both can be tuned by the user depending on the specific domain: the significance level and the goodness measure. Significance is an absolute threshold such that any (specialised) complexes below the threshold will not be considered for selecting the best complex (but they are still used for further specialisation in the *star*). Goodness is a measure of the quality of the complexes so it is used to order the complexes that are above the significance threshold to select the best complex.

Several difference functions can be chosen to guide the search for a good rule in the CN2/AQ system, for example:

- "Number of correctly classified examples divided by total number covered". This is the traditional AQ evaluation function.

- Entropy, similar to the information gain measure used by ID3 (Quinlan, 1986) and other decision tree algorithms.

- The Laplacian error estimate: $Accuracy\ a(n, n_c, k) = (n - n_c + k - 1)/(n + k)$ where n is the total number of examples covered by the rule, n_c is the number of positive examples covered by the rule and k is the number of classes in the problem.

---

[3] The intersection of set **A** with set **B** is the set $\{\mathbf{x} \wedge \mathbf{y} | \mathbf{x} \in \mathbf{A}, \mathbf{y} \in \mathbf{B}\}$. For example, using '.' to abbreviate '$\wedge$', $\{a.b, a.c, b.d\}$ intersected with $\{a, b, c, d\}$ is $\{a.b, a.b.c, a.b.d, a.c, a.c.d, b.d, b.c.d\}$. If we now remove unchanged elements in this set we obtain $\{a.b.c, a.b.d, a.c.d, b.c.d\}$.

CN2 uses one of these criteria according to the user's choice to order the goodness of rules.

To test significance, CN2 uses the entropy statistic. This is given by:

$$2 \sum_{i=1}^{n} p_i \log(p_i/q_i),$$

where the distribution $p_1, \ldots, p_n$ is the observed frequency distribution of examples among classes satisfying a given complex and $q_1, \ldots, q_n$ is the expected frequency distribution of the same number of examples under the assumption that the complex selects examples randomly. This is taken as the $N = \sum p_i$ covered examples distributed among classes with the same probability as that of examples in the entire training set. This statistic provides an information-theoretic measure of the (non-commutative) distance between the two distributions. The user provides a threshold of significance below which rules are rejected.

Missing values

Similar to NewID, CN2 can deal with unknown or don't-care values. During rule generation, a similar policy of handling unknowns and don't-cares is followed: unknowns are split into fractional examples and don't-cares are duplicated.

Each rule produced by CN2 is associated with a set of counts which corresponds to the number of examples, covered by the rule, belonging to each class. Strictly speaking, for the ordered rules the counts attached to rules when writing the rule set should be those encountered during rule generation. However, for unordered rules, the counts to attach are generated *after* rule generation in a second pass, following the execution policy of splitting an example with unknown attribute value into *equal* fractions for each value rather than the Laplace-estimated fractions used during rule generation.

When normally executing unordered rules without unknowns, for each rule which fires the class distribution (*i.e.* distribution of training examples among classes) attached to the rule is collected. These are then summed. Thus a training example satisfying two rules with attached class distributions [8,2] and [0,1] has an expected distribution [8,3] which results in c_1 being predicted, or $[c_1 : c_2] = [8/11 : 3/11]$ if probabilistic classification is desired. The built-in rule executer follows the first strategy (the example is classed simply c_1).

With unordered CN2 rules, an attribute test whose value is unknown in the training example causes the example to be examined. If the attribute has three values, 1/3 of the example is deemed to have passed the test and thus the final class distribution is weighted by 1/3 when collected. A similar rule later will again cause 1/3 of the example to pass the test. A don't-care value is always deemed to have passed the attribute test in full (*i.e.* weight 1). The normalisation of the class counts means that an example with a don't-care can only count as a single example during testing, unlike NewID where it may count as representing several examples.

With ordered rules, a similar policy is followed, except after a rule has fired absorbing, say, 1/3 of the testing example, only the remaining 2/3s are sent down the remainder of the rule list. The first rule will cause $1/3 \times class\ frequency$ to be collected, but a second similar rule will cause $2/3 \times 1/3 \times class\ frequency$ to be collected. Thus the fraction of the example gets less and less as it progresses down the rule list. A don't-care value always passes the attribute test in full, and thus no fractional example remains to propagate further down the rule list.

Numeric attributes and rules

For numeric attributes, CN2 will partition the values into two subsets and test which subset each example belongs to. The drawback with a naïve implementation of this is that it requires $2^n - 1$ evaluations where n is the number of attribute values. Breiman *et al.* (1984) proved that in the special case where there are two class values it is possible to find an optimal split with $n - 1$ comparisons. In the general case heuristic methods must be used.

The AQ algorithm produces an unordered set of rules, whereas the version of the CN2 algorithm used in StatLog produces an ordered list of rules. Unordered rules are on the whole more comprehensible, but require also that they are qualified with some numeric confidence measure to handle any clashes which may occur. With an ordered list of rules, clashes cannot occur as each rule in the list is considered to have precedence over all subsequent rules.

Relation between CN2 and AQ

There are several differences between these two algorithms; however, it is possible to show that strong relationships exist between the two, so much so that simple modifications of the CN2 system can be introduced to enable it to emulate the behaviour of the AQ algorithm. See Michalski & Larson (1978).

AQ searches for rules which are *completely consistent* with the training data, whereas CN2 may prematurely halt specialisation of a rule when no further rules above a certain *threshold* of statistical significance can be generated via specialisation. Thus, the behaviour of AQ in this respect is equivalent to setting the threshold to zero.

When generating specialisations of a rule, AQ considers only specialisations which exclude a *specific negative example* from the coverage of a rule, whereas CN2 considers all specialisations. However, specialisations generated by CN2 which don't exclude any negative examples will be rejected, as they do not contribute anything to the predictive accuracy of the rule. Thus, the two algorithms search the same space in different ways.

Whereas published descriptions of AQ leave open the choice of evaluation function to use during search, the published norm is that of "number of correctly classified examples divided by total examples covered". The original CN2 algorithm uses *entropy* as its evaluation function. To obtain a synthesis of the two systems, the choice of evaluation function can be user-selected during start of the system.

AQ generates order-independent rules, whereas CN2 generates an ordered list of rules. To modify CN2 to produce order-independent rules requires a change to the evaluation function, and a change to the way examples are removed from the training set between iterations of the complex-finding algorithm. The basic search algorithm remains unchanged.

5.2.8 ITrule

Goodman & Smyth's (1989) ITrule algorithm uses a function called the J-measure to rank the hypotheses during decision rule construction. Its output is a set of probability rules, which are the most informative selected from the possible rules depending on the training data.

The algorithm iterates through each attribute (including the class attribute) value in turn to build rules. It keeps a ranked list of the K best rules determined to that point of the algorithm execution (K is the size of the beam search). The J-measure of the Kth rule is used as the running minimum to determine whether a new rule should be inserted into the rule list. For each attribute value the algorithm must find all possible conditions to add to the left hand side of an over-general rule to specialise it. Or it may decide to drop a condition to generalise an over-specific rule. The rules considered are those limited by the minimum running J-measure value, which prevents the algorithm from searching a large rule space.

Three points should be noted. First, ITrule produces rules for each attribute value. So it can also capture the dependency relationships between attributes, between attributes and classes and between class values. Secondly, ITrule not only specialises existing rules but also generalises them if the need arises. Specialisation is done through adding conditions to the left hand side of the rule and generalisation is done through dropping conditions. Finally, ITrule only deals with categorical examples so it generally needs to convert numeric attributes and discrete values.

Evaluation function: the J-measure

Let a be an attribute with values in the set $\{a_i | i = 1, ..., l\}$ and b be an attribute with values in $\{b_i | i = 1, ..., m\}$. The J-measure is a method for calculating the information content $I(a|b = b_j)$ of attribute a given the value of attribute $b = b_j$. It is

$$J(a|b = b_j) = \sum_{i=1}^{l} p(a_i|b_j) ln(\frac{p(a_i|b_j)}{p(a_i)}),$$

where $p(a_i|b_j)$ is the conditional probability of $a = a_i$ given $b = b_j$ and $p(a_i)$ is the *a priori* probability of $a = a_i$. These can normally be estimated from the (conditional) relative frequency of the value of a_i. When the distribution is uniform and the data set is sufficient such estimates can be reasonable accurate. The ITrule algorithms uses a maximum entropy estimator:

$$p = \frac{\alpha + n + 1}{\alpha + \beta + N + 2}$$

where α and β are parameters of an initial density estimate, n is the number of the (conditional) event $a = a_i$ in the data and N is the (conditional) total number of a.

The average information content is therefore defined as:

$$J_{avg}(a|b = b_j) = \sum_{j=1}^{m} p(b_j) J(a|b = b_j) = p(b_j) J(a|b = b_j).$$

The above is true because it takes into account the fact that the probabilities of other values of b are zero. The first term $p(b_j)$ can be interpreted as a measure of the simplicity of the hypothesis that a is related to b. The second term $J(a|b = b_j)$ is equal to the cross-entropy of the variable a with the condition "a is dependent on the event $b = b_j$". Cross-entropy is known to measure the goodness of fit between two distributions; see Goodman & Smyth (1989).

Rule searching strategy

ITrule performs both generalisation and specialisation. It starts with a model driven strategy much like CN2. But its rules all have probability attached from the beginning. So a universal rule will be

If *All Conditions* **Then** *Current Class* **with probability** 1.

To specialise a rule such as one with current J-value $J_{avg}(a|b = b_j)$ it calculates the all possible values of $J_{avg}(a|b = b_j, c = c_k)$ for attribute c. If $J_{avg}(a|b = b_j, c = c_k) > J_{avg}(a|b = b_j)$ then it insert the new rule with specialised condition $c = c_k$ into the rule list. This process continues until no rule can be produced to cover remaining examples. To generalise a rule, with the current j-measure value $J_{avg}(a|b = b_j, c = c_k)$ it requires

$$J_{avg}(a|b = b_j) > \alpha J_{avg}(a|b = b_j, c = c_k),$$

where $\alpha = \frac{p(b=b_j, c=c_k)}{p(b=b_j)}$. Namely the increase in simplicity is sufficiently compensated for by the decrease in cross-entropy.

5.3 BEYOND THE COMPLEXITY BARRIER

All ML designers, whether rule-oriented or tree-oriented agree that, to the extent that the data permits, mental fit is an indispensible hall-mark. Thus, discussing requirements of rule learning systems Clark & Niblett (1989) state that "for the sake of comprehensibility, the induced rules should be as short as possible. However, when noise is present, overfitting can lead to long rules. Thus, to induce short rules, one must usually relax the requirement that the induced rules be consistent with all the training data." Such measures constitute the analogue of "pruning" of trees. But tree pruning and rule-set simplification measures may encounter complexity barriers that limit how much can be done in the direction of mental fit while retaining acceptable accuracy. When this occurs, are there other directions in which descriptive adequacy can still be sought?

5.3.1 Trees into rules

A tree that after pruning still remains too big to be comprehensible is a sign that a more powerful description language is required. A modest, but often effective, step starts by recognising that there is no intrinsic difference in expressive power between rulesets and trees, yet rule languages seem to lend themselves more to user-friendliness. A successful exploitation of this idea takes the form of a compressive re-organisation of induced trees into rule-sets. Quinlan's trees-into-rules algorithm (see his 1993 book for the most recent version) starts with the set formed from a C4.5 decision tree by identifying each root-to-leaf path with a rule. Each rule is simplified by successively dropping conditions (attribute-tests) in the specific-to-general style illustrated at the beginning of this chapter. The difference lies in the sophistication of criteria used for retracting a trial generalisation when it is found to result in inclusion of cases not belonging to the rule's decision class. In the noise-free taxonomy problem of the earlier tutorial example, a single "false positive" was taken to bar dropping the given condition. As with CN2 and some other rule-learners, a statistical criterion is substituted. Quinlan's is based on forming from the training set "pessimistic" estimates of the accuracy that a candidate rule would show on a test set.

When specific-to-general simplification has run its course for each class in turn, a final scan is made over each ruleset for any that, in the context of the other rules, are not contributing to the ruleset's accuracy. Any such passengers are dropped. The end of this stage leaves as many subsets of if-then rules ("covers" in the earlier terminology) as there are classes, *i.e.* one subset for each class. These subsets are then ordered prior to use for classifying new cases. The ordering principle first applies the subset which on the training set gives fewest false positives. The one with most false positives is the last to be applied. By that time some of the false-positive errors that it could have made have been pre-empted by other rule-sets. Finally a default class is chosen to which all cases which do not match any rule are to be assigned. This is calculated from the frequency statistics of such left-overs in the training set. Whichever class appears most frequently among these left-overs is selected as the default classification.

Rule-structured classifiers generated in this way turn out to be smaller, and better in "mental fit", than the trees from which the process starts. Yet accuracy is found to be fully preserved when assayed against test data. A particularly interesting feature of Quinlan's (1993) account, for which space allows no discussion here, is his detailed illustration of the Minimum Description Length (MDL) Principle, according to which the storage costs of rulesets and of their exceptions are expressed in a common information-theoretic coinage. This is used to address a simplification problem in building rule-sets that is essentially similar to the regulation of the pruning process in decision trees. The trade-off in each case is between complexity and predictive accuracy.

5.3.2   Manufacturing new attributes

If a user-friendly description still cannot be extracted more radical treatment may be required. The data-description language's vocabulary may need extending with new combinations formed from the original primitive attributes. The effects can be striking.

Consider the problem of classifying as "illegal" or "legal" the chessboard positions formed by randomly placing the three pieces White king, White rook and Black king. Combinatorially there are 64^3 positions, or 262,144. Assume that it is White's turn to move. Approximately two thirds of the positions are then illegal. Two or more pieces may have been placed on the same square, or the two kings may be diagonally or directly adjacent. Additionally positions in which the Black king is in check from the White rook are also illegal (recall that it is White to move).

A problem is presented for inductive analysis as a training set of n cases sampled randomly from the total space of possible 3-piece placements, as shown in Table 5.2.

Given sufficiently large n, Table 5.2 constitutes what McCarthy and Hayes (1969) termed an "epistemologically adequate" representation: it supplies whatever facts are in principle needed to obtain solutions. But for decision-tree learning, the representation is not "heuristically adequate". Michie & Bain (1992) applied a state-of-the-art decision-tree learner (XpertRule) of roughly similar power to C4.5, to training sets of 700 examples. The resulting 27-node tree performed on test data with only 69% accuracy, not differing significantly from that achievable by making the default conjecture "illegal" for every case.

The next step was to augment the six attributes with fifteen new ones, manufactured by forming all possible pairwise differences among the original six. With the augmented attribute set, two random partitions of a file of 999 cases were made into a training set of 698 and a test set of 301. Trees of 99% and 97% accuracy now resulted, with 49 nodes and 41 nodes respectively.

For making these very successful constructions the algorithm seized on just six attributes, all newly manufactured, namely the three pairwise differences among attributes 1, 3, and 5, and the three among attributes 2, 4, and 6. In this way, even though in a verbose and contorted style, it was able to express in decision-tree language certain key

Table 5.2: The six attributes encode a position according to the scheme: a1 = file(BK); a2 = rank (BK); a3 = file(WR); a4 = rank(WR); a5 = file(BK); a6 = rank(BK).

ID no.	a1	a2	a3	a4	a5	a6	class
1	7	8	1	7	6	8	yes
2	6	5	8	4	6	8	no
3	2	3	3	5	8	7	no
4	2	2	5	7	5	1	yes
..	..	..	..	..	..	..	. . .
..	..	..	..	..	..	..	. . .
n-1	2	7	5	3	2	3	yes
n	7	1	5	4	3	6	no

sub-descriptions, – such as the crucial same-file and same-rank relation between White rook and Black king. Whenever one of these relations holds it is a good bet that the position is illegal.

The gain in classification accuracy is impressive, yet no amount of added training data could inductively refine the above "excellent bet" into a certainty. The reason again lies with persisting limitations of the description language. To define the cases where the classifier's use of samefile(WR, BK) and samerank(WR, BK) lets it down, one needs to say that this happens if and only if the WK is *between* the WR and BK. Decision-tree learning, with attribute-set augmented as described, can patch together subtrees to do duty for samefile and samerank. But an equivalent feat for a sophisticated three-place relation such as "between" is beyond the expressive powers of an attribute-value propositional-level language. Moreover, the decision-tree learner's constructions were described above as "very successful" on purely operational grounds of accuracy relative to the restricted amount of training material, *i.e.* successful in predictivity. In terms of "descriptivity" the trees, while not as opaque as those obtained with primitive attributes only, were still far from constituting intelligible theories.

5.3.3   Inherent limits of propositional-level learning

Construction of theories of high descriptivity is the shared goal of human analysts and of ML. Yet the propositional level of ML is too weak to fully solve even the problem here illustrated. The same task, however, was proved to be well within the powers (1) of Dr. Jane Mitchell,a gifted and experienced human data analyst on the academic staff of Strathclyde University, and (2) of a predicate-logic ML system belonging to the Inductive Logic Programming (ILP) family described in Chapter 12. The two independently obtained theories were complete and correct. One theory-discovery agent was human, namely a member of the academic staff of a University Statistics department. The other was an ILP learner based on Muggleton & Feng's (1990) GOLEM, with "Closed World Specialization" enhancements (Bain, private communication). In essentials the two theories closely approximated to the one shown below in the form of four if-then rules. These are here given in english after back-interpretation into chess terms. Neither of the learning agents had any knowledge of the meaning of the task, which was simply presented as in Table 5.2. They did not know that it had anything to do with chess, nor even with objects placed on plane surfaces. The background knowledge given to the ILP learner was similar in amount to that earlier given to XpertRule in the form of manufactured attributes.

1.   **if** WR and BK either occupy same file **and** WK is not directly between
      or if they occupy the same rank **and** WK is not directly between
      then the position is illegal;

2.   **if** WK and BK either are vertically adjacent
      or are horizontally adjacent
      or are diagonally adjacent
      then the position is illegal;

3.   **if** any two pieces are on the same square
      then the position is illegal;

4.   **otherwise** the position is legal.

Construction of this theory requires certain key sub-concepts, notably of "directly between". Definitions were invented by the machine learner, using lower-level concepts such as "less-than", as background knowledge. "Directly between" holds among the three co-ordinate pairs if either the first co-ordinates are all equal and the second co-ordinates are in ascending or descending progression, or the second co-ordinates are all equal and the first co-ordinates show the progression. Bain's ILP package approached the relation piece-wise, *via* invention of "between-file" and "between-rank". The human learner doubtless came ready-equipped with some at least of the concepts that the ML system had to invent. None the less, with unlimited access to training data and the use of standard statistical analysis and tabulation software, the task of theory building still cost two days of systematic work. Human learners given hours rather than days constructed only partial theories, falling far short even of operational adequacy (see also Muggleton, S.H., Bain, M., Hayes-Michie, J.E. and Michie, D. (1989)).

Bain's new work has the further interest that learning takes place incrementally, by successive refinement, a style sometimes referred to as "non-monotonic". Generalisations made in the first pass through training data yield exceptions when challenged with new data. As exceptions accumulate they are themselves generalised over, to yield sub-theories which qualify the main theory. These refinements are in turn challenged, and so forth to any desired level.

The KRK illegality problem was originally included in StatLog's datasets. In the interests of industrial relevance, artificial problems were not retained except for expository purposes. No connection, however, exists between a data-set's industrial importance and its intrinsic difficulty. All of the ML algorithms tested by StatLog were of propositional type. If descriptive adequacy is a desideratum, none can begin to solve the KRK-illegal problem. It would be a mistake, however, to assume that problems of complex logical structure do not occur in industry. They can be found, for example, in trouble-shooting complex circuitry (Pearce, 1989), in inferring biological activity from specifications of macromolecular structure in the pharmaceutical industry (see last section of Chapter 12) and in many other large combinatorial domains. As Inductive Logic Programming matures and assimilates techniques from probability and statistics, industrial need seems set to explore these more powerful ML description languages.

5.3.4   A human-machine compromise: structured induction

In industrial practice more mileage can be got from decision-tree and rule learning than the foregoing account might lead one to expect. Comparative trials like StatLog's, having a scientific end in view, necessarily exclude approaches in which the algorithm's user intervenes interactively to help it. The inability of propositional learning to invent new attributes can be by-passed in practical contexts where human-computer interaction can plug the gap. From this, an approach known as "structured induction" has come to dominate commercial ML. The method, originated by Shapiro & Niblett (1982) (see also Shapiro, 1987) assigns the task of attribute-invention to the user, in a manner that partitions the problem into a hierarchy of smaller problems. For each smaller problem a solution tree is separately induced.

Structured induction is closely related to the software discipline of "structured programming". For large problems the industrial stream of ML work will continue to flow along this human-computer channel. It may for some time remain exceptional for problem complexity to force users to look beyond rule-based ML and multivariate statistics. Because the StatLog ground-rules of comparative trials necessarily barred the user from substantive importation of domain-specific knowledge, structured induction does not figure in this book. But industrially oriented readers may find advantage in studying cases of the method's successful field use. One such account by Leech (1986) concerned process and quality control in uranium refining. A well-conceived application of structured decision-tree induction transformed the plant from unsatisfactory to highly satisfactory operation, and is described in sufficient detail to be used as a working paradigm. Similar experience has been reported from other industries (see Michie, 1991, for review).

6

Neural Networks

R. Rohwer (1), M. Wynne-Jones (1) and F. Wysotzki (2)
(1) Aston University[1] and (2) Fraunhofer-Institute

6.1 INTRODUCTION

The field of Neural Networks has arisen from diverse sources, ranging from the fascination of mankind with understanding and emulating the human brain, to broader issues of copying human abilities such as speech and the use of language, to the practical commercial, scientific, and engineering disciplines of pattern recognition, modelling, and prediction. For a good introductory text, see Hertz *et al.* (1991) or Wasserman (1989).

Linear discriminants were introduced by Fisher (1936), as a statistical procedure for classification. Here the space of attributes can be partitioned by a set of hyperplanes, each defined by a linear combination of the attribute variables. A similar model for logical processing was suggested by McCulloch & Pitts (1943) as a possible structure bearing similarities to neurons in the human brain, and they demonstrated that the model could be used to build any finite logical expression. The McCulloch-Pitts neuron (see Figure 6.1) consists of a weighted sum of its inputs, followed by a non-linear function called the em activation function, originally a threshold function. Formally,

$$
y_k = \begin{cases} 1 \text{ if } \sum_j w_{kj} x_j - \mu_k \geq 0 \\ \\ 0 \text{ otherwise} \end{cases}
\tag{6.1}
$$

Other neuron models are quite widely used, for example in Radial Basis Function networks, which are discussed in detail in Section 6.2.3.

Networks of McCulloch-Pitts neurons for arbitrary logical expressions were hand-crafted, until the ability to learn by reinforcement of behaviour was developed in Hebb's book 'The Organisation of Behaviour' (Hebb, 1949). It was established that the functionality of neural networks was determined by the strengths of the connections between neurons; Hebb's learning rule prescribes that if the network responds in a desirable way to a given input, then the weights should be adjusted to increase the probability of a similar

---

[1]*Address for correspondence*: Dept. of Computer Science and Applied Mathematics, Aston University, Birmingham B4 7ET, U.K.

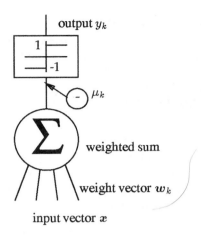

output y_k

weighted sum

weight vector w_k

input vector x

Fig. 6.1: McCulloch and Pitts neuron.

response to similar inputs in the future. Conversely, if the network responds undesirably to an input, the weights should be adjusted to decrease the probability of a similar response.

A distinction is often made, in pattern recognition, between *supervised* and *unsupervised* learning. The former describes the case where the the training data, measurements on the surroundings, are accompanied by labels indicating the class of event that the measurements represent, or more generally a desired response to the measurements. This is the more usual case in classification tasks, such as those forming the empirical basis of this book. The supervised learning networks described later in this chapter are the Perceptron and Multi Layer Perceptron (MLP), the Cascade Correlation learning architecture, and Radial Basis Function networks.

Unsupervised learning refers to the case where measurements are not accompanied by class labels. Networks exist which can model the structure of samples in the measurement, or attribute space, usually in terms of a probability density function, or by representing the data in terms of cluster centres and widths. Such models include Gaussian mixture models and Kohonen networks.

Once a model has been made, it can be used as a classifier in one of two ways. The first is to determine which class of pattern in the training data each node or neuron in the model responds most strongly to, most frequently. Unseen data can then be classified according to the class label of the neuron with the strongest activation for each pattern. Alternatively, the Kohonen network or mixture model can be used as the first layer of a Radial Basis Function network, with a subsequent layer of weights used to calculate a set of class probabilities. The weights in this layer are calculated by a linear one-shot learning algorithm (see Section 6.2.3), giving radial basis functions a speed advantage over non-linear training algorithms such as most of the supervised learning methods. The first layer of a Radial Basis Function network can alternatively be initialised by choosing a subset of the training data points to use as centres.

6.2   SUPERVISED NETWORKS FOR CLASSIFICATION

In supervised learning, we have an instance of data, i, comprising an attribute vector $\mathbf{X}_i$ and a target vector $\mathbf{Y}_i$. We process $\mathbf{X}_i$ with a network, to produce an output y_i, which has the same form as the target vector $\mathbf{Y}_i$.

The parameters of the network w are modified to optimise the match between outputs and targets, typically by minimising the total squared error

$$E = \frac{1}{2} \sum_i (\mathbf{y}_i - \mathbf{Y}_i)^2.$$

It might seem more natural to use a percentage misclassification error measure in classification problems, but the total squared error has helpful smoothness and differentiability properties. Although the total squared error was used for training in the StatLog trials, percentage misclassification in the trained networks was used for evaluation.

6.2.1   Perceptrons and Multi Layer Perceptrons

The activation of the McCulloch-Pitts neuron has been generalised to the form

$$y_j = f_j \left(\sum_i w_{ji} X_i \right) \tag{6.2}$$

where the activation function, f_j can be any non-linear function. The nodes have been divided into an *input layer I* and an *output layer O*. The threshold level, or bias of Equation (6.1) has been included in the sum, with the assumption of an extra component in the vector X whose value is fixed at 1. Rosenblatt studied the capabilities of groups of neurons in a single layer, and hence all acting on the same input vectors; this structure was termed the Perceptron (Rosenblatt, 1958), and Rosenblatt proposed the Perceptron Learning Rule for learning suitable weights for classification problems (Rosenblatt, 1962). When f is a hard threshold function (*i.e.*, discontinuously jumps from a lower to an upper limiting value), Equation (6.2) defines a non-linear function across a hyperplane in the attribute space; with a threshold activation function the neuron output is simply 1 on one side of the hyperplane and 0 on the other. When combined in a perceptron structure, neurons can segment the attribute space into regions, and this forms the basis of the capability of perceptron networks to perform classification.

Minsky and Papert pointed out, however, that many real world problems do not fall into this simple framework, citing the exclusive-or problem as the simplest example. Here it is necessary to isolate two convex regions, joining them together in a single class. They showed that while this was not possible with a perceptron network, it can be done with a two layer perceptron structure (Minsky & Papert, 1969). This formed the Multi Layer Perceptron (MLP) which is widely in use today, although the Perceptron Learning Rule (also called the Delta Rule) could not be generalised to find weights for this structure.

A learning rule was proposed in 1985 which allows the multi layer perceptron to learn. This *Generalised Delta Rule* (Section 6.2.2) defines a notion of back-propagation of error derivatives through the network (Werbos, 1974; Hinton *et al.*, 1985 and 1986), and enables a large class of models with different connection structures, or *architectures* to be trained. These publications initiated the recent academic interest in neural networks, and the field subsequently came to the attention of industrial users.

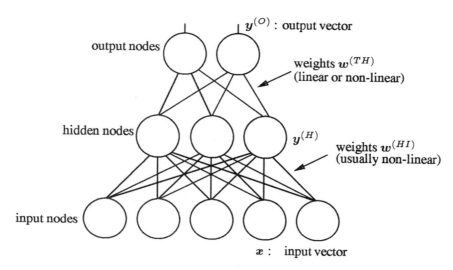

Fig. 6.2: MLP Structure.

6.2.2   Multi Layer Perceptron structure and functionality

Figure 6.2 shows the structure of a standard two-layer perceptron. The inputs form the *input nodes* of the network; the outputs are taken from the *output nodes*. The middle layer of nodes, visible to neither the inputs nor the outputs, is termed the *hidden layer*, and unlike the input and output layers, its size is not fixed. The hidden layer is generally used to make a *bottleneck*, forcing the network to make a simple model of the system generating the data, with the ability to generalise to previously unseen patterns.

The operation of this network is specified by

$$y_i^{(H)} \;=\; f^{(H)}\left(\sum_j w_{ij}^{(HI)} x_j\right)$$

$$y_i \;=\; f^{(T)}\left(\sum_j w_{ij}^{(TH)} y_j^{(H)}\right) \tag{6.3}$$

This specifies how input pattern vector x is mapped into output pattern vector $y^{(0)}$, via the hidden pattern vector $y^{(H)}$, in a manner parameterised by the two layers of weights $\mathbf{w}^{(HI)}$ and $\mathbf{w}^{(TH)}$. The univariate functions $f^{(\cdot)}$ are typically each set to

$$f(x) = \frac{1}{1 + e^{-x}} \tag{6.4}$$

which varies smoothly from 0 at $-\infty$ to 1 at ∞, as a threshold function would do abruptly.

If the number of hidden layer nodes is less than the number of degrees of freedom inherent in the training data, the activations of the hidden nodes tend to form an orthogonal set of variables, either linear or non-linear combinations of the attribute variables, which span as large a subspace of the problem as possible. With a little extra constraint on the network, these internal variables form a linear or non-linear principal component representation of the attribute space. If the data has noise added that is not an inherent part of the generating system, then the principal component network acts as a filter of the lower-variance noise signal, provided the signal to noise ratio of the data is sufficiently high. This property gives MLPs the ability to generalise to previously unseen patterns, by modelling only the important underlying structure of the generating system. The hidden nodes can be regarded as detectors of abstract features of the attribute space.

Universal Approximators and Universal Computers

In the Multilayer Perceptron (MLP) such as the two-layer version in Equation (6.3), the output-layer node values y are functions of the input-layer node values X (and the weights w). It can be shown (Funahashi, 1989) that the two-layer MLP can approximate an arbitrary continuous mapping arbitrarily closely if there is no limit to the number of hidden nodes. In this sense the MLP is a universal function approximator. This theorem does not imply that more complex MLP architectures are pointless; it can be more efficient (in terms of the number of nodes and weights required) to use different numbers of layers for different problems. Unfortunately there is a shortage of rigorous principles on which to base a choice of architecture, but many heuristic principles have been invented and explored. Prominent among these are *symmetry principles* (Lang *et al.*, 1990; Le Cun *et al.*, 1989) and *constructive algorithms* (Wynne-Jones, 1991).

The MLP is a *feedforward* network, meaning that the output vector y is a function of the input vector X and some parameters w; we can say

$$y = F(x; w) \tag{6.5}$$

for some vector function F given in detail by (6.3) in the 2-layer case. It is also possible to define a recurrent network by feeding the outputs back to the inputs. The general form of a recurrent perceptron is

$$y_i(t + 1) = f\left(\sum_j w_{ij} y_j(t)\right),$$

which could be written

$$y(t + 1) = F(y(t); w)$$

This is a discrete-time model; continuous-time models governed by a differential equation of similar structure are also studied.

Recurrent networks are universal computers in the sense that given an infinite number of nodes, they can emulate any calculation which can be done on a Universal Turing machine. (The infinite number of nodes is needed to simulate the infinite Turing tape.) This result is easily proved for hard-threshold recurrent perceptrons by sketching a 1-node network which performs not-AND and another which functions as a FLIP-FLOP. These elements are all that are required to build a computer.

This chapter focuses on feedforward neural network models because they are simpler to use, better understood, and closely connected with statistical classification methods. However recurrent networks attract a great deal of research interest because of their potential to serve as a vehicle for bringing statistical methods to bear on algorithm design (Rohwer 1991a, 1991b, 1992; Rohwer *et al.*, 1992; Shastri & Ajjanagadde 1993).

Training MLPs by nonlinear regression

In neural network parlance, *training* is the process of fitting network parameters (its weights) to given data. The training data consists of a set of examples of corresponding inputs and desired outputs, or "targets". Let the ith example be given by input X_{ji} for input dimension j and target Y_{ji} for target dimension j. Usually a least-squares fit is obtained by finding the parameters which minimise the *error measure*

$$E = \tfrac{1}{2} \sum_i \sum_j (y_{ji} - Y_{ji})^2 \tag{6.6}$$

where y_{ji} are the output values obtained by substituting the inputs X_{ji} for x_j in (6.3). If the fit is perfect, $E = 0$; otherwise $E > 0$.

Probabilistic interpretation of MLP outputs

If there is a one-to-many relationship between the inputs and targets in the training data, then it is not possible for any mapping of the form (6.5) to perform perfectly. It is straightforward to show (Bourlard & Wellekens, 1990) that if a probability density $P(\mathbf{Y}|\mathbf{X})$ describes the data, then the minimum of (6.6) is attained by the map taking $\mathbf{X}$ to the average target

$$\int d\mathbf{Y} P(\mathbf{Y}|\mathbf{X})\mathbf{Y} \tag{6.7}$$

Any given network might or not be able to approximate this mapping well, but when trained as well as possible it will form its best possible approximation to this mean. Many commonly-used error measures in addition to (6.6) share this property (Hampshire & Pearlmuter, 1990).

Usually classification problems are represented using *one-out-of-N* output coding. One output node is allocated for each class, and the target vector $\mathbf{Y}_i$ for example i is all 0's except for a 1 on the node indicating the correct class. In this case, the value computed by the jth target node can be directly interpreted as the probability that the input pattern belongs to class j. Collectively the outputs express $P(\mathbf{Y}|\mathbf{X})$. This not only provides helpful insight, but also provides a principle with which neural network models can be combined with other probabilistic models (Bourlard & Wellekens, 1990) .

The probabilistic interpretation of the the output nodes leads to a natural error measure for classification problems. Given that the value y_{ji} output by the jth target node given the ith training input $\mathbf{X}_i$, is $P(Y_{ji} = 1)$, so $1 - y_{ji}$ is $P(Y_{ji} = 0)$, the probability of the entire collection of training outputs $\mathbf{Y}$ is

$$P(\mathbf{Y}) = \prod_{ji} y_{ji}{}^{Y_{ji}} \left(1 - y_{ji}\right)^{1-Y_{ji}} \tag{6.8}$$

This is the exponential of the *cross-entropy*,

$$E = \sum_i \sum_j \left(Y_{ji} \log y_{ji} + (1 - Y_{ji}) \log(1 - y_{ji})\right) \tag{6.9}$$

Therefore the cross-entropy can be used as an error measure instead of a sum of squares (6.6). It happens that its minimum also lies at the average target (6.7), so the network outputs can still be interpreted probabilistically, and furthermore the minimisation of cross-entropy is equivalent to maximisation of the likelihood of the training data in classification problems.[2]

---

[2] The cross-entropy (6.9) has this interpretation when an input can simultaneously be a member of any number of classes, and membership of one class provides no information about membership of another. If an input can

The probabilistic interpretation of MLP outputs in classification problems must be made with some caution. It only applies if the network is trained to its minimum error, and then only if the training data accurately represents the underlying probability density $P(\mathbf{Y}|\mathbf{X})$. The latter condition is problematic if $\mathbf{X}$ belongs to a continuous space or a large discrete set, because technically a large or infinite amount of data is required. This problem is intimately related to the overtraining and generalisation issues discussed below.

For the theoretical reasons given here, the cross-entropy is the most appropriate error measure for use in classification problems, although practical experience suggests it makes little difference. The sum of squares was used in the StatLog neural network trials.

Minimisation methods

Neural network models are trained by adjusting their weight matrix parameters w so as to minimise an error measure such as (6.6). In the simplest cases the network outputs are linear in the weights, making (6.6) quadratic. Then the minimal error can be found by solving a linear system of equations. This special case is discussed in Section 6.2.3 in the context of Radial Basis Function networks, which have this property. In the generic, nonlinear case the minimisation is accomplished using a variant of *Gradient Descent*. This produces a *local* minimum, a w from which any infinitesimal change increases E, but not necessarily the *global* minimum of $E(\mathbf{w})$.

First order gradient based methods

The *gradient* $\nabla E(\mathbf{w})$ of $E(\mathbf{w})$ is the vector field of derivatives of E:

$$\nabla E(\mathbf{w}) = \left(\frac{dE(\mathbf{w})}{dw_1}, \frac{dE(\mathbf{w})}{dw_2}, \ldots\right)$$

(a *field* because the vector depends on w) A linear approximation to $E(\mathbf{w})$ in the infinitesimal vicinity of an arbitrary weight matrix $\mathbf{w}^0$ is given by

$$E(\mathbf{w}) = E(\mathbf{w}^0) + \nabla E(\mathbf{w}^0) \cdot (\mathbf{w} - \mathbf{w}^0) \tag{6.10}$$

Clearly then, at any point w of the parameter space (weight space) of the network, the vector ∇E points in the direction of fastest increase of E; *i.e.*, of all the infinitesimal changes $\delta \mathbf{w}$ (of a given magnitude) which one could make to w, a change in the direction of ∇E increases E the most. Consequently an adjustment of w in the direction of $-\nabla E$ provides the maximum possible decrease in E. The basic strategy in gradient descent is to compute the gradient and adjust the weights in the opposite direction.

The problem with this method is that the theorem on maximal descent only applies to infinitesimal adjustments. The gradient changes as well as the error, so the optimal direction for (infinitesimal) descent changes when w is adjusted. The *Pure* Gradient Descent algorithm requires a *step size* parameter η, chosen small enough for $\eta \nabla E$ to be effectively infinitesimal so far as obtaining descent is concerned, but otherwise as large as possible, in the interests of speed. The weights are repeatedly adjusted by

$$\mathbf{w} \leftarrow \mathbf{w} - \eta \nabla E(\mathbf{w}) \tag{6.11}$$

until the error E fails to descend.

In practice, trial and error is used to look for the largest step size η which will work. With large step sizes, the gradient will tend to change dramatically with each step. A

---

belong to one and only one class, then the simple entropy, obtained by dropping the terms involving $(1 - y)$, should be used.

popular heuristic is to use a moving average of the gradient vector in order find a systematic tendency. This is accomplished by adding a *momentum* term to (6.11), involving a parameter $\alpha \lesssim 1$:

$$\mathbf{w} \leftarrow \mathbf{w} - \eta \nabla E(\mathbf{w}) + \alpha \delta \mathbf{w}_{\text{old}}$$

Here $\delta \mathbf{w}_{\text{old}}$ refers to the most recent weight change.

These methods offer the benefit of simplicity, but their performance depends sensitively on the parameters η and α (Toolenaere, 1990). Different values seem to be appropriate for different problems, and for different stages of training in one problem. This circumstance has given rise to a plethora of heuristics for adaptive *variable step size* algorithms (Toolenaere, 1990; Silva & Almeida, 1990; Jacobs, 1988) .

Second-Order methods

The underlying difficulty in first order gradient based methods is that the linear approximation (6.10) ignores the curvature of $E(\mathbf{w})$. This can be redressed by extending (6.10) to the quadratic approximation,

$$E(\mathbf{w}) = E(\mathbf{w}^0) + \nabla E(\mathbf{w}^0) \cdot \delta \mathbf{w} + \delta \mathbf{w} \nabla \nabla E(\mathbf{w}^0) \delta \mathbf{w}$$

where $\nabla \nabla E$ is the matrix with components $\frac{d^2 E}{dw_i dw_j}$, called the inverse *Hessian* (or the Hessian, depending on conventions), and $\delta \mathbf{w} = \mathbf{w} - \mathbf{w}^0$. The change $\delta \mathbf{w} = -\frac{1}{2} H \nabla E$, where $H^{-1} = \nabla \nabla E$, brings $\mathbf{w}$ to a stationary point of this quadratic form. This may be a minimum, maximum, or saddle point. If it is a minimum, then a step in that direction seems a good idea; if not, then a positive or negative step (whichever has a negative projection on the gradient) in the *conjugate gradient* direction, $H \nabla E$, is at least not unreasonable. Therefore a large class of algorithms has been developed involving the conjugate gradient.

Most of these algorithms require explicit computation or estimation of the Hessian H. The number of components of H is roughly half the square of the number of components of $\mathbf{w}$, so for large networks involving many weights, such algorithms lead to impractical computer memory requirements. But one algorithm, generally called *the* conjugate gradient algorithm, or the *memoryless* conjugate gradient algorithm, does not. This algorithm maintains an estimate of the conjugate direction without directly representing H.

The conjugate gradient algorithm uses a sequence of *linesearches*, one-dimensional searches for the minimum of $E(\mathbf{w})$, starting from the most recent estimate of the minimum and searching for the minimum in the direction of the current estimate of the conjugate gradient. Linesearch algorithms are comparatively easy because the issue of direction choice reduces to a binary choice. But because the linesearch appears in the inner loop of the conjugate gradient algorithm, efficiency is important. Considerable effort therefore goes into it, to the extent that the linesearch is typically the most complicated module of a conjugate gradient implementation. Numerical round-off problems are another design consideration in linesearch implementations, because the conjugate gradient is often nearly orthogonal to the gradient, making the variation of $E(\mathbf{w})$ along the conjugate gradient especially small.

The update rule for the conjugate gradient direction s is

$$\mathbf{s} \leftarrow -\nabla E + \alpha \mathbf{s}_{\text{old}} \qquad\qquad (6.12)$$

where

$$\alpha = \frac{(\nabla E - \nabla E_{\text{old}}) \cdot \nabla E}{\nabla E_{\text{old}} \cdot \nabla E_{\text{old}}} \tag{6.13}$$

(This is the *Polak-Ribiere* variant; there are others.) Somewhat intricate proofs exist which show that if E were purely quadratic in w, s were initialised to the gradient, and the linesearches were performed exactly, then s would converge on the conjugate gradient and E would converge on its minimum after as many iterations of (6.12) as there are components of w. In practice good performance is often obtained on much more general functions using very imprecise linesearches. It is necessary to augment (6.13) with a rule to reset s to $-\nabla E$ whenever s becomes too nearly orthogonal to the gradient for progress to continue.

An implementation of the conjugate gradient algorithm will have several parameters controlling the details of the linesearch, and others which define exactly when to reset s to $-\nabla E$. But unlike the step size and momentum parameters of the simpler methods, the performance of the conjugate gradient method is relatively insensitive to its parameters if they are set within reasonable ranges. All algorithms are sensitive to process for selecting initial weights, and many other factors which remain to be carefully isolated.

Gradient calculations in MLPs

It remains to discuss the computation of the gradient $\nabla E(\text{w})$ in the case of an MLP neural network model with an error measure such as (6.6). The calculation is conveniently organised as a *back propagation of error* (Rumelhart *et al.*, 1986; Rohwer & Renals, 1988). For a network with a single layer of hidden nodes, this calculation proceeds by propagating node output values y forward from the input to output layers for each training example, and then propagating quantities δ related to the output errors backwards through a linearised version of the network. Products of δs and ys then give the gradient. In the case of a network with an input layer (I), a single hidden layer (H), and an output or target layer (T), the calculation is:

$$y_i^{(H)} = f^{(H)}\left(\sum_j w_{ij}^{(HI)} x_j\right)$$

$$y_i = f^{(T)}\left(\sum_j w_{ij}^{(TH)} y_j^{(H)}\right)$$

$$\delta_{ji}^{(T)} = (y_{ji} - Y_{ji})$$

$$\delta_{ji}^{(H)} = \sum_k \delta_{ki}^{(T)} f_{ki}^{\prime(T)} w_{kj}^{(TH)}$$

$$dE/dw_{jk}^{(TH)} = \sum_i \delta_{ji}^{(T)} f_{ji}^{\prime(T)} y_{ki}^{(H)} \tag{6.14}$$

$$dE/dw_{jk}^{(HI)} = \sum_i \delta_{ji}^{(H)} f_{ji}^{\prime(H)} X_{ki} \tag{6.15}$$

The index i is summed over training examples, while the js and ks refer to nodes, and

$$f_{ki}^{\prime(\cdot)} = \left.\frac{d}{dx} f(x)\right|_{x = f^{-1}\left(y_{ki}^{(\cdot)}\right)}$$

This network architecture was used in the work reported in this book.

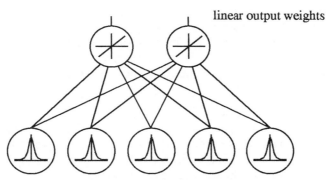

linear output weights

non-linear receptive fields in attribute space

Fig. 6.3:   A Radial Basis Function Network.

Online vs. Batch

Note that both the error E (6.6) and the gradient ∇E (6.14, 6.15) are a sum over examples. These could be estimated by randomly selecting a subset of examples for inclusion in the sum. In the extreme, a single example might be used for each gradient estimate. This is a *Stochastic Gradient* method. If a similar strategy is used without random selection, but with the data taken in the order it comes, the method is an *Online* one. If a sum over all training data is performed for each gradient calculation, then the method is a *Batch* variety.

Online and Stochastic Gradient methods offer a considerable speed advantage if the approximation is serviceable. For problems with large amounts of training data they are highly favoured. However, these approximations cannot be used directly in the conjugate gradient method, because it is built on procedures and theorems which assume that E is a given function of w which can be evaluated precisely so that meaningful comparisons can be made at nearby arguments. Therefore the stochastic gradient and Online methods tend to be used with simple step-size and momentum methods. There is some work on finding a compromise method (Møller, 1993).

6.2.3   Radial Basis Function networks

The radial basis function network consists of a layer of units performing linear or non-linear functions of the attributes, followed by a layer of weighted connections to nodes whose outputs have the same form as the target vectors. It has a structure like an MLP with one hidden layer, except that each node of the the hidden layer computes an arbitrary function of the inputs (with Gaussians being the most popular), and the transfer function of each output node is the trivial identity function. Instead of "synaptic strengths" the hidden layer has parameters appropriate for whatever functions are being used; for example, Gaussian widths and positions. This network offers a number of advantages over the multi layer perceptron under certain conditions, although the two models are computationally equivalent.

These advantages include a linear training rule once the locations in attribute space of the non-linear functions have been determined, and an underlying model involving localised functions in the attribute space, rather than the long-range functions occurring in perceptron-based models. The linear learning rule avoids problems associated with local minima; in particular it provides enhanced ability to make statments about the accuracy of the probabilistic interpretation of the outputs in Section 6.2.2.

Figure 6.3 shows the structure of a radial basis function; the non-linearities comprise a position in attribute space at which the function is located (often referred to as the function's *centre*), and a non-linear function of the distance of an input point from that centre, which can be any function at all. Common choices include a gaussian response function, $\exp(-x^2)$ and inverse multiquadrics ($[z^2 + c^2]^{-\frac{1}{2}}$), as well as non-local functions such as thin plate splines ($z^2 \log z$) and multiquadrics ($[z^2 + c^2]^{\frac{1}{2}}$). Although it seems counter-intuitive to try and produce an interpolating function using non-localised functions, they are often found to have better interpolating properties *in the region populated by the training data*.

The Radial Basis Function network approach involves the expansion or pre-processing of input vectors into a high-dimensional space. This attempts to exploit a theorem of Cover (1965) which implies that a classification problem cast in a high-dimensional space is more likely to be linearly separable than would be the case in a low-dimensional space.

Training: choosing the centres and non-linearities

A number of methods can be used for choosing the centres for a radial basis function network. It is important that the distribution of centres in the attribute space should be similar to, or at least cover the same region as the training data. It is assumed that the training data is representative of the problem, otherwise good performance cannot be expected on future unseen patterns.

A first order technique for choosing centres is to take points on a square grid covering the region of attribute space covered by the training data. Alternatively, better performance might be expected if the centres were sampled at random from the training data itself, using some or all samples, since the more densely populated regions of the attribute space would have a higher resolution model than sparser regions. In this case, it is important to ensure that at least one sample from each class is used as a prototype centre. In the experiments in this book, the number of samples required from each class was calculated before sampling, thereby ensuring this condition was met.

When centre positions are chosen for Radial Basis Function networks with localised non-linear functions such as Gaussian receptive fields, it is important to calculate suitable variances, or spreads for the functions. This ensures that large regions of space do not occur between centres, where no centres respond to patterns, and conversely, that no pair of centres respond nearly identically to all patterns. This problem is particularly prevalent in high dimensional attribute spaces because volume depends sensitively on radius. For a quantitative discussion of this point, see Prager & Fallside (1989). In the experiments reported in this book, the standard deviations of the Gaussian functions were set separately for each coordinate direction to the distance to the nearest centre in that direction, multiplied by an arbitrary scaling parameter (set to 1.0).

Other methods include using a 'principled' clustering technique to position the centres, such as a Gaussian Mixture model or a Kohonen network. These models are discussed in Section 6.3.

Training: optimising the weights

As mentioned in Section 6.2.2, radial basis function networks are trained simply by solving a linear system. The same problem arises in ordinary linear regression, the only difference being that the input to the linear system is the output of the hidden layer of the network, not the attribute variables themselves. There are a few subtleties however, which are discussed here. Let $y_{ki}^{(H)}$ be the output of the kth radial basis function on the ith example. The output of each target node j is computed using the weights w_{jk} as

$$y_{ji} = \sum_k w_{jk} y_{ki}^{(H)} \qquad (6.16)$$

Let the desired output for example i on target node j be Y_{ji}. The error measure (6.6) written out in full is then

$$E(\mathbf{w}) = \tfrac{1}{2} \sum_{ji} \left(\sum_k w_{jk} y_{ki}^{(H)} - Y_{ji} \right)^2 \qquad (6.17)$$

which has its minimum where the derivative

$$\frac{dE}{dw_{rs}} = \sum_k \sum_i w_{rk} y_{ki}^{(H)} y_{ji}^{(H)} - \sum_i Y_{ri} y_{si}^{(H)} \qquad (6.18)$$

vanishes. Let $\mathbf{R}$ be the correlation matrix of the radial basis function outputs,

$$R_{jk} = \sum_i y_{ki}^{(H)} y_{ji}^{(H)}. \qquad (6.19)$$

The weight matrix $\mathbf{w}^*$ which minimises E lies where the gradient vanishes:

$$\mathbf{w}_{jk}^* = \sum_r \sum_i Y_{ji} y_{ri}^{(H)} \left(\mathbf{R}^{-1} \right)_{rk} \qquad (6.20)$$

Thus, the problem is solved by inverting the square $H \times H$ matrix $\mathbf{R}$, where H is the number of radial basis functions.

The matrix inversion can be accomplished by standard methods such as LU decomposition (Renals & Rohwer, 1989) and (Press *et. al.*, 1988) if $\mathbf{R}$ is neither singular nor nearly so. This is typically the case, but things can go wrong. If two radial basis function centres are very close together a singular matrix will result, and a singular matrix is guaranteed if the number of training samples is not at least as great as H. There is no practical way to ensure a non-singular correlation matrix. Consequently the safest course of action is to use a slightly more computationally expensive singular value decomposition method. Such methods provide an approximate inverse by diagonalising the matrix, inverting only the eigenvalues which exceed zero by a parameter-specified margin, and transforming back to the original coordinates. This provides an optimal minimum-norm approximation to the inverse in the least-mean-squares sense.

Another approach to the entire problem is possible (Broomhead & Lowe, 1988). Let n be the number of training examples. Instead of solving the $H \times H$ linear system given by the derivatives of E (6.18), this method focuses on the linear system embedded in the error formula (6.17) itself:

$$\sum_k w_{jk} y_{ki}^{(H)} = Y_{ji} \qquad (6.21)$$

Unless $n = H$, this is a rectangular system. In general an exact solution does not exist, but the optimal solution in the least-squares sense is given by the pseudo-inverse (Kohonen, 1989) $\mathbf{y}^{(H)+}$ of $\mathbf{y}^{(H)}$, the matrix with elements $y_{ji}^{(H)}$:

$$\mathbf{w}^* = \mathbf{Y} \mathbf{y}^{(H)+} \qquad (6.22)$$

This formula is applied directly. The identity $\mathbf{Y}^+ = \tilde{\mathbf{Y}}(\mathbf{Y}\tilde{\mathbf{Y}})^+$, where $\tilde{}$ denotes the matrix transpose, can be applied to (6.22) to show that the pseudo-inverse method gives the same result as (6.20):

$$\mathbf{w}^* = \mathbf{Y}\tilde{\mathbf{y}}^{(H)}\left(\mathbf{y}^{(H)}\tilde{\mathbf{y}}^{(H)}\right)^+ \tag{6.23}$$

The requirement to invert or pseudo-invert a matrix dependent on the entire dataset makes this a batch method. However an online variant is possible, known as *Kalman Filtering* (Scalero & Tepedelenlioglu, 1992). It is based on the somewhat remarkable fact that an exact expression exists for updating the inverse correlation $\mathbf{R}^{-1}$ if another example is added to the sum (6.19), which does not require recomputation of the inverse.

6.2.4   Improving the generalisation of Feed-Forward networks

Constructive algorithms and pruning

A number of techniques have emerged recently, which attempt to improve on the perceptron and multilayer perceptron training algorithms by changing the architecture of the networks as training proceeds. These techniques include *pruning* useless nodes or weights, and *constructive algorithms* where extra nodes are added as required. The advantages include smaller networks, faster training times on serial computers, and increased generalisation ability, with a consequent immunity to noise. In addition, it is frequently much easier to interpret what the trained network is doing. As was noted earlier, a minimalist network uses its hidden layer to model as much of the problem as possible in the limited number of degrees of freedom available in its hidden layer. With such a network, one can then begin to draw analogies with other pattern classifying techniques such as decision trees and expert systems.

To make a network with good generalisation ability, we must determine a suitable number of hidden nodes. If there are too few, the network may not learn at all, while too many hidden nodes lead to over-learning of individual samples at the expense of forming a near optimal model of the data distributions underlying the training data. In this case, previously unseen patterns are labeled according to the nearest neighbour, rather than in accordance with a good model of the problem. An easy to read introduction to the issues invloved in over-training a network can be found in Geman (1992). Early constructive algorithms such as *Upstart* (Frean, 1990a, 1990b) and the *Tiling Algorithm* (Mézard & Nadal, 1989) built multi-layer feed-forward networks of perceptron units (Rosenblatt, 1958), which could be applied to problems involving binary input patterns. Convergence of such algorithms is guaranteed if the data is linearly separable, and use of the Pocket algorithm (Gallant, 1985) for training allows an approximate solution to be found for non linearly-separable datasets. These networks do not usually include a stopping criterion to halt the creation of new layers or nodes, so every sample in the training data is learned. This has strong repercussions if the training set is incomplete, has noise, or is derived from a classification problem where the distributions overlap.

Later methods apply to more general problems and are suitable for statistical classification problems (Ash, 1989; Fahlman & Lebière, 1990; Hanson, 1990; Refenes & Vithlani, 1991, and Wynne-Jones, 1992, 1993) . They often build a single hidden layer, and incorporate stopping criteria which allow them to converge to solutions with good generalisation ability for statistical problems. *Cascade Correlation* (Fahlman & Lebière, 1990) is an example of such a network algorithm, and is described below.

Pruning has been carried out on networks in three ways. The first is a heuristic approach based on identifying which nodes or weights contribute little to the mapping. After these have been removed, additional training leads to a better network than the original. An alternative technique is to include terms in the error function, so that weights tend to zero under certain circumstances. Zero weights can then be removed without degrading the network performance. This approach is the basis of *regularisation*, discussed in more detail below. Finally, if we define the sensitivity of the global network error to the removal of a weight or node, we can remove the weights or nodes to which the global error is least sensitive. The sensitivity measure does not interfere with training, and involves only a small amount of extra computational effort. A full review of these techniques can be found in Wynne-Jones (1991).

Cascade Correlation: A Constructive Feed-Forward network

Cascade Correlation is a paradigm for building a feed-forward network as training proceeds in a supervised mode (Fahlman & Lebière, 1990) . Instead of adjusting the weights in a fixed architecture, it begins with a small network, and adds new hidden nodes one by one, creating a multi-layer structure. Once a hidden node has been added to a network, its input-side weights are frozen and it becomes a permanent feature-detector in the network, available for output or for creating other, more complex feature detectors in later layers. Cascade correlation can offer reduced training time, and it determines the size and topology of networks automatically.

Cascade correlation combines two ideas: first the cascade architecture, in which hidden nodes are added one at a time, each using the outputs of all others in addition to the input nodes, and second the maximisation of the correlation between a new unit's output and the residual classification error of the parent network. Each node added to the network may be of any kind. Examples include linear nodes which can be trained using linear algorithms, threshold nodes such as single perceptrons where simple learning rules such as the Delta rule or the Pocket Algorithm can be used, or non-linear nodes such as sigmoids or Gaussian functions requiring Delta rules or more advanced algorithms such as Fahlman's Quickprop (Fahlman, 1988a, 1988b). Standard MLP sigmoids were used in the StatLog trials.

At each stage in training, each node in a pool of candidate nodes is trained on the residual error of the parent network. Of these nodes, the one whose output has the greatest correlation with the error of the parent is added permanently to the network. The error function minimised in this scheme is S, the sum over all output units of the magnitude of the correlation (or, more precisely, the covariance) between V, the candidate unit's value, and $E_{i,o}$, the residual error observed at output unit o for example i. S is defined by:

$$ S = \sum_o \left| \sum_i (V_i - \overline{V})(E_{i,o} - \overline{E_o}) \right| $$

The quantities $\overline{V}$ and $\overline{E_o}$ are the values of V and E_o averaged over all patterns.

In order to maximise S, the partial derivative of the error is calculated with respect to each of the weights coming into the node, w_j. Thus:

$$\frac{\partial S}{\partial w_j} = \sum_{i,o} \sigma_o (E_{i,o} - \overline{E_o}) f_i' I_{j,i} \qquad (6.24)$$

where σ_o is the sign of the correlation between the candidate's value and the output o, f_i' is the derivative for pattern i of the candidate unit's activation function withe respect to the sum of its inputs, and $I_{j,i}$ is the input the candidate unit receives for pattern i.

The partial derivatives are used to perform gradient ascent to maximise S. When S no longer improves in training for any of the candidate nodes, the best candidate is added to the network, and the others are scrapped.

In benchmarks on a toy problem involving classification of data points forming two interlocked spirals, cascade correlation is reported to be ten to one hundred times faster than conventional back-propagation of error derivatives in a fixed architecture network. Empirical tests on a range of real problems (Yang & Honavar, 1991) indicate a speedup of one to two orders of magnitude with minimal degradation of classification accuracy. These results were only obtained after many experiments to determine suitable values for the many parameters which need to be set in the cascade correlation implementation. Cascade correlation can also be implemented in computers with limited precision (Fahlman, 1991b), and in recurrent networks (Hoehfeld & Fahlman, 1991).

Bayesian regularisation

In recent years the formalism of Bayesian probability theory has been applied to the treatment of feedforward neural network models as nonlinear regression problems. This has brought about a greatly improved understanding of the generalisation problem, and some new techniques to improve generalisation. None of these techniques were used in the numerical experiments described in this book, but a short introduction to this subject is provided here.

A reasonable scenario for a Bayesian treatment of feedforward neural networks is to presume that each target training data vector $\mathbf{Y}$ was produced by running the corresponding input training vector $\mathbf{X}$ through some network and corrupting the output with noise from a stationary source. The network involved is assumed to have been drawn from a probability distribution $P(\mathbf{w})$, which is to be estimated. The most probable $\mathbf{w}$ in this distribution can be used as the optimal classifier, or a more sophisticated average over $P(\mathbf{w})$ can be used. (The latter technique is *marginalisation* (MacKay, 1992a).)

The notation used here for probability densities is somewhat cavalier. In discussions involving several probability density functions, the notation should distinguish one density function from another, and further notation should be used when such a density is indicated at a particular point; for example, $P_{\mathbf{w}}$ can designate the density function over weights, and $P_{\mathbf{w}}(\mathbf{w})$ would designate this density at the particular point $\mathbf{w}$, which confusingly and unsignificantly has the same name as the label index of P. However, a tempting opportunity to choose names which introduce this confusion will arise in almost every instance that a density function is mentioned, so we shall not only succumb to the temptation, but furthermore adopt the common practice of writing $P(\mathbf{w})$ when $P_{\mathbf{w}}(\mathbf{w})$ is meant, in order to be concise. Technically, this is an appalling case of using a function argument name (which is ordinarily arbitrary) to designate the function.

The Bayesian analysis is built on a probabilistic interpretation of the error measure used in training. Typically, as in Equations (6.6) or (6.9), it is additive over input-output pairs

$\mathbf{Y}$; *i.e.* it can be expressed as

$$E(\mathbf{Y}; \mathbf{w}) = \sum_p e(\mathbf{Y}_p; \mathbf{w}) \tag{6.25}$$

for some function e, where $\mathbf{Y}$ is all the training data, the set of input-output pairs in the sum. $\mathbf{Y}$ is composed of all the input data $\mathbf{X}$, regarded as fixed, and all the target data $\mathbf{Y}$, regarded as a noise-corrupted, $\mathbf{w}$-dependent function of $\mathbf{X}$, drawn from a distribution with density function $P(\mathbf{Y}|\mathbf{w})$ (or technically $P(\mathbf{Y}|\mathbf{w}, \mathbf{X})$). The Bayesian argument requires the assumption that $P(\mathbf{Y}|\mathbf{w})$ is a function of E alone. Thus, different choices of E correspond to different probabilistic interpretations. Given this assumption, and the assumption that training data samples are produced independently of each other,

$$P(\{\mathbf{Y}_1, \mathbf{Y}_2\}|\mathbf{w}) = P(\mathbf{Y}_1; \mathbf{w})P(\mathbf{Y}_2; \mathbf{w}) \tag{6.26}$$

the relationship between $E(\mathbf{Y}; \mathbf{w})$ and $P(\mathbf{Y}|\mathbf{w})$ can only have the form

$$P(\mathbf{Y}|\mathbf{w}) = \frac{1}{Z_Y} e^{-\beta E(\mathbf{Y};\mathbf{w})} \tag{6.27}$$

for some parameter β. Z_Y is the normalisation term

$$Z_Y = \int d\mathbf{Y} e^{-\beta E(\mathbf{Y};\mathbf{w})}, \tag{6.28}$$

an integral over all possible target training data sets of the size under consideration.

If e in (6.25) is a function only of $\mathbf{y}_p - \mathbf{Y}_p$, as is (6.6), then Z_Y turns out to be independent of $\mathbf{w}$, a result which is useful later[3]. The only common form of e which does not have this form is the cross-entropy (6.9). But this is normally used in classification problems, in which case (6.9) and (6.8) together justify the assumption that $P(\mathbf{Y}|\mathbf{w})$ depends only on $E(\mathbf{Y}; \mathbf{w})$ and imply for (6.28) that $\beta = 1$ and $Z_Y = 1$, so Z_Y is still independent of $\mathbf{w}$.

Density (6.27) can also be derived from somewhat different assumptions using a maximum-entropy argument (Bilbro & van den Bout, 1992). It plays a prominent role in thermodynamics, and thermodynamics jargon has drifted into the neural networks literature partly in consequence of the analogies it underlies.

The probability of the weights given the data $P(\mathbf{w}|\mathbf{Y})$ is of greater interest than the probability of the data given the weights $P(\mathbf{Y}|\mathbf{w})$ (the *likelihood*), but unfortunately the additivity argument does not go through for this. Instead, Bayes' rule

$$P(\mathbf{w}|\mathbf{Y}) = \frac{P(\mathbf{Y}|\mathbf{w})P^0(\mathbf{w})}{P(\mathbf{Y})} \tag{6.29}$$

can be used to convert $P(\mathbf{Y}|\mathbf{w})$ from Equation (6.27), and a prior over the weights $P^0(\mathbf{w})$, into the desired distribution. The probability of the data $P(\mathbf{Y})$ is given by the normalisation condition as

$$P(\mathbf{Y}) = \int d\mathbf{w} P(\mathbf{Y}|\mathbf{w})P^0(\mathbf{w}) \tag{6.30}$$

---

[3] There is a further technicality; the integral (6.28) over target data must be with respect to uniform measure, which may not always be reasonable.

Bayesian methods inevitably require a prior, $P^0(\mathbf{w})$ in this case. $P^0(\mathbf{w})$ must express the notion that some weight matrices are more reasonable, *a priori*, than others. As discussed above, this is normally expressed through regularisation terms added to the error measure. For example, the view that large weights are unreasonable might be expressed by adding a "weight decay" term of the form $\alpha\mathbf{w} \cdot \mathbf{w}$ to $E(\mathbf{Y}; \mathbf{w})$.

Typically, the regularisation error $\alpha E(\mathbf{w})$ is additive over the weights and an independence assumption like (6.26) is reasonable, so given that the prior depends only on the regularisation term, then it has the form

$$P^0(\mathbf{w}) = \frac{1}{Z^0} e^{-\alpha E(\mathbf{w})}$$

where Z^0 is given by normalisation.

Assembling all the pieces, the posterior probability of the weights given the data is

$$P(\mathbf{w}|\mathbf{Y}) = \frac{e^{-\beta E\left(\mathbf{Y};\mathbf{w}\right)-\alpha E(\mathbf{w})}}{\int d\mathbf{w}' e^{-\beta E\left(\mathbf{Y};\mathbf{w}'\right)-\alpha E(\mathbf{w}')}} \tag{6.31}$$

provided that (6.28) does not depend on $\mathbf{w}$. This ensures that the denominator of (6.31) does not depend on $\mathbf{w}$, so the usual training process of minimising $E(\mathbf{Y}; \mathbf{w}) + \frac{\alpha}{\beta}E(\mathbf{w})$ finds the maximum of $P(\mathbf{w}|\mathbf{Y})$.

The Bayesian method helps with one of the most troublesome steps in the regularisation approach to obtaining good generalisation, deciding the values of the regularisation parameters. The ratio α/β expresses the relative importance of smoothing and data-fitting, which deserves to be decided in a principled manner. The Bayesian *Evidence* formalism provides a principle and an implementation. It can be computationally demanding if used precisely, but there are practicable approximations.

The Evidence formalism simply assumes a prior distribution over the regularisation parameters, and sharpens it using Bayes' rule:

$$P(\alpha, \beta|\mathbf{Y}) = \frac{P(\mathbf{Y}|\alpha, \beta)P^0(\alpha, \beta)}{P(\mathbf{Y})} \tag{6.32}$$

If a uniform prior $P^0(\alpha, \beta)$ is assumed, then the most likely regularisation parameters are those which maximise the *evidence* $P(\mathbf{Y}|\alpha, \beta)$, which is given by (6.30), the denominator of (6.29). Note with reference to (6.29) that the goal of maximising the evidence opposes the goal of maximising $P(\mathbf{w}|\mathbf{Y})$; the regularisation parameters α and β, and the weights $\mathbf{w}$ are optimised for opposing purposes. This expresses the Bayesian quantification of the compromise between data fitting and smoothing.

This method of setting regularisation parameters does not provide a guarantee against overfitting (Wolpert, 1992), but it helps. In setting the regularisation parameters by maximising (6.30) $P(\mathbf{Y})$, one attempts to find a prior $P^0(\mathbf{w})$ under which "usually" networks $\mathbf{w}$ fit the data $\mathbf{Y}$ well. This objective is not diametrically opposed to the later objective of selecting the best-fitting $\mathbf{w}$. Indeed, the distribution $P(\mathbf{w})$ which maximises the evidence is one which is concentrated on a single overfit $\mathbf{w}$. This is prevented only if the the distribution of weight matrices parameterised by the regularisation parameters does not include such highly concentrated distributions. Therefore it remains an art to select reasonable functional forms for the regularisers, but once selected, the determination of the parameters themselves is a matter of calculation. The art of selecting regularisation functions has become an interesting research area (Nowlan & Hinton, 1992).

The calculation of (6.32) involves an integration which is generally non-trivial, but which can be done easily in a Gaussian approximation. Typically this is good enough. This requires computation of the second derivatives of the error measure, which is prohibitive for large problems, but in this case a further approximation is possible and often adequate (MacKay, 1992b).

6.3 UNSUPERVISED LEARNING

Interest in Unsupervised Learning has increased greatly in recent years. It offers the possibility of exploring the structure of data without guidance in the form of class information, and can often reveal features not previously expected or known about. These might include the division of data that was previously thought to be a single uniform cluster, into a number of smaller groups, each with separate identifiable properties. The clusters found offer a model of the data in terms of cluster centres, sizes and shapes, which can often be described using less information, and in fewer parameters than were required to store the entire training data set. This has obvious advantages for storing, coding, and transmitting stochastically generated data; if its distribution in the attribute space is known, equivalent data can be generated from the model when required.

While general, unsupervised learning methods such as Boltzmann machines are computationally expensive, iterative clustering algorithms such as Kohonen networks, K-means clustering and Gaussian Mixture models offer the same modelling power with greatly reduced training time. Indeed, while class labels are not used to constrain the structure learned by the models, freedom from this constraint coupled with careful initialisation of the models using any prior information available about the data, can yield very quick and effective models. These models, known collectively as *Vector Quantizers*, can be used as the non-linear part of supervised learning models. In this case a linear part is added and trained later to implement the mapping from activation in different parts of the model, to probable classes of event generating the data.

6.3.1 The K-means clustering algorithm

The principle of clustering requires a representation of a set of data to be found which offers a model of the distribution of samples in the attribute space. The K-means algorithm (for example, Krishnaiah & Kanal, 1982) achieves this quickly and efficiently as a model with a fixed number of cluster centres, determined by the user in advance. The cluster centres are initially chosen from the data, and each centre forms the *code vector* for the patch of the input space in which all points are closer to that centre than to any other. This division of the space into patches is known as a *Voronoi tessellation*. Since the initial allocation of centres may not form a good model of the probability distribution function (PDF) of the input space, there follows a series of iterations where each cluster centre is moved to the mean position of all the training patterns in its tessellation region.

A generalised variant of the K-means algorithm is the Gaussian Mixture Model, or Adaptive K-means. In this scheme, Voronoi tessellations are replaced with soft transitions from one centre's receptive field to another's. This is achieved by assigning a variance to each centre, thereby defining a Gaussian kernel at each centre. These kernels are mixed

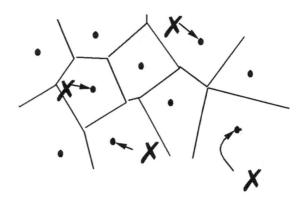

Fig. 6.4:   K-Means clustering: within each patch the centre is moved to the mean position of the patterns.

together by a set of mixing weights to approximate the PDF of the input data, and an efficient algorithm exists to calculate iteratively a set of mixing weights, centres, and variances for the centres (Dubes & Jain, 1976, and Wu & Chan, 1991). While the number of centres for these algorithms is fixed in advance in more popular implementations, some techniques are appearing which allow new centres to be added as training proceeds. (Wynne-Jones, 1992 and 1993)

6.3.2   Kohonen networks and Learning Vector Quantizers

Kohonen's network algorithm (Kohonen, 1984) also provides a Voronoi tessellation of the input space into patches with corresponding code vectors. It has the additional feature that the centres are arranged in a low dimensional structure (usually a string, or a square grid), such that nearby points in the topological structure (the string or grid) map to nearby points in the attribute space. Structures of this kind are thought to occur in nature, for example in the mapping from the ear to the auditory cortex, and the retinotopic map from the retina to the visual cortex or optic tectum.

In training, the *winning node* of the network, which is the nearest node in the input space to a given training pattern, moves towards that training pattern, while dragging with its neighbouring nodes in the network topology. This leads to a smooth distribution of the network topology in a non-linear subspace of the training data.

Vector Quantizers that conserve topographic relations between centres are also particularly useful in communications, where noise added to the coded vectors may corrupt the representation a little; the topographic mapping ensures that a small change in code vector is decoded as a small change in attribute space, and hence a small change at the output. These models have been studied extensively, and recently unified under the framework of Bayes' theory (Luttrell, 1990, 1993).

Although it is fundamentally an unsupervised learning algorithm, The Learning Vector Quantizer can be used as a *supervised* vector quantizer, where network nodes have class labels associated with them. The Kohonen Learning Rule is used when the winning node represents the same class as a new training pattern, while a difference in class between the winning node and a training pattern causes the node to move *away* from the training pattern by the same distance. Learning Vector Quantizers are reported to give excellent performance in studies on statistical and speech data (Kohonen *et al.*, 1988).

6.3.3   RAMnets

One of the oldest practical neurally-inspired classification algorithms is still one of the best. It is the n-tuple recognition method introduced by Bledsoe & Browning (1959) and Bledsoe (1961) , which later formed the basis of a commercial product known as Wisard (Aleksander *et al.*, 1984) . The algorithm is simple. The patterns to be classified are bit strings of a given length. Several (let us say N) sets of n bit locations are selected randomly. These are the n-tuples. The restriction of a pattern to an n-tuple can be regarded as an n-bit number which constitutes a 'feature' of the pattern. A pattern is classified as belonging to the class for which it has the most features in common with at least 1 pattern in the training data.

To be precise, the class assigned to unclassified pattern u is

$$\underset{c}{\operatorname{argmax}} \left(\sum_{i=1}^{N} \Theta \left(\sum_{v \in C_c} \delta_{\alpha_i(u),\alpha_i(v)} \right) \right) \tag{6.33}$$

where C_c is the set of training patterns in class c, $\Theta(x) = 0$ for $\Theta \leq 0$, $\Theta(x) = 1$ for $\Theta > 0$, $\delta_{i,j}$ is the Kronecker delta ($\delta_{i,j} = 1$ if $i = j$ and 0 otherwise.) and $\alpha_i(u)$ is the ith feature of pattern u:

$$\alpha_i(u) = \sum_{j=0}^{n-1} u_{\eta_i(j)} 2^j \tag{6.34}$$

Here u_i is the ith bit of u and $\eta_i(j)$ is the jth bit of the ith n-tuple.

With C classes to distinguish, the system can be implemented as a set of NC RAMS, in which the memory content $m_{ci\alpha}$ at address α of the ith RAM allocated to class c is

$$m_{ci\alpha} = \Theta \left(\sum_{v \in C_c} \delta_{\alpha,\alpha_i(v)} \right) \tag{6.35}$$

Thus $m_{ci\alpha}$ is set if any pattern of C_c has feature α and unset otherwise. Recognition is accomplished by tallying the set bits in the RAMS of each class at the addresses given by the features of the unclassified pattern.

RAMnets are impressive in that they can be trained faster than MLPs or radial basis function networks by orders of magnitude, and often provide comparable results. Experimental comparisons between RAMnets and other methods can be found in Rohwer & Cressy (1989) .

6.4   DIPOL92

This is something of a hybrid algorithm, which has much in common with both logistic discrimination and some of the nonparametric statistical methods. However, for historical reasons it is included here.

6.4.1   Introduction

DIPOL92 is a learning algorithm which constructs an optimised piecewise linear classifier by a two step procedure. In the first step the initial positions of the discriminating hyperplanes are determined by pairwise linear regression. To optimise these positions in relation to the misclassified patterns an error criterion function is defined. This function is then minimised by a gradient descent procedure for each hyperplane separately. As an option in the case of non–convex classes (e.g. if a class has a multimodal probability distribution) a clustering procedure decomposing the classes into appropriate subclasses can be applied. (In this case DIPOL92 is really a three step procedure.)

Seen from a more general point of view DIPOL92 is a combination of a statistical part (regression) with a learning procedure typical for artificial neural nets. Compared with most neural net algorithms an advantage of DIPOL92 is the possibility to determine the number and initial positions of the discriminating hyperplanes (corresponding to "neurons") a priori, *i.e.* before learning starts. Using the clustering procedure this is true even in the case that a class has several distinct subclasses. There are many relations and similarities between statistical and neural net algorithms but a systematic study of these relations is still lacking.

Another distinguishing feature of DIPOL92 is the introduction of Boolean variables (signs of the normals of the discriminating hyperplanes) for the description of class regions on a symbolic level and using them in the decision procedure. This way additional layers of "hidden units" can be avoided.

DIPOL92 has some similarity with the MADALINE-system (Widrow, 1962) which is also a piecewise linear classification procedure. But instead of applying a majority function for class decision on the symbolic level (as in the case of MADALINE) DIPOL92 uses more general Boolean descriptions of class and subclass segments, respectively. This extends the variety of classification problems which can be handled considerably.

6.4.2   Pairwise linear regression

Suppose that $X \subset \Re^p$ is the set of data $x = (x_1, \ldots, x_p)$. Then linear regression is used to discriminate between two classes A_1 and A_2 by defining the dependent variable b as follows:

$$\begin{aligned} \text{if} \quad & x \epsilon A_1, \quad \text{then} \quad b = +1 \\ \text{if} \quad & x \epsilon A_2, \quad \text{then} \quad b = -1 \end{aligned}$$

Let W be the linear regression function $W : X \to \Re$ with $W(x) = w_0 + w_1 x_1 + \ldots + w_p x_p$. Then a pattern x is correctly classified if

$$\begin{aligned} W(x) > 0 \quad & \text{for} \quad x \epsilon A_1 \\ W(x) < 0 \quad & \text{for} \quad x \epsilon A_2 \end{aligned}$$

For each pair of classes a discriminating regression function can be calculated.

6.4.3   Learning procedure

The following criterion function is defined. For all misclassified patterns the squared distances from the corresponding decision hyperplane multiplied by the costs for these misclassifications are summed up. Suppose that $W = 0$ defines the decision hyperplane between the classes A_1 and A_2, respectively. Then let m_1 be the set of all misclassified patterns of class A_1, *i.e.*, $x \epsilon A_1$ and $W(x) < 0$, let m_2 be the set of all misclassified patterns of class A_2, *i.e.*, $x \epsilon A_2$ and $W(x) > 0$, and let $c(i, j)$ be the costs of the misclassification of the class A_i into the class A_j. We then minimise:

$$F(W) = c(1,2) \sum_{x \epsilon m_1} \frac{W(x)^2}{\|x\|^2} + c(2,1) \sum_{x \epsilon m_2} \frac{W(x)^2}{\|x\|^2}$$

This means that costs are included explicitly in the learning procedure which consists of minimizing the criterion function with respect to $w_0, w_1, \ldots, w_m$ by a gradient descent algorithm for each decision surface successively.

6.4.4   Clustering of classes

To handle also problems with non–convex (especially non simply–connected class regions), one can apply a clustering procedure before the linear regression is carried out. For solving the clustering problem a minimum–squared–error algorithm is used. Suppose that a class A_k has been partitioned into q_k clusters $A_{k(i)}$ $(i = 1, \ldots, q_k)$ with k_i elements and mean vectors s_i given by

$$s_i = \frac{1}{k_i} \sum_{x \epsilon A_{k(i)}} x$$

Then the criterion function

$$J = \sum_{i=1}^{q_k} \sum_{x \epsilon A_{k(i)}} \|x - s_i\|^2$$

is calculated. Patterns are moved from one cluster to another if such a move will improve the criterion function J. The mean vectors and the criterion function are updated after each pattern move. Like hill–climbing algorithms in general, these approaches guarantee local but not global optimisation. Different initial partitions and sequences of the training patterns can lead to different solutions. In the case of clustering the number of two–class problems increases correspondingly.

  We note that by the combination of the clustering algorithm with the regression technique the number and initial positions of discriminating hyperplanes are fixed a priori (*i.e.* before learning) in a reasonable manner, even in the case that some classes have multimodal distributions (i.e consist of several subclasses). Thus a well known bottleneck of artificial neural nets can at least be partly avoided.

6.4.5   Description of the classification procedure

If the discriminating hyperplanes were calculated then any pattern $x = (x_1, \ldots, x_p)$ (contained in the training set or not) can be classified, *i.e.*, the class predicted. For the pairwise discrimination of the q classes $q^* = q(q - 1)/2$ hyperplanes W^i are calculated (in the case of clustering the number q is changed into $q + n_{clust}$). The following q^*-dimensional vector V_k is formed for each class A_k : if the function W^i discriminates the classes A_1 and A_2, then the i-th component $V_{k,i}$ is equal to 1, if $A = A_1$, is equal to -1, if $A = A_2$, and is equal to 0 in all other cases. On the basis of the discriminant functions a vector function sw is defined for each pattern x

$$sw : X \rightarrow \{1, 0, -1\}^{q^*}$$

with

$$sw(x)_i = \text{sign}(W^i(x))$$

For each class A_k the function

$$S_k : X \rightarrow G$$

(G is the set of integers) is defined by

$$S_k(x) = \sum_{i=1}^{q^*} V_{k,i} * sw(x)_i$$

A pattern x is uniquely classified by the discriminating hyperplanes W^i ($i = 1, \ldots, q^*$) into the class A_k if

$$S_k(x) = q - 1,$$

i.e., with respect to the $q - 1$ hyperplanes, which discriminate the class A_k from the other $q - 1$ classes, the pattern x is placed in the halfspace, belonging to class A_k ($V_{k,i}$ and $W^i(x)$ have the same sign for all $V_{k,i} \neq 0$). For all other classes j, $j \neq k$, $S_j < q - 1$ is valid, because at least with respect to the hyperplane, which discriminates class j from class A_k the pattern x is placed in the halfspace of class A_k ($V_{j,i}$ and $W^i(x)$ have not the same sign).

A pattern x is not uniquely classified if

$$\max_j S_j(x) < q - 1$$

In this case all classes j were determined with $S_j(x) = \max_j S_j(x)$. If there is only one such class then x will be assigned to this class. If there are several classes let M be the set of the classes with this property, $M = \{j_1, \ldots, j_l\}$. For each class j_i all hyperplanes discriminating the class j_i against all other classes are found. Those of the hyperplanes $W_{j_i}^r$ for each class j_i are selected for which x is misclassified, *i.e.*, for each class j_i a set of hyperplanes $H_{j_i} = \{W_{j_i}^1, \ldots, W_{j_i}^r\}$ is determined for which x is not in the halfspace of class j_i. The Euclidian distance of x to all these hyperplanes $W_{j_i}^s$ are calculated. x is assigned to that class for which the minimum

$$\min_{j_i \epsilon M} \min_{s=1,\ldots,r} W_{j_i}^s(x)$$

is reached.

7

Methods for Comparison

R. J. Henery
University of Strathclyde[1]

7.1 ESTIMATION OF ERROR RATES IN CLASSIFICATION RULES

In testing the accuracy of a classification rule, it is widely known that error rates tend to be biased if they are estimated from the same set of data as that used to construct the rules. At one extreme, if a decision tree for example is allowed to grow without limit to the number of leaves in the tree, it is possible to classify the given data with 100% accuracy, in general at the expense of creating a very complex tree-structure. In practice complex structures do not always perform well when tested on unseen data, and this is one case of the general phenomenon of over-fitting data. Of course, overfitting is of most concern with noisy data, *i.e.* data in which 100% correct classification is impossible in principle as there are conflicting examples. However, the problem also arises with noise-free datasets, where, in principle, 100% correct classification is possible. Among the StatLog datasets, for example, there is one dataset (Shuttle) that is probably noise free, and it is possible to classify the given data 100% correctly. However, certain classes are represented so infrequently that we cannot be sure what the true classification procedure should be. As a general rule, we expect that very simple structures should be used for noisy data, and very complex structures only for data that are noise-free. What is clear is that we should adjust the complexity to suit the problem at hand, otherwise the procedure will be biased.

For example, most decision tree procedures (such as CART by Breiman *et al.*, 1984) restrict the size of the decision tree by pruning, *i.e.* by cutting out some branches if they do not lead to useful dichotomies of the data. Even if some measure of pruning is added to avoid over-fitting the data, the apparent error-rate, estimated by applying the induced rule on the original data, is usually over-optimistic. One way of correcting for this bias is to use two independent samples of data: one to learn the rule and another to test it. A method that is more suitable for intermediate sample sizes (of order 1000) is cross-validation, which first came to prominence when Lachenbruch & Mickey (1968) suggested the leave-one-out procedure. A closely related method, which is used for small sample sizes, is the bootstrap

---
[1]*Address for correspondence*: Department of Statistics and Modelling Science, University of Strathclyde, Glasgow G1 1XH, U.K.

procedure of Efron (1983). These three methods of estimating error rates are now described briefly.

7.1.1   Train-and-Test

The essential idea is this: a sample of data (the training data) is given to enable a classification rule to be set up. What we would like to know is the proportion of errors made by this rule when it is up-and-running, and classifying new observations without the benefit of knowing the true classifications. To do this, we test the rule on a second independent sample of new observations (the test data) whose true classifications are known but are not told to the classifier. The predicted and true classifications on the test data give an unbiased estimate of the error rate of the classifier. To enable this procedure to be carried out from a given set of data, a proportion of the data is selected at random (usually about 20-30%) and used as the test data. The classifier is trained on the remaining data, and then tested on the test data. There is a slight loss of efficiency here as we do not use the full sample to train the decision rule, but with very large datasets this is not a major problem. We adopted this procedure when the number of examples was much larger than 1000 (and allowed the use of a test sample of size 1000 or so). We often refer to this method as "one-shot" train-and-test.

7.1.2   Cross-validation

For moderate-sized samples, the procedure we adopted was cross-validation. In its most elementary form, cross-validation consists of dividing the data into m subsamples. Each sub-sample is predicted via the classification rule constructed from the remaining $(m - 1)$ subsamples, and the estimated error rate is the average error rate from these m subsamples. In this way the error rate is estimated efficiently and in an unbiased way. The rule finally used is calculated from all the data. The leave-one-out method of Lachenbruch & Mickey (1968) is of course m-fold cross-validation with m equal to the number of examples. Stone (1974) describes cross-validation methods for giving unbiased estimates of the error rate.

A practical difficulty with the use of cross-validation in computer-intensive methods such as neural networks is the m-fold repetition of the learning cycle, which may require much computational effort.

7.1.3   Bootstrap

The more serious objection to cross-validation is that the error estimates it produces are too scattered, so that the confidence intervals for the true error-rate are too wide. The bootstrap procedure gives much narrower confidence limits, but the penalty paid is that the estimated error-rates are optimistic (i.e. are biased downwards). The trade-off between bias and random error means that, as a general rule, the bootstrap method is preferred when the sample size is small, and cross-validation when the sample size is large. In conducting a comparative trial between methods on the same dataset, the amount of bias is not so important so long as the bias is the same for all methods. Since the bootstrap represents the best way to reduce variability, the most effective way to conduct comparisons in small datasets is to use the bootstrap. Since it is not so widely used in classification trials as perhaps it should be, we give an extended description here, although it must be admitted that we did not use the bootstrap in any of our trials as we judged that our samples were large enough to use either cross-validation or train-and-test.

In statistical terms, the bootstrap is a non-parametric procedure for estimating parameters generally and error-rates in particular. The basic idea is to re-use the original dataset (of size n) to obtain new datasets also of size n by re-sampling with replacement. See Efron (1983) for the definitive introduction to the subject and Crawford (1989) for an application to CART. Breiman *et al.* (1984) note that there are practical difficulties in applying the bootstrap to decision trees.

In the context of classification, the bootstrap idea is to replicate the whole classification experiment a large number of times and to estimate quantities like bias from these replicate experiments. Thus, to estimate the error rate in small samples (of size n say), a large number B of bootstrap replicate samples are created, each sample being a replicate (randomly chosen) of the original sample. That is, a random sample of size n is taken from the original sample by sampling **with replacement**. Sampling with replacement means, for example, that some data points will be omitted (on average about $1/e = 37\%$ of data will not appear in the bootstrap sample). Also, some data points will appear more than once in the bootstrap sample. Each bootstrap sample is used to construct a classification rule which is then used to predict the classes of those original data that were **unused** in the training set (so about $1/e = 37\%$ of the original data will be used as test set). This gives one estimate of the error rate for each bootstrap sample. The average error rates over all bootstrap samples are then combined to give an estimated error rate for the original rule. See Efron (1983) and Crawford (1989) for details. The main properties of the bootstrap have been summarised by Efron(1983) as follows.

Properties of cross-validation and bootstrap
Efron (1983) gives the following properties of the bootstrap as an estimator of error-rate. By taking B very large (Efron recommends approximately 200), the statistical variability in the average error rate e_{EFRON} is small, and for small sample size n, this means that the bootstrap will have very much smaller statistical variability than the cross-validation estimate.

The bootstrap and cross-validation estimates are generally close for large sample sizes, and the ratio between the two estimates approaches unity as the sample size tends to infinity.

The bootstrap and cross-validation methods tend to be closer for smoother cost-functions than the 0-1 loss-function implicit in the error rates discussed above. However the Bootstrap may be biased, even for large samples.

The effective sample size is determined by the number in the smallest classification group. Efron (1983) quotes a medical example with n = 155 cases, but primary interest centres on the 33 patients that died. The effective sample size here is 33.

For large samples, group-wise cross-validation may give better results than the leave-one-out method, although this conclusion seems doubtful.

7.1.4 Optimisation of parameters

Frequently it is desirable to tune some parameter to get the best performance from an algorithm: examples might be the amount of pruning in a decision tree or the number of hidden nodes in the multilayer perceptron. When the objective is to minimise the error-rate of the tree or perceptron, the training data might be divided into two parts: one to build the tree or perceptron, and the other to measure the error rate. A plot of error-rate against the parameter will indicate what the best choice of parameter should be. However, the error rate corresponding to this choice of parameter is a biased estimate of the error rate of the classification rule when tested on unseen data. When it is necessary to optimise a parameter in this way, we recommend a three-stage process for very large datasets: (i) hold back 20% as a test sample; (ii) of the remainder, divide into two, with one set used for building the rule and the other for choosing the parameter; (iii) use the chosen parameter to build a rule for the complete training sample (containing 80% of the original data) and test this rule on the test sample.

Thus, for example, Watkins (1987) gives a description of cross-validation in the context of testing decision-tree classification algorithms, and uses cross-validation as a means of selecting better decision trees. Similarly, in this book, cross-validation was used by Backprop in finding the optimal number of nodes in the hidden layer, following the procedure outlined above. This was done also for the trials involving Cascade. However, cross-validation runs involve a greatly increased amount of computational labour, increasing the learning time m−fold, and this problem is particularly serious for neural networks.

In StatLog, most procedures had a tuning parameter that can be set to a default value, and where this was possible the default parameters were used. This was the case, for example, with the decision trees: generally no attempt was made to find the optimal amount of pruning, and accuracy and "mental fit" (see Chapter 5) is thereby sacrificed for the sake of speed in the learning process.

7.2   ORGANISATION OF COMPARATIVE TRIALS

We describe in this section what we consider to be the ideal setup for comparing classification procedures. It not easy to compare very different algorithms on a large number of datasets, and in practice some compromises have to be made. We will not detail the compromises that we made in our own trials, but attempt to set out the ideals that we tried to follow, and give a brief description of the UNIX-based procedures that we adopted. If a potential trialist wishes to perform another set of trials, is able to cast the relevant algorithms into the form that we detail here, and moreover is able to work within a UNIX environment, then we can recommend that he uses our test procedures. This will guarantee comparability with the majority of our own results.

In the following list of desiderata, we use the notation *file1, file2, ...* to denote arbitrary files that either provide data or receive output from the system. Throughout we assume that files used for training/testing are representative of the population and are statistically similar to each other.

1.   **Training Phase**. The most elementary functionality required of any learning algorithm, is to be able to take data from one file *file1* (by assumption *file1* contains known classes) and create the rules.

   - (Optionally) The resulting rules (or parameters defining the rule) may be saved to another file *file3*;
   - (Optionally) A cost matrix (in *file2* say) can be read in and used in building the rules

2.   **Testing Phase**. The algorithm can read in the rules and classify unseen data, in the following sequence:

- Read in the rules or parameters from the training phase (either passed on directly from the training phase if that immediately precedes the testing phase or read from the file *file3*)
- Read in a set of unseen data from a file *file4* with true classifications that are hidden from the classifier
- (Optionally) Read in a cost matrix from a file *file5* (normally *file5* = *file2*) and use this cost matrix in the classification procedure
- (Optionally) Output the classifications to a file *file6*
- If true classifications were provided in the test file *file4*, output to file *file7* a confusion matrix whose rows represent the true classifications and whose columns represent the classifications made by the algorithm

The two steps above constitute the most basic element of a comparative trial, and we describe this basic element as a simple Train-and-Test (TT) procedure. All algorithms used in our trials were able to perform the Train-and-Test procedure.

7.2.1   Cross-validation

To follow the cross-validation procedure, it is necessary to build an outer loop of control procedures that divide up the original file into its component parts and successively use each part as test file and the remaining part as training file. Of course, the cross-validation procedure results in a succession of mini-confusion matrices, and these must be combined to give the overall confusion matrix. All this can be done within the Evaluation Assistant shell provided the classification procedure is capable of the simple Train-and-Test steps above. Some more sophisticated algorithms may have a cross-validation procedure built in, of course, and if so this is a distinct advantage.

7.2.2   Bootstrap

The use of the bootstrap procedure makes it imperative that combining of results, files etc. is done automatically. Once again, if an algorithm is capable of simple Train-and-Test, it can be embedded in a bootstrap loop using Evaluation Assistant (although perhaps we should admit that we never used the bootstrap in any of the datasets reported in this book).

7.2.3   Evaluation Assistant

Evaluation Assistant is a tool that facilitates the testing of learning algorithms on given datasets and provides standardised performance measures. In particular, it standardises timings of the various phases, such as training and testing. It also provides statistics describing the trial (mean error rates, total confusion matrices, etc. etc.). It can be obtained from J. Gama of the University of Porto. For details of this, and other publicly available software and datasets, see Appendices A and B. Two versions of Evaluation Assistant exist:
- Command version (EAC)
- Interactive version (EAI)
The command version of Evaluation Assistant (EAC) consists of a set of basic commands that enable the user to test learning algorithms. This version is implemented as a set of C-shell scripts and C programs.

The interactive version of Evaluation Assistant (EAI) provides an interactive interface that enables the user to set up the basic parameters for testing. It is implemented in C and the interactive interface exploits X windows. This version generates a customised version of some EAC scripts which can be examined and modified before execution.

Both versions run on a SUN SPARCstation and other compatible workstations.

7.3   CHARACTERISATION OF DATASETS

An important objective is to investigate why certain algorithms do well on some datasets and not so well on others. This section describes measures of datasets which may help to explain our findings. These measures are of three types: (i) very simple measures such as the number of examples; (ii) statistically based, such as the skewness of the attributes; and (iii) information theoretic, such as the information gain of attributes. We discuss information theoretic measures in Section 7.3.3. There is a need for a measure which indicates when decision trees will do well. Bearing in mind the success of decision trees in image segmentation problems, it seems that some measure of multimodality might be useful in this connection.

Some algorithms have built in measures which are given as part of the output. For example, CASTLE measures the Kullback-Leibler information in a dataset. Such measures are useful in establishing the validity of specific assumptions underlying the algorithm and, although they do not always suggest what to do if the assumptions do not hold, at least they give an indication of internal consistency.

The measures should continue to be elaborated and refined in the light of experience.

7.3.1   Simple measures

The following descriptors of the datasets give very simple measures of the complexity or size of the problem. Of course, these measures might advantageously be combined to give other measures more appropriate for specific tasks, for example by taking products, ratios or logarithms.

Number of observations, N

This is the **total** number of observations in the **whole dataset**. In some respects, it might seem more sensible to count only the observations in the training data, but this is generally a large fraction of the total number in any case.

Number of attributes, p

The total number of attributes in the data as used in the trials. Where categorical attributes were originally present, these were converted to binary indicator variables.

Number of classes, q

The total number of classes represented in the entire dataset.

Number of binary attributes, Bin.att

The total number of number of attributes that are binary (including categorical attributes coded as indicator variables). By definition, the remaining $p -$ Bin.att attributes are numerical (either continuous or ordered) attributes.

7.3.2   Statistical measures

The following measures are designed principally to explain the performance of statistical algorithms, but are likely to be more generally applicable. Often they are much influenced by the simple measures above. For example, the skewness measure often reflects the number of binary attributes, and if this is so, the skewness and kurtosis are directly related to each other. However, the statistical measures in this section are generally defined only for continuous attributes. Although it is possible to extend their definitions to include discrete and even categorical attributes, the most natural measures for such data are the information theoretic measures discussed in section 7.3.3.

Test statistic for homogeneity of covariances

The covariance matrices are fundamental in the theory of linear and quadratic discrimination detailed in Sections 3.2 and 3.3, and the key in understanding when to apply one and not the other lies in the homogeneity or otherwise of the covariances. One measure of the lack of homogeneity of covariances is the geometric mean ratio of standard deviations of the populations of individual classes to the standard deviations of the sample, and is given by SD_ratio (see below). This quantity is related to a test of the hypothesis that all populations have a common covariance structure, *i.e.* to the hypothesis $H_0 : \Sigma_1 = \Sigma_2 = \ldots = \Sigma_q$ which can be tested via Box's M test statistic:

$$M = \gamma \sum_{i=1}^{q} (n_i - 1) \log |S_i^{-1} S|,$$

where

$$\gamma = 1 - \frac{2p^2 + 3p - 1}{6(p + 1)(q - 1)} \left\{ \sum \frac{1}{n_i - 1} - \frac{1}{n - q} \right\},$$

and S_i and S are the unbiased estimators of the i–th sample covariance matrix and the pooled covariance matrix respectively. This statistic has an asymptotic $\chi^2_{p(p+1)(q-1)/2}$ distribution: and the approximation is good if each n_i exceeds 20, and if q and p are both much smaller than every n_i.

In datasets reported in this volume these criteria are not always met, but the M–statistic can still be computed, and used as a characteristic of the data. The M–statistic can be re-expressed as the geometric mean ratio of standard deviations of the individual populations to the pooled standard deviations, via the expression

$$SD\_ratio = \exp \left\{ \frac{M}{p \sum_{i=1}^{q} (n_i - 1)} \right\}.$$

The SD_ratio is strictly greater than unity if the covariances differ, and is equal to unity if and only if the M-statistic is zero, *i.e.* all individual covariance matrices are equal to the pooled covariance matrix.

In every dataset that we looked at the M–statistic is significantly different from zero, in which case the SD_ratio is significantly greater than unity.

Mean absolute correlation coefficient, corr.abs

The set of correlations ρ_{ij} between all pairs of attributes give some indication of the interdependence of the attributes, and a measure of that interdependence may be calculated as follows. The correlations ρ_{ij} between all pairs of attributes are calculated for each class separately. The absolute values of these correlations are averaged over all pairs of attributes and over all classes giving the measure corr.abs $= \rho$ which is a measure of interdependence between attributes.

If corr.abs is near unity, there is much redundant information in the attributes and some procedures, such as logistic discriminants, may have technical problems associated with this. Also, CASTLE, for example, may be misled substantially by fitting relationships to the attributes, instead of concentrating on getting right the relationship between the classes and the attributes.

Canonical discriminant correlations

Assume that, in p—dimensional space, the sample points from one class form clusters of roughly elliptical shape around its population mean. In general, if there are q classes, the q means lie in a $q-1$ dimensional subspace. On the other hand, it happens frequently that the classes form some kind of sequence, so that the population means are strung out along some curve that lies in k—dimensional space, where $k < q - 1$. The simplest case of all occurs when $k = 1$ and the population means lie along a straight line. *Canonical discriminants* are a way of systematically projecting the mean vectors in an optimal way to maximise the ratio of between-mean distances to within-cluster distances, successive discriminants being orthogonal to earlier discriminants. Thus the first canonical discriminant gives the best single linear combination of attributes that discriminates between the populations. The second canonical discriminant is the best single linear combination orthogonal to the first, and so on. The success of these discriminants is measured by the canonical correlations. If the first canonical correlation is close to unity, the q means lie along a straight line nearly. If the $k + 1$th canonical correlation is near zero, the means lie in k—dimensional space.

Proportion of total variation explained by first k (=1,2,3,4) canonical discriminants

This is based on the idea of describing how the means for the various populations differ in attribute space. Each class (population) mean defines a point in attribute space, and, at its simplest, we wish to know if there is some simple relationship between these class means, for example, if they lie along a straight line. The sum of the first k eigenvalues of the canonical discriminant matrix divided by the sum of all the eigenvalues represents the "proportion of total variation" explained by the first k canonical discriminants. The total variation here is tr(Σ). We calculate, as fractk, the values of

$$(\lambda_1 + \ldots + \lambda_k)/(\lambda_1 + \lambda_2 + \ldots + \lambda_p) \qquad \text{for} \qquad k = 1, 2, 3, 4$$

This gives a measure of collinearity of the class means. When the classes form an ordered sequence, for example soil types might be ordered by wetness, the class means typically lie along a curve in low dimensional space. The λ's are the squares of the canonical correlations. The significance of the λ's can be judged from the χ^2 statistics produced by "manova". This representation of linear discrimination, which is due to Fisher (1936), is discussed also in Section 3.2.

Departure from normality

The assumption of multivariate normality underlies much of classical discrimination procedures. But the effects of departures from normality on the methods are not easily or clearly understood. Moreover, in analysing multiresponse data, it is not known how robust classical procedures are to departures from multivariate normality. Most studies on robustness depend on simulation studies. Thus, it is useful to have measures for verifying the reasonableness of assuming normality for a given dataset. If available, such a measure would be helpful in guiding the subsequent analysis of the data to make it more normally distributed, or suggesting the most appropriate discrimination method. Andrews *et al.*

(1973), whose excellent presentation we follow in this section, discuss a variety of methods for assessing normality.

With multiresponse data, the possibilities for departure from joint normality are many and varied. One implication of this is the need for a variety of techniques with differing sensitivities to the different types of departure and to the effects that such departures have on the subsequent analysis.

Of great importance here is the degree of commitment one wishes to make to the coordinate system for the multiresponse observations. At one extreme is the situation where the interest is completely confined to the observed coordinates. In this case, the marginal distributions of each of the observed variables and conditional distributions of certain of these given certain others would be the objects of interest.

At the other extreme, the class of all nonsingular linear transformations of the variables would be of interest. One possibility is to look at all possible linear combinations of the variables and find the maximum departure from univariate normality in these combinations (Machado, 1983). Mardia *et al.* (1979) give multivariate measures of skewness and kurtosis that are invariant to affine transformations of the data: critical values of these statistics for small samples are given in Mardia (1974). These measures are difficult to compare across datasets with differing dimensionality. They also have the disadvantage that they do not reduce to the usual univariate statistics when the attributes are independent.

Our approach is to concentrate on the original coordinates by looking at their marginal distributions. Moreover, the emphasis here is on a measure of non-normality, rather than on a test that tells us how statistically significant is the departure from normality. See Ozturk & Romeu (1992) for a review of methods for testing multivariate normality.

Univariate skewness and kurtosis

The usual measure of univariate skewness (Kendall *et al.*, 1983) is γ_1, which is the ratio of the mean cubed deviation from the mean to the cube of the standard deviation

$$\gamma_1 = E(X - \mu)^3 / \sigma^3$$

although, for test purposes, it is usual to quote the square of this quantity: $\beta_1 = \gamma_1^2$. Another measure is defined via the ratio of the fourth moment about the mean to the fourth power of the standard deviation:

$$\beta_2 = E(X - \mu)^4 / \sigma^4.$$

The quantity $\beta_2 - 3$ is generally known as the kurtosis of the distribution. However, we will refer to β_2 itself as the measure of kurtosis: since we only use this measure relative to other measurements of the same quantity within this book, this slight abuse of the term kurtosis may be tolerated. For the normal distribution, the measures are $\beta_1 = 0$ and $\beta_2 = 3$, and we will say that the skewness is zero and the kurtosis is 3, although the usual definition of kurtosis gives a value of zero for a normal distribution.

Mean skewness and kurtosis

Denote the skewness statistic for attribute i in population A_j by $\gamma_1(i, j)$. As a single measure of skewness for the whole dataset, we quote the mean of the absolute value of $\gamma_1(i, j)$, averaged over all attributes and over all populations. This gives the measure $skew\_abs$. For a normal population, $skew\_abs$ is zero: for uniform and exponential variables, the theoretical values of $skew\_abs$ are zero and 2 respectively. Similarly, we find the mean of the univariate standardised fourth moment $\beta_2(i, j)$, averaged over all attributes and populations. This gives the measure β_2. For a normal population, $\beta_2 = 3$ exactly, and the corresponding figures for uniform and exponential variables are 1.8 and 9, respectively.

Univariate skewness and kurtosis of correlated attributes

The univariate measures above have very large variances if the attributes are highly correlated. It may therefore be desirable to transform to uncorrelated variables before finding the univariate skewness and kurtosis measures. This may be achieved via the symmetric inverse square-root of the covariance matrix. The corresponding kurtosis and skewness measure (*kurt_inv* and *skew_inv* say) may be more reliable for correlated attributes. By construction, these measures reduce to the univariate values if the attributes are uncorrelated. Although they were calculated for all the datasets, these particular measures are not quoted in the tables, as they are usually similar to the univariate statistics.

7.3.3   Information theoretic measures

For the most part, the statistical measures above were based on the assumption of continuous attributes. The measures we discuss now are motivated by information theory and are most appropriate for discrete (and indeed categorical) attributes, although they are able to deal with continuous attributes also. For this reason, these measures are very much used by the machine learning community, and are often used as a basis for splitting criteria when building decision trees. They correspond to the deviance statistics that arise in the analysis of contingency tables (McCullagh & Nelder, 1989). For a basic introduction to the subject of information theory, see, for example, Jones (1979).

Entropy of attributes, $\bar{H}(X)$

Entropy is a measure of randomness in a random variable. In general terms the entropy $H(X)$ of a discrete random variable X is defined as the sum

$$H(X) = -\sum_i q_i \log_2 q_i$$

where q_i is the probability that X takes on the i'th value. Conventionally, logarithms are to base 2, and entropy is then said to be measured in units called "bits" (binary information units). In what follows, all logarithms are to base 2. The special cases to remember are:

- Equal probabilities (uniform distribution). The entropy of a discrete random variable is maximal when all q_i are equal. If there are k possible values for X, the maximal entropy is $\log k$.
- Continuous variable with given variance. Maximal entropy is attained for normal variables, and this maximal entropy is $0.5 \log(2\pi\sigma e)$.

In the context of classification schemes, the point to note is that an attribute that does not vary at all, and therefore has zero entropy, contains no information for discriminating between classes.

The entropy of a collection of attributes is not simply related to the individual entropies, but, as a basic measure, we can average the entropy over all the attributes and take this as a global measure of entropy of the attributes collectively. Thus, as a measure of entropy of the attributes we take the $H(X)$ averaged over all attributes $X_1, ..., X_p$:

$$\bar{H}(X) = p^{-1} \sum_i H(X_i)$$

This measure is strictly appropriate only for independent attributes.

The definition of entropy for continuous distributions is analogous to the discrete case, with an integral replacing the summation term. This definition is no use for empirical data, however, unless some very drastic assumptions are made (for example assuming that the data have a normal distribution), and we are forced to apply the discrete definition to all empirical data. For the measures defined below, we discretised all numerical data into equal-length intervals. The number of intervals was chosen so that there was a fair expectation that there would be about ten observations per cell in the two-way table of attribute by class. As there are dq cells in a two-way table of attribute (with d discrete levels) by class (with q classes), and there are N examples, this means choosing $N/dq = 10$. The simplest, but not the best, procedure is to divide the range of the attribute into d equal intervals. A more refined procedure would have the number and width of intervals varying from attribute to attribute, and from dataset to dataset. Unless the data are very extensive, the estimated entropies, even for discrete variables, are likely to be severely biased. Blyth (1958) discusses methods of reducing the bias.

Entropy of classes, $H(C)$

In many of our datasets, some classes have very low probabilities of occurrence, and, for practical purposes, the very infrequent classes play little part in the assessment of classification schemes. It is therefore inappropriate merely to count the number of classes and use this as a measure of complexity. An alternative is to use the entropy $H(C)$ of the class probability distribution:

$$H(C) = -\sum_i \pi_i \log \pi_i$$

where π_i is the prior probability for class A_i. Entropy is related to the average length of a variable length coding scheme, and there are direct links to decision trees (see Jones, 1979 for example). Since class is essentially discrete, the class entropy $H(C)$ has maximal value when the classes are equally likely, so that $H(C)$ is at most $\log q$, where q is the number of classes. A useful way of looking at the entropy $H(C)$ is to regard $2^{H(C)}$ as an effective number of classes.

Joint entropy of class and attribute, $H(C, X)$

The joint entropy $H(C, X)$ of two variables C and X is a measure of total entropy of the combined system of variables, *i.e.* the pair of variables (C, X). If p_{ij} denotes the joint probability of observing class A_i and the j-th value of attribute X, the joint entropy is defined to be:

$$H(C, X) = -\sum_{ij} p_{ij} \log p_{ij}.$$

This is a simple extension of the notion of entropy to the combined system of variables.

Mutual information of class and attribute, $\bar{M}(C, X)$

The mutual information $M(C, X)$ of two variables C and X is a measure of common information or entropy shared between the two variables. If the two variables are independent, there is no shared information, and the mutual information $M(C, X)$ is zero. If p_{ij} denotes the joint probability of observing class A_i and the j-th value of attribute X, if the marginal probability of class A_i is π_i, and if the marginal probability of attribute X taking on its j-th value is q_j, then the mutual information is defined to be (note that there is no minus sign):

$$M(C, X) = \sum_{ij} p_{ij} \log(\frac{p_{ij}}{\pi_i q_j}).$$

Equivalent definitions are:

$$M(C, X) = H(C) + H(X) - H(C, X)$$
$$M(C, X) = H(C) - H(C|X)$$
$$M(C, X) = H(X) - H(X|C)$$

The conditional entropy $H(C|X)$, for example, which we have not yet defined, may be defined formally by the equation in which it appears above, but it has a distinct meaning, namely, the entropy (*i.e.* randomness or noise) of the class variable that is *not* removed by knowing the value of the attribute X. Minimum mutual information $M(C, X)$ is zero, and this occurs when class and attribute are independent. The maximum mutual information $M(C, X)$ occurs when one of $H(C|X)$ or $H(X|C)$ is zero. Suppose, for example, that $H(C|X)$ is zero. This would mean that the value of class is fixed (non-random) once the value of X is known. Class C is then completely predictable from the attribute X, in the sense that attribute X contains all the information needed to specify the class. The corresponding limits of $M(C, X)$ are

$$0 \le M(C, X) \le \min(H(C), H(X)).$$

Since there are many attributes, we have tabulated an average of the mutual information $M(C, X)$ taken over all attributes $X_1, \ldots, X_p$:

$$\bar{M}(C, X) = p^{-1} \sum_i M(C, X_i)$$

This average mutual information gives a measure of how much useful information about classes is provided by the average attribute.

Mutual information may be used as a splitting criterion in decision tree algorithms, and is preferable to the gain ratio criterion of C4.5 (Pagallo & Haussler, 1990).

Equivalent number of attributes, EN.attr

The information required to specify the class is $H(C)$, and no classification scheme can be completely successful unless it provides at least $H(C)$ bits of useful information. This information is to come from the attributes taken together, and it is quite possible that the useful information $M(C, X)$ of all attributes together (here X stands for the vector of attributes $(X_1, \ldots, X_p)$) is greater than the sum of the individual informations $M(C, X_1) + \ldots + M(C, X_p)$. However, in the simplest (but most unrealistic) case that all attributes are independent, we would have

$$M(C, X) = M(C, X_1) + \ldots + M(C, X_p)$$

In this case the attributes contribute independent bits of useful information for classification purposes, and we can count up how many attributes would be required, on average, by taking the ratio between the class entropy $H(C)$ and the average mutual information $\bar{M}(C, X)$. Of course, we might do better by taking the attributes with highest mutual information, but, in any case, the assumption of independent useful bits of information is very dubious in any case, so this simple measure is probably quite sufficient:

$$\text{EN.attr} = \frac{H(C)}{\bar{M}(C, X)}$$

Noisiness of attributes, NS.ratio

If the useful information is only a small fraction of the total information, we may say that there is a large amount of noise. Thus, take $\bar{M}(C, X)$ as a measure of useful information about class, and $\bar{H}(X) - \bar{M}(C, X)$ as a measure as non-useful information. Then large values of the ratio

$$\text{NS.ratio} = \frac{\bar{H}(X) - \bar{M}(C, X)}{\bar{M}(C, X)}$$

imply a dataset that contains much irrelevant information (noise). Such datasets could be condensed considerably without affecting the performance of the classifier, for example by removing irrelevant attributes, by reducing the number of discrete levels used to specify the attributes, or perhaps by merging qualitative factors. The notation NS.ratio denotes the Noise-Signal-Ratio. Note that this is the reciprocal of the more usual Signal-Noise-Ratio (SNR).

Irrelevant attributes

The mutual information $M(C, X_i)$ between class and attribute X_i can be used to judge if attribute X_i could, of itself, contribute usefully to a classification scheme. Attributes with small values of $M(C, X_i)$ would not, by themselves, be useful predictors of class. In this context, interpreting the mutual information as a deviance statistic would be useful, and we can give a lower bound to statistically significant values for mutual information. Suppose that attribute X and class are, in fact, statistically independent, and suppose that X has d distinct levels. Assuming further that the sample size N is large, then it is well known that the deviance statistic $2N M(C, X)$ is approximately equal to the *chi-square* statistic for testing the independence of attribute and class (for example Agresti, 1990). Therefore $2N M(C, X)$ has an approximate $\chi^2_{(q-1)(d-1)}$ distribution, and order of magnitude calculations indicate that the mutual information contributes significantly (in the hypothesis testing sense) if its value exceeds $(d-1)(q-1)/N$, where q is the number of classes, N is the number of examples, and d is the number of discrete levels for the attribute.

In our measures, d is the number of levels for integer or binary attributes, and for continuous attributes we chose $d = N/10q$ (so that, on average, there were about 10 observations per cell in the two-way table of attribute by class), but occasionally the number of levels for so-called continuous attributes was less than $d = N/10q$. If we adopt a critical level for the $\chi^2_{(q-1)(d-1)}$ distribution as twice the number of degrees of freedom, for the sake of argument, we obtain an approximate critical level for the mutual information as $2(q-1)(d-1)/2N$. With our chosen value of d, this is of order $1/10$ for continuous attributes.

We have not quoted any measure of this form, as almost all attributes are relevant in this sense (and this measure would have little information content!). In any case, an equivalent measure would be the difference between the actual number of attributes and the value of EN.attr.

Correlated normal attributes

When attributes are correlated, the calculation of information measures becomes much more difficult, so difficult, in fact, that we have avoided it altogether. The above univariate measures take no account of any lack of independence, and are therefore very crude approximations to reality. There are, however, some simple results concerning the multivariate normal distribution, for which the entropy is

$$0.5 \log(2\pi e |\Sigma|)$$

where $|\Sigma|$ is the determinant of the covariance matrix of the variables. Similar results hold for mutual information, and there are then links with the statistical measures elaborated in Section 7.3.2. Unfortunately, even if such measures were used for our datasets, most datasets are so far from normality that the interpretation of the resulting measures would be very questionable.

7.4 PRE-PROCESSING

Usually there is no control over the form or content of the vast majority of datasets. Generally, they are already converted from whatever raw data was available into some "suitable" format, and there is no way of knowing if the manner in which this was done was consistent, or perhaps chosen to fit in with some pre-conceived type of analysis. In some datasets, it is very clear that some very drastic form of pre-processing has already been done – see Section 9.5.4, for example.

7.4.1 Missing values

Some algorithms (*e.g.* Naive Bayes, CART, CN2, Bayes Tree, NewID, C4.5, Cal5, AC^2) can deal with missing values, whereas others require that the missing values be replaced. The procedure Discrim was not able to handle missing values, although this can be done in principle for linear discrimination for certain types of missing value. In order to get comparable results we settled on a general policy of replacing all missing values. Where an attribute value was missing it was replaced by the *global mean* or *median* for that attribute. If the class value was missing, the whole observation was omitted. Usually, the proportion of cases with missing information was very low. As a separate exercise it would be of interest to learn how much information is lost (or gained) in such a strategy by those algorithms that can handle missing values.

Unfortunately, there are various ways in which missing values might arise, and their treatment is quite different. For example, a clinician may normally use the results of a blood-test in making a diagnosis. If the blood-test is not carried out, perhaps because of faulty equipment, the blood-test measurements are missing for that specimen. A situation that may appear similar, results from doing measurements on a subset of the population, for example only doing pregnancy tests on women, where the test is not relevant for men (and so is missing for men). In the first case, the measurements are missing at random, and in the second the measurements are structured, or hierarchical. Although the treatment of these two cases should be radically different, the necessary information is often lacking. In at least one dataset (technical), it would appear that this problem arises in a very extreme manner, as it would seem that missing values are coded as zero, and that a large majority of observations is zero.

7.4.2 Feature selection and extraction

Some datasets are so large that many algorithms have problems just entering the data, and the sheer size of the dataset has to be reduced. In this case, to achieve uniformity, a data reduction process was performed in advance of the trials. Again it is of interest to note which algorithms can cope with the very large datasets. There are several ways in which data reduction can take place. For example, the Karhunen-Loeve transformation can be used with very little loss of information – see Section 9.6.1 for an example. Another way of reducing the number of variables is by a stepwise procedure in a Linear Discriminant procedure, for example. This was tried on the "Cut50" dataset, in which a version "Cut20" with number of attributes reduced from 50 to 20 was also considered. Results for both these versions are presented, and make for an interesting paired comparison: see the section on paired comparisons for the Cut20 dataset in Section 10.2.2.

In some datasets, particularly image segmentation, extra relevant information can be included. For example, we can use the prior knowledge that examples which are "neighbours" are likely to have the same class. A dataset of this type is considered in Section 9.6.5 in which a satellite image uses the fact that attributes of neighbouring pixels can give useful information in classifying the given pixel.

Especially in an exploratory study, practitioners often combine attributes in an attempt to increase the descriptive power of the resulting decision tree/rules etc. For example, it might be conjectured that it is the sum of two attributes $x_1 + x_2$ that is important rather than each attribute separately. Alternatively, some ratios are included such as $x_1/(x_1 + x_2)$. In our trials we did not introduce any such combinations. On the other hand, there existed already some linear combinations of attributes in some of the datasets that we looked at. We took the view that these combinations were included because the dataset provider thought that these particular combinations were potentially useful. Although capable of running on attributes with linear dependencies, some of the statistical procedures prefer attributes that are linearly independent, so when it came to running LDA (Discrim), QDA (Quadisc) and logistic discrimination (Logdisc) we excluded attributes that were linear combinations of others. This was the case for the Belgian Power data which is described in section 9.5.5. Although, in principle, the performance of linear discriminant procedures is not affected by the presence of linear combinations of attributes, in practice the resulting singularities are best avoided for numerical reasons.

As the performance of statistical procedures is directly related to the statistical properties of the attributes, it is generally advisable to transform the attributes so that their marginal distributions are as near normal as possible. Each attribute is considered in turn, and some transformation, usually from the power-law family, is made on the attribute. Most frequently, this is done by taking the square-root, logarithm or reciprocal transform. These transforms may help the statistical procedures: in theory, at least, they have no effect on non-parametric procedures, such as the decision trees, or Naive Bayes.

7.4.3 Large number of categories

We describe now the problems that arise for decision trees and statistical algorithms alike when an attribute has a large number of categories. Firstly, in building a decision tree, a potential split of a categorical attribute is based on some partitioning of the categories, one partition going down one side of the split and the remainder down the other. The number of potential splits is 2^L where L is the number of different categories (levels) of the attribute. Clearly, if L is much larger than ten, there is an enormous computational load, and the tree takes a very long time to train. However, there is a computational shortcut that applies to two-class problems (see Clark & Pregibon, 1992 for example). The shortcut method is not implemented in all StatLog decision-tree methods. With the statistical algorithms, a categorical attribute with L categories (levels) needs $L - 1$ binary variables for a complete specification of the attribute.

Now it is a fact that decision trees behave differently for categorical and numerical data. Two datasets may be logically equivalent, yet give rise to different decision trees. As a trivial example, with two numerical attributes X and Y, statistical algorithms would probably see exactly the same predictive value in the pair of attributes $(X + Y, X - Y)$ as in the original pair (X, Y), yet the decision trees would be different, as the decision boundaries would now be at an angle of 45 degrees. When categorical attributes are replaced by binary variables the decision trees will be very different, as most decision tree procedures look at all possible subsets of attribute values when considering potential splits. There is the additional, although perhaps not so important, point that the interpretation of the tree is rendered more difficult.

It is therefore of interest to note where decision tree procedures get almost the same accuracies on an original categorical dataset and the processed binary data. NewID, as run by ISoft for example, obtained an accuracy of 90.05% on the processed DNA data and 90.80% on the original DNA data (with categorical attributes). These accuracies are probably within what could be called experimental error, so it seems that NewID does about as well on either form of the DNA dataset.

In such circumstances, we have taken the view that *for comparative purposes* it is better that all algorithms are run on exactly the same preprocessed form. This way we avoid differences in preprocessing when comparing performance. When faced with a new application, it will pay to consider very carefully what form of preprocessing should be done. This is just as true for statistical algorithms as for neural nets or machine learning.

7.4.4 Bias in class proportions

First, some general remarks on potential bias in credit datasets. We do not know the way in which the credit datasets were collected, but it is very probable that they were biased in the following way. Most credit companies are very unwilling to give credit to all applicants. As a result, data will be gathered for only those customers who were given credit. If the credit approval process is any good at all, the proportion of bad risks among all applicants will be significantly higher than in the given dataset. It is very likely also, that the profiles of creditors and non-creditors are very different, so rules deduced from the creditors will have much less relevance to the target population (of all applicants).

When the numbers of good and bad risk examples are widely different, and one would expect that the bad risk examples would be relatively infrequent in a well managed lending concern, it becomes rather awkward to include all the data in the training of a classification procedure. On the one hand, if we are to preserve the true class proportions in the training sample, the total number of examples may have to be extremely large in order to guarantee sufficient bad risk examples for a reliable rule. On the other hand, if we follow the common practice in such cases and take as many bad risk examples as possible, together with a matching number of good risk examples, we are constructing a classification rule with its boundaries in the wrong places. The common practice is to make an adjustment to the boundaries to take account of the true class proportions. In the case of two classes, such an adjustment is equivalent to allocating different misclassification costs (see Sections 2.6 and 10.2.1). For example, if the true bad risk proportion is 5%, and a rule is trained on an artificial sample with equal numbers of good and bad risks, the recommendation would be to classify as bad risk only those examples whose assessed posterior odds of being bad risk were 19 to 1 (95% to 5%). This is equivalent to learning on the artificial sample, with the cost of misclassifying bad risks as 19 times that of misclassifying good risk examples. For such a procedure to work, it is necessary that a classification procedure returns class probabilities as its output, and the user can then allocate according to his prior probabilities (or according to misclassification costs). Many decision trees, CART and Bayes tree for example, now output class probabilities rather than classes. But the majority of decision trees in this project do not do so. And, in any case, it is by no means true that this artificial procedure is, in fact, a proper procedure at all. Consider again the case where bad risks form 5% of the population, and suppose that we are given a single normally distributed variable (say "bank balance") on which to classify. For simplicity, suppose also that good and bad risk customers differ only in their mean bank balance. When trained on an artificial sample with equal good and bad risks, a decision tree method would, correctly, divide the population into two regions above and below the midpoint between the two mean bank balances. In the artificial sample there will be a proportion, p say, of good examples above this boundary and, approximately, p bad examples below the boundary. So, for example, if a potential customer has bank balance above this boundary, we can assess the class probabilities as p for being good and $1 - p$ for bad. No matter what adjustment is made for the true prior odds of being bad risk, it is clear that the allocation rule can only take one of two forms: either allocate everyone to being good (or bad); or allocate good or bad according as bank balance is above or below the established boundary. In the situation we have described, however, it is clear that it is the boundary that should move, rather than adjust the probabilities. The way to modify the procedure is to overgrow the tree and then to take the costs and/or priors into account when pruning. See Michie & Attar (1991) for further details.

7.4.5   Hierarchical attributes

It often happens that information is relevant only to some of the examples. For example, certain questions in a population census may apply only to the householder, or certain medical conditions apply to females. There is then a hierarchy of attributes: primary variables refer to all members (*Sex* is a primary attribute); secondary attributes are only relevant when the appropriate primary attribute is applicable (*Pregnant* is secondary to *Sex* = Female); tertiary variables are relevant when a secondary variable applies (*Duration of pregnancy* is tertiary to *Pregnant* = True); and so on. Note that testing all members of a population for characteristics of pregnancy is not only pointless but wasteful. Decision tree methods are readily adapted to deal with such hierarchical datasets, and the algorithm AC^2 has been so designed.

The Machine Fault dataset (see Section 9.5.7), which was created by ISoft, is an example of a hierarchical dataset, with some attributes being present for one subclass of examples and not for others. Obviously AC^2 can deal with this dataset in its original form, but, from the viewpoint of the other algorithms, the dataset is unreadable, as it has a variable number of attributes. Therefore, an alternative version needs to be prepared. Of course, the flat form has lost some of the information that was available in the hierarchical structure of the data. The fact that AC^2 does best on this dataset when it uses this hierarchical information suggests that the hierarchical structure is related to the decision class.

Coding of hierarchical attributes

Hierarchical attributes can be coded into flat format without difficulty, in that a one-to-one correspondence can be set up between the hierarchically structured data and the flat format. We illustrate the procedure for an artificial example. Consider the primary attribute *Sex*. When *Sex* takes the value "male", the value of attribute *Baldness* is recorded as one of (Yes No), but when *Sex* takes the value "female" the attribute *Baldness* is simply "Not applicable". One way of coding this information in flat format is to give two attributes, with x_1 denoting *Sex* and x_2 *Baldness*. The three possible triples of values are (1 1), (1 0) and (0 0). In this formulation, the primary variable is explicitly available through the value of x_1, but there is the difficulty, here not too serious, that when x_2 is equal to 0, it is not clear whether this means "not bald" or "not applicable". Strictly, there are three possible values for x_2: "bald", "not bald" and "not applicable", the first two possibilities applying only to males. This gives a second formulation, in which the two attributes are lumped together into a single attribute, whose possible values represent the possible states of the system. In the example, the possible states are "bald male", "not bald male" and "female". Of course, none of the above codings enables ordinary classifiers to make use of the hierarchical structure: they are designed merely to represent the information in flat form with the same number of attributes per example. Breiman *et al.* (1984) indicate how hierarchical attributes may be programmed into a tree-building procedure. A logical flag indicates if a test on an attribute is permissible, and for a secondary attribute this flag is set to "true" only when the corresponding primary attribute has already been tested.

7.4.6   Collection of datasets

For the most part, when data are gathered, there is an implicit understanding that the data will be analysed by a certain procedure, and the data-gatherer usually sets down the data in a format that is acceptable to that procedure. For example, if linear discriminants are to be used, it is inappropriate to include linear combinations of existing attributes, yet the judicious use of sums or differences can make all the difference to a decision tree procedure. In other cases, the data may have some additional structure that cannot be incorporated in the given procedure, and this structure must be removed, or ignored in some way.

7.4.7   Preprocessing strategy in StatLog

The general strategy with datasets was to circulate the datasets exactly as received, and 11 datasets were sent out in exactly the same format as they came in. For these 11 datasets, the only processing was to permute the order of the examples. In four datasets substantial preprocessing was necessary, and in three of these datasets it is possible that the resulting dataset has lost some vital information, or has been biased in some way. For example, the credit management dataset was processed to make the class proportions representative. Another source of potential bias is the way in which categorical attributes are treated — a problem that is most acute in the DNA dataset.

8

Review of Previous Empirical Comparisons

R. J. Henery
University of Strathclyde[1]

8.1 INTRODUCTION

It is very difficult to make sense of the multitude of empirical comparisons that have been made. So often, the results are apparently in direct contradiction, with one author claiming that decision trees are superior to neural nets, and another making the opposite claim. Even allowing for differences in the types of data, it is almost impossible to reconcile the various claims that are made for this or that algorithm as being faster, or more accurate, or easier, than some other algorithm. There are no agreed objective criteria by which to judge algorithms, and in any case subjective criteria, such as how easy an algorithm is to program or run, are also very important when a potential user makes his choice from the many methods available.

Nor is it much help to say to the potential user that a particular neural network, say, is better for a particular dataset. Nor are the labels *neural network* and *Machine Learning* particularly helpful either, as there are different types of algorithms within these categories. What is required is some way of categorising the datasets into types, with a statement that for such-and-such a type of dataset, such-and-such a type of algorithm is likely to do well.

The situation is made more difficult because rapid advances are being made in all three areas: Machine Learning, Neural Networks and Statistics. So many comparisons are made between, say, a state-of-the-art neural network and an outmoded Machine Learning procedure like ID3.

8.2 BASIC TOOLBOX OF ALGORITHMS

Before discussing the various studies, let us make tentative proposals for candidates in future comparative trials, *i.e.* let us say what, in our opinion, form the basis of a toolbox of good classification procedures. In doing so, we are implicitly making a criticism of any comparative studies that do not include these basic algorithms, or something like them. Most are available as public domain software. Any that are not can be made available

---

[1] *Address for correspondence*: Department of Statistics and Modelling Science, University of Strathclyde, Glasgow G1 1XH, U.K.

from the database of algorithms administered from Porto (see Appendix B). So there is no excuse for not including them in future studies!

1. We should probably always include the linear discriminant rule, as it is sometimes best, but for the other good reason that is a standard algorithm, and the most widely available of all procedures.

2. On the basis of our results, the k-nearest neighbour method was often the outright winner (although if there are scaling problems it was sometimes outright loser too!) so it would seem sensible to include k-nearest neighbour in any comparative studies. Although the generally good performance of k-nearest neighbour is well known, it is surprising how few past studies have involved this procedure, especially as it is so easy to program.

3. In many cases where k-nearest neighbour did badly, the decision-tree methods did relatively well, for example in the (non-cost-matrix) credit datasets. So some kind of decision tree should be included.

4. Yet again, some of the newer statistical procedures got very good results when all other methods were struggling. So we would also recommend the inclusion of, say, SMART as a modern statistical procedure.

5. Representing neural networks, we would probably choose LVQ and/or radial basis functions, as these seem to have a distinct edge over the version of backpropagation that we used. However, as the performance of LVQ seems to mirror that of k-NN rather closely, we would recommend inclusion of RBF rather than LVQ if k-NN is already included.

Any comparative study that does not include the majority of these algorithms is clearly not aiming to be complete. Also, any comparative study that looks at only two procedures cannot give reliable indicators of performance, as our results show.

8.3   DIFFICULTIES IN PREVIOUS STUDIES

Bearing in mind our choice of potential candidates for comparative studies, it will quickly become obvious that most previous studies suffer from the major disadvantage that their choice of algorithms is too narrow. There are many other sources of difficulty, and before giving detailed consideration of past empirical studies, we list the pitfalls that await anyone carrying out comparative studies. Of course, our own study was not entirely free from them either.

*   The choice of algorithms is too narrow;
*   In many cases, the authors have developed their own pet algorithm, and are expert in their own field, but they are not so expert in other methods, resulting in a natural bias against other methods;
*   The chosen algorithms may not represent the state of the art;
*   The datasets are usually small or simulated, and so not representative of real-life applications;
*   There is a substantial bias in the choice of dataset, in simulations especially, giving a substantial bias in favour of certain algorithms;
*   Often the choice of criteria is biased in favour of one type of algorithm, sometimes even using unrealistic cost criteria.

- Especially across comparative studies, there may be problems due to differences in the way the data were pre-processed, for example by removing or replacing missing values, or transforming categorical to numerical attributes.
- The class definitions may be more suited to some algorithms than others. Also, the class proportions in the training set may well differ substantially from the population values - often deliberately so.
- Some comparative studies used variant, but not identical, datasets and algorithms.

We have attempted to minimise the above problems in our own study, for example, by adopting a uniform policy for missing values and a uniform manner of dealing with categorical variables in some, but not all, of the datasets.

8.4 PREVIOUS EMPIRICAL COMPARISONS

While it is easy to criticise past studies on the above grounds, nonetheless many useful comparative studies have been carried out. What they may lack in generality, they may gain in specifics, the conclusion being that, for at least one dataset, algorithm A is superior (faster or more accurate ...) than algorithm B. Other studies may also investigate other aspects more fully than we did here, for example, by studying learning curves, *i.e.* the amount of data that must be presented to an algorithm before it learns something useful. In studying particular characteristics of algorithms, the role of simulations is crucial, as it enables controlled departures from assumptions, giving a measure of robustness etc.. (Although we have used some simulated data in our study, namely the *Belgian* datasets, this was done because we believed that the simulations were very close to the real-world problem under study, and it was hoped that our trials would help in understanding this particular problem.)

Here we will not discuss the very many studies that concentrate on just one procedure or set of cognate procedures: rather we will look at cross-disciplinary studies comparing algorithms with widely differing capabilities. Among the former however, we may mention comparisons of symbolic (ML) procedures in Clark & Boswell (1991), Sammut (1988), Quinlan *et al.* (1986) and Aha (1992); statistical procedures in Cherkaoui & Cleroux (1991), Titterington *et al.* (1981) and Remme *et al.* (1980), and neural networks in Huang *et al.* (1991), Fahlman (1991a), Xu *et al.* (1991) and Ersoy & Hong (1991). Several studies use simulated data to explore various aspects of performance under controlled conditions, for example, Cherkaoui & Cleroux (1991) and Remme *et al.* (1980).

8.5 INDIVIDUAL RESULTS

Particular methods may do well in some specific domains and for some performance measures, but not in all applications. For example, k-nearest neighbour performed very well in recognising handwritten characters (Aha, 1992) and (Kressel, 1991) but not as well on the sonar-target task (Gorman & Sejnowski, 1988).

8.6 MACHINE LEARNING vs. NEURAL NETWORK

With the recent surge in interest in both Machine Learning and Neural Networks, there are many recent studies comparing algorithms from these two areas. Commonly, such studies do not include any statistical algorithms: for example Fisher & McKusick (1989) and Shavlik *et al.* (1989) and Shavlik *et al.* (1989) used a relatively old symbolic algorithm

ID3, which has been repeatedly shown to be less effective than its successors (NewID and C4.5 in this book).

Kirkwood *et al.* (1989) found that a symbolic algorithm, ID3, performed better than discriminant analysis for classifying the gait cycle of artificial limbs. Tsaptsinos *et al.* (1990) also found that ID3 was more preferable on an engineering control problem than two neural network algorithms. However, on different tasks other researchers found that a higher order neural network (HONN) performed better than ID3 (Spivoska & Reid, 1990) and back-propagation did better than CART (Atlas *et al.*, 1991). Gorman & Sejnowski (1988) reported that back-propagation outperformed nearest neighbour for classifying sonar targets, whereas some Bayes algorithms were shown to be better on other tasks (Shadmehr & D'Argenio, 1990).

More extensive comparisons have also been carried out between neural network and symbolic methods. However, the results of these studies were inconclusive. For example, whereas Weiss & Kulikowski (1991) and Weiss & Kapouleas (1989) reported that back-propagation performed worse than symbolic methods (*i.e.* CART and PVM), Fisher & McKusick (1989) and Shavlik *et al.* (1989) indicated that back-propagation did as well or better than ID3. Since these are the most extensive comparisons to date, we describe their findings briefly and detail their limitations in the following two paragraphs.

First, Fisher & McKusick (1989) compared the accuracy and learning speed (*i.e.* the number of example presentations required to achieve asymptotic accuracy) of ID3 and back-propagation. This study is restricted in the selection of algorithms, evaluation measures, and data sets. Whereas ID3 cannot tolerate noise, several descendants of ID3 can tolerate noise more effectively (for example, Quinlan, 1987b), which would improve their performance on many noisy data sets. Furthermore, their measure of speed, which simply counted the number of example presentations until asymptotic accuracy was attained, unfairly favours ID3. Whereas the training examples need be given to ID3 only once, they were repeatedly presented to back-propagation to attain asymptotic accuracies. However, their measure ignored that back-propagation's cost per example presentation is much lower than ID3's. This measure of speed was later addressed in Fisher *et al.* (1989), where they defined speed as the product of total example presentations and the cost per presentation. Finally, the only data set with industrial ramifications used in Fisher & McKusick (1989) is the Garvan Institute's thyroid disease data set. We advocate using more such data sets.

Second, Mooney *et al.* (1989) and Shavlik *et al.* (1991) compared similar algorithms on a larger collection of data sets. There were only three algorithms involved (*i.e.* ID3, perceptron and back-propagation). Although it is useful to compare the relative performance of a few algorithms, the symbolic learning and neural network fields are rapidly developing; there are many newer algorithms that can also solve classification tasks (for example, CN2 (Clark & Boswell, 1991), C4.5 (Quinlan, 1987b), and radial basis networks (Poggio & Girosi, 1990). Many of these can outperform the algorithms selected here. Thus, they should also be included in a broader evaluation. In both Fisher & McKusick (1989), Mooney *et al.* (1989) and Shavlik *et al.* (1991), data sets were separated into a collection of training and test sets. After each system processed a training set its performance, in terms of error rate and training time, was measured on the corresponding test set. The final error rate was the geometric means of separate tests. Mooney *et al.* (1989) and Shavlik *et al.* (1991) measured speed differently from Fisher *et al.* (1989); they used the length of training. In both measures, Mooney *et al.* (1989) and Shavlik *et al.* (1991) and Fisher *et al.* (1990) found that back-propagation was significantly slower than ID3. Other significant characteristics are: 1) they varied the number of training examples and studied the effect on the performance that this will have; and 2) they degenerated data in several ways and investigated the sensitivity of the algorithms to the quality of data.

8.7 STUDIES INVOLVING ML, k-NN AND STATISTICS

Thrun, Mitchell, and Cheng (1991) conducted a co-ordinated comparison study of many algorithms on the MONK's problem. This problem features 432 simulated robots classified into two classes using six attributes. Although some algorithms outperformed others, there was no apparent analysis of the results. This study is of limited practical interest as it involved simulated data, and, even less realistically, was capable of error-free classification.

Other small-scale comparisons include Huang & Lippmann (1987), Bonelli & Parodi (1991) and Sethi & Otten (1990), who all concluded that the various neural networks performed similarly to, or slightly better than, symbolic and statistical algorithms.

Weiss & Kapouleas (1989) involved a few (linear) discriminants and ignored much of the new development in modern statistical classification methods. Ripley (1993) compared a diverse set of statistical methods, neural networks, and a decision tree classifier on the Tsetse fly data. This is a restricted comparison because it has only one data set and includes only one symbolic algorithm. However, some findings are nevertheless interesting. In accuracy, the results favoured nearest neighbour, the decision tree algorithm, back-propagation and projection pursuit. The decision tree algorithm *rapidly* produced most *interpretable* results. More importantly, Ripley (1993) also described the "degree of frustration" in getting some algorithms to produce the eventual results (whereas others, for example, Fisher & McKusick (1989) and Shavlik *et al.* (1991) did not). The neural networks were bad in this respect: they were very sensitive to various system settings (for example, hidden units and the stopping criterion) and they generally converged to the final accuracies slowly.

Of course, the inclusion of statistical algorithms does not, of itself, make the comparisons valid. For example, statisticians would be wary of applying a Bayes algorithm to the four problems involved in Weiss & Kapouleas (1989) because of the lack of basic information regarding the prior and posterior probabilities in the data. This same criticism could be applied to many, if not most, of the datasets in common use. The class proportions are clearly unrealistic, and as a result it is difficult to learn the appropriate rule. Machine Learning algorithms in particular are generally not adaptable to changes in class proportions, although it would be straightforward to implement this.

8.8 SOME EMPIRICAL STUDIES RELATING TO CREDIT RISK

As this is an important application of Machine Learning methods, we take some time to mention some previous empirical studies concerning credit datasets.

8.8.1 Traditional and statistical approaches

An empirical study of a point awarding approach to Credit Scoring is made by Häussler (1979, 1981a, 1981b). Fahrmeir *et al.* (1984) compare the results of a point awarding approach with the results obtained by the linear discriminant. In Von Stein & Ziegler (1984) the authors use the *k*-nearest neighbour approach to analyse the problem of prognosis and surveillance of corporate credit risk. Linear discriminant is applied by Bretzger (1991) to early risk recognition in disposition credits. In a comprehensive study of corporate credit granting reported in Srinivisan & Kim (1987), the authors evaluate various approaches including parametric, nonparametric and Judgemental classification procedures. Within the nonparametric approaches they use a "recursive partitioning" method based on the decision tree concept. Their results show that this "recursive partitioning" approach performs better than the others.

8.8.2   Machine Learning and Neural Networks

Several empirical studies deal with credit-scoring problem using machine learning and neural networks. The CART method (Breiman *et al.*, 1984) is used by Hofmann (1990) to analyse consumer credit granting. Hofmann concludes that CART has major advantages over discriminant analysis and emphasises the ability of CART to deal with mixed datasets containing both qualitative and quantitative attributes.

Carter & Catlett (1987) use machine learning in assessing credit card applications. Besides decision trees they also apply probability trees (that produce probability values to the final nodes of the tree). This means that the algorithm is able decide for a good or bad credit risk with a certain probability attached as well as incorporating costs.

One example of the application of neural networks to solving the credit scoring problem is reported in Schumann *et al.* (1992).

Michie (1989) reports a case where the aim of the credit-granting procedure was to keep the bad debt rate among those granted credit down to 9%. While some procedures accepted only 20% of applications, the ML procedure was able to double the proportion of acceptances while keeping the bad-debt rate within bounds. ML procedures almost always output a Yes-No decision, and this may be inconvenient in situations where costs may vary from applicant to applicant. In some situations, the bad-debt risk could be allowed to rise to say 18%, but it would be necessary to re-train the decision tree, using a different pruning parameter.

9

Dataset Descriptions and Results

Various StatLog partners
See Appendix C for a full list[1]

9.1 INTRODUCTION

We group the dataset results according to domain type, although this distinction is perhaps arbitrary at times. There are three credit datasets, of which two follow in the next section; the third dataset (German credit) involved a cost matrix, and so is included in Section 9.4 with other cost matrix datasets. Several of the datasets involve image data of one form or another. In some cases we are attempting to classify each pixel, and thus segment the image, and in other cases, we need to classify the whole image as an object. Similarly the data may be of raw pixel form, or else processed data. These datasets are given in Section 9.3. The remainder of the datasets are harder to group and are contained in Section 9.5. See the appendices for general availability of datasets, algorithms and related software.

The tables contain information on time, memory and error rates for the training and test sets. The time has been standardised for a SUN IPC workstation (quoted at 11.1 SPECs), and for the cross-validation studies the quoted times are the average for each cycle. The unit of memory is the maximum number of pages used during run time. This quantity is obtained from the set time UNIX command and includes the program requirements as well as data and rules stored during execution. Ideally, we would like to decompose this quantity into memory required by the program itself, and the amount during the training, and testing phase, but this was not possible. A page is currently 4096 bytes, but the quoted figures are considered to be very crude. Indeed, both time and memory measurements should be treated with great caution, and only taken as a rough indication of the truth.

In all tables we quote the error rate for the "Default" rule, in which each observation is allocated to the most common class. In addition there is a "rank" column which orders the algorithms on the basis of the error rate for the test data. Note, however, that this is not the only measure on which they could be ranked, and many practitioners will place great importance on time, memory, or interpretability of the algorithm's "classifying rule". We use the notation '*' for missing (or not applicable) information, and 'FD' to indicate that

---

[1] *Address for correspondence*: Charles Taylor, Department of Statistics, University of Leeds, Leeds LS2 9JT, U.K.

an algorithm failed on that dataset. We tried to determine reasons for failure, but with little success. In most cases it was a "Segmentation Violation" probably indicating a lack of memory.

In Section 9.6, we present both the statistical and information-based measures for all of the datasets, and give an interpreation for a few of the datasets.

9.2   CREDIT DATASETS

9.2.1   Credit management (Cred.Man)

This dataset was donated to the project by a major British engineering company, and comes from the general area of credit management, that is to say, assessing methods for pursuing debt recovery. Credit Scoring (CS) is one way of giving an objective score indicative of credit risk: it aims to give a numerical score, usually containing components from various factors indicative of risk, by which an objective measure of credit risk can be obtained. The aim of a credit scoring system is to assess the risk associated with each application for credit. Being able to assess the risk enables the bank to improve their pricing, marketing and debt recovery procedures. Inability to assess the risk can result in lost business. It is also important to assess the determinants of the risk: Lawrence & Smith (1992) state that payment history is the overwhelming factor in predicting the likelihood of default in mobile home credit cases. Risk assessment may influence the severity with which bad debts are pursued. Although it might be thought that the proper end product in this application should be a risk factor or probability assessment rather than a yes-no decision, the dataset was supplied with pre-allocated classes. The aim in this dataset was therefore to classify customers (by simple train-and-test) into one of the two given classes. The classes can be interpreted as the method by which debts will be retrieved, but, for the sake of brevity, we refer to classes as "good" and "bad" risk.

Table 9.1: Previously obtained results for the original Credit management data, with equal class proportions (* supplied by the Turing Institute, ** supplied by the dataset providers).

algorithm	error rate
NewID*	0.05
CN2*	0.06
Neural Net**	0.06

The original dataset had 20 000 examples of each class. To make this more representative of the population as a whole (where approximately 5% of credit applicants were assessed – by a human – as bad risk), the dataset used in the project had 20 000 examples with 1000 of these being class 1 (bad credit risk) and 19 000 class 2 (good credit risk). As is common when the (true) proportion of bad credits is very small, the default rule (to grant credit to all applicants) achieves a small error rate (which is clearly 5% in this case). In such circumstances the credit-granting company may well adopt the default strategy for the sake of good customer relations –see Lawrence & Smith (1992). However, most decision tree algorithms do worse than the default if they are allowed to train on the given data which is strongly biased towards bad credits (typically decision tree algorithms have an error rate of around 6% error rate). This problem disappears if the training set has the proper class proportions. For example, a version of CART(the Splus module tree()) obtained an error rate

Table 9.2: Results for the Credit management dataset (2 classes, 7 attributes, (train, test)=
(15 000, 5 000) observations).

Algorithm	Max. Storage	Time (sec.) Train	Test	Error Rate Train	Test	Rank
Discrim	68	32.2	3.8	0.031	0.033	13
Quadisc	71	67.2	12.5	0.051	0.050	21
Logdisc	889	165.6	14.2	0.031	0.030	8
SMART	412	27930.0	5.4	0.021	0.020	1
ALLOC80	220	22069.7	*	0.033	0.031	10
k-NN	108	124187.0	968.0	0.028	0.088	22
CASTLE	48	370.1	81.4	0.051	0.047	19
CART	FD	FD	FD	FD	FD	
IndCART	1656	423.1	415.7	0.010	0.025	6
NewID	104	3035.0	2.0	0.000	0.033	13
AC^2	7250	5418.0	3607.0	0.000	0.030	8
Baytree	1368	53.1	3.3	0.002	0.028	7
NaiveBay	956	24.3	2.8	0.041	0.043	16
CN2	2100	2638.0	9.5	0.000	0.032	12
C4.5	620	171.0	158.0	0.014	0.022	3
ITrule	377	4470.0	1.9	0.041	0.046	18
Cal5	167	553.0	7.2	0.018	0.023	4
Kohonen	715	*	*	0.037	0.043	16
DIPOL92	218	2340.0	57.8	0.020	0.020	1
Backprop	148	5950.0	3.0	0.020	0.023	4
RBF	253	435.0	26.0	0.033	0.031	10
LVQ	476	2127.0	52.9	0.024	0.040	15
Default	*	*	*	0.051	0.047	19

of 5.8% on the supplied data but only 2.35% on the dataset with proper class proportions, whereas linear discriminants obtained an error rate of 5.4% on the supplied data and 2.35% on the modified proportions. (The supplier of the credit management dataset quotes error rates for neural nets and decision trees of around 5–6% also when trained on the 50-50 dataset). Note that the effective bias is in favour of the non-statistical algorithms here, as statistical algorithms can cope, to a greater or lesser extent, with prior class proportions that differ from the training proportions.

In this dataset the classes were chosen by an expert on the basis of the given attributes (see below) and it is hoped to replace the expert by an algorithm rule in the future. All attribute values are numeric. The dataset providers supplied the performance figures for algorithms which have been applied to the data drawn from the same source.Note that the figures given in Table 9.1 were achieved using the original dataset with equal numbers of examples of both classes.

The best results (in terms of error rate) were achieved by SMART, DIPOL92 and the tree algorithms C4.5 and Cal5. SMART is very time consuming to run: however, with credit type datasets small improvements in accuracy can save vast amounts of money so this has to be considered if sacrificing accuracy for time. k-NN did badly due to irrelevant attributes; with a variable selection procedure, it obtained an error rate of 3.1%. CASTLE, Kohonen, ITrule and Quadisc perform poorly (the result for Quadisc equalling the default rule). CASTLE uses only attribute 7 to generate the rule, concluding that this is the only relevant attribute for the classification. Kohonen works best for datasets with equal class distributions which is not the case for the dataset as preprocessed here. At the cost of significantly increasing the CPU time, the performance might be improved by using a larger Kohonen net.

The best result for the Decision Tree algorithms was obtained by C4.5 which used the smallest tree with 62 nodes. Cal5 used 125 nodes and achieved a similar error rate; NewID and AC^2 used 448 and 415 nodes, respectively, which suggests that they over trained on this dataset.

9.2.2   Australian credit (Cr.Aust)

Table 9.3: Results for the Australian credit dataset (2 classes, 14 attributes, 690 observations, 10-fold cross-validation).

Algorithm	Max. Storage	Time (sec.) Train	Test	Error Rate Train	Test	Rank
Discrim	366	31.8	6.7	0.139	0.141	3
Quadisc	353	30.5	7.2	0.185	0.207	21
Logdisc	329	21.0	18.0	0.125	0.141	3
SMART	762	246.0	0.2	0.090	0.158	13
ALLOC80	102	876.9	*	0.194	0.201	19
k-NN	758	3.0	7.0	0.000	0.181	15
CASTLE	62	46.8	5.3	0.144	0.148	8
CART	149	68.4	1.6	0.145	0.145	6
IndCART	668	34.2	32.7	0.081	0.152	10
NewID	28	15.2	0.3	0.000	0.181	15
AC^2	404	400.0	14.0	0.000	0.181	15
Baytree	524	7.2	0.4	0.000	0.171	14
NaiveBay	420	3.7	0.4	0.136	0.151	9
CN2	215	42.0	3.0	0.001	0.204	20
C4.5	62	6.0	1.0	0.099	0.155	12
ITrule	124	173.6	0.6	0.162	0.137	2
Cal5	128	24.0	2.2	0.132	0.131	1
Kohonen	FD	FD	FD	FD	FD	
DIPOL92	52	55.6	2.0	0.139	0.141	3
Backprop	147	1369.8	0.0	0.087	0.154	11
RBF	231	12.2	2.4	0.107	0.145	6
LVQ	81	260.8	7.2	0.065	0.197	18
Default	*	*	*	0.440	0.440	22

The aim is to devise a rule for assessing applications for credit cards. The dataset has been studied before (Quinlan, 1987a, 1993) . Interpretation of the results is made difficult because the attributes and classes have been coded to preserve confidentiality, however examples of likely attributes are given for another credit data set in Section 9.4.3. For our purposes, we replaced the missing values by the overall medians or means (5% of the examples had some missing information).

Due to the confidentiality of the classes, it was not possible to assess the relative costs of errors nor to assess the prior odds of good to bad customers. We decided therefore to use the default cost matrix. The use of the default cost matrix is not realistic. In practice it is generally found that it is very difficult to beat the simple rule: "Give credit if (and only if) the applicant has a bank account". We do not know, with this dataset, what success this default rule would have. The results were obtained by 10-fold cross validation.

The best result here was obtained by Cal5, which used only an average of less than 6 nodes in its decision tree. By contrast AC^2 and NewID used around 70 nodes and achieved higher error rates, which suggests that pruning is necessary.

9.3   IMAGE DATASETS

9.3.1   Handwritten digits (Dig44)

This dataset consists of 18 000 examples of the digits 0 to 9 gathered from postcodes on letters in Germany. The handwritten examples were digitised onto images with 16×16 pixels and 256 grey levels. They were read by one of the automatic address readers built by a German company. These were initially scaled for height and width but not "thinned" or rotated in a standard manner. An example of each digit is given in Figure 9.1.

Fig. 9.1: Hand-written digits from German postcodes (16 x 16 pixels).

The dataset was divided into a training set with 900 examples per digit and a test set with 900 examples per digit. Due to lack of memory, very few algorithms could cope with the full dataset. In order to get comparable results we used a version with 16 attributes prepared by averaging over 4×4 neighbourhoods in the original images.

For the k-NN classifier this averaging resulted in an increase of the error rate from 2.0% to 4.7%, whereas for Discrim the error rate increased from 7.4% to 11.4%. Backprop could also cope with all 256 attributes but when presented with all 9000 examples in the training set took an excessively long time to train (over two CPU days).

The fact that k-NN and LVQ do quite well is probably explained by the fact that they make the fewest restrictive assumptions about the data. Discriminant analysis, on the other hand, assumes that the data follows a multi-variate normal distribution with the attributes obeying a common covariance matrix and can model only linear aspects of the data. The fact that Quadisc, using a reduced version of the dataset, does better than Discrim, using either the full version or reduced version, shows the advantage of being able to model non-linearity. CASTLE approximates the data by a polytree and this assumption is too restrictive in this case. Naive Bayes assumes the attributes are conditionally independent. That Naive Bayes does so badly is explained by the fact that the attributes are clearly not conditionally independent, since neighbouring pixels are likely to have similar grey levels. It is surprising that Cascade does better than Backprop, and this may be attributed to the

Table 9.4: Results for the 4 × 4 digit dataset (10 classes, 16 attributes, (train, test) = (9000, 9000) observations).

Algorithm	Max. Storage	Time (sec.)		Error Rate		Rank
		Train	Test	Train	Test	
Discrim	252	65.3	30.2	0.111	0.114	12
Quadisc	324	194.4	152.0	0.052	0.054	2
Logdisc	1369	5110.2	138.2	0.079	0.086	10
SMART	337	19490.6	33.0	0.096	0.104	11
ALLOC80	393	1624.0	7041.0	0.066	0.068	5
k-NN	497	2230.7	2039.2	0.016	0.047	1
CASTLE	116	252.6	4096.8	0.180	0.170	20
CART	240	251.6	40.8	0.180	0.160	19
IndCART	884	3614.5	50.6	0.011	0.154	17
NewID	532	500.7	112.5	0.080	0.150	16
AC^2	770	10596.0	22415.0	*	0.155	18
Baytree	186	1117.0	59.8	0.015	0.140	14
NaiveBay	129	42.7	61.8	0.220	0.233	23
CN2	1926	3325.9	119.9	0.000	0.134	13
$C4.5^2$	248	778.1	60.6	0.041	0.149	15
ITrule	504	1800.1	9000	*	0.222	22
Cal5	1159	571.0	55.2	0.118	0.220	21
Kohonen	646	67176.0	2075.1	0.051	0.075	7
DIPOL92	110	191.2	43.6	0.065	0.072	6
Backprop	884	28910.0	110.0	0.072	0.080	8
RBF	268	1400.0	250.0	0.080	0.083	9
LVQ	249	1342.6	123.0	0.040	0.061	3
Cascade	2442	19171.0	1.0	0.064	0.065	4
Default	*	*	*	0.900	0.900	24

Backprop procedure being trapped in a local minimum or to having insufficient time to train. Either way, Backprop should really do better here, and one suggestion would be to start the Backprop procedure with the parameters found from Cascade. In this project we ran all algorithms independently, without reference to others, and we did not try to hybridise or run procedures in tandem, although there is no doubt that there would be great benefit from pooling the results.

The above dataset is close to "raw" pixel data. A minimum of processing has been carried out, and the results could almost certainly be improved upon using deformable templates or some other statistical pattern recognition technique. Note, however, that comparison of performance across handwritten digit datasets should not be made, since they vary widely in quality. In this dataset only zeroes and sevens with strokes are used, and there are a few intentional "mistakes", for example a digitised "!" is classified as a 1, and the capital "B" is classed as an 8.

The original 256 attribute dataset has been analysed by Kressel (1991) using (i) a multilayer perceptron with one hidden layer and (ii) linear discriminants with selected quadratic terms. Both methods achieved about 2% error rates on the test set. (2.24% for the linear/quadratic classifier and 1.91% errors for the MLP). hidden layer.

9.3.2   Karhunen-Loeve digits (KL)

Table 9.5: Results for the KL digits dataset (10 classes, 40 attributes, (train, test) = (9000, 9000) observations).

Algorithm	Max. Storage	Time (sec.) Train	Test	Error Rate Train	Test	Rank
Discrim	306	87.1	53.9	0.070	0.075	10
Quadisc	1467	1990.2	1647.8	0.016	0.025	3
Logdisc	1874	31918.3	194.4	0.032	0.051	7
SMART	517	174965.8	57.7	0.043	0.057	9
ALLOC80	500	23239.9	23279.3	0.000	0.024	2
k-NN	500	0.0	6706.4	0.000	0.020	1
CASTLE	779	4535.4	56052.7	0.126	0.135	12
CART	FD	FD	FD	FD	FD	
IndCART	341	3508.0	46.9	0.003	0.170	16
NewID	1462	779.0	109.0	0.000	0.162	13
AC^2	1444	15155.0	937.0	0.000	0.168	15
Baytree	289	1100.4	53.0	0.006	0.163	14
NaiveBay	1453	64.9	76.0	0.205	0.223	20
CN2	732	2902.1	99.7	0.036	0.180	17
C4.5	310	1437.0	35.5	0.050	0.180	17
ITrule	1821	*	8175.0	*	0.216	19
Cal5	1739	3053.4	64.3	0.128	0.270	21
Kohonen	FD	FD	FD	FD	FD	
DIPOL92	221	462.8	80.0	0.030	0.039	5
Backprop	1288	129600.0	4.0	0.041	0.049	6
RBF	268	1700.0	580.0	0.048	0.055	8
LVQ	368	1692.1	158.1	0.011	0.026	4
Cascade	2540	10728.0	1.0	0.063	0.075	10
Default	*	*	*	0.900	0.900	22

An alternative data reduction technique (to the 4×4 averaging above) was carried out using the first 40 principal components. It is interesting that, with the exception of Cascade correlation, the order of performance of the algorithms is virtually unchanged (see Table 9.5) and that the error rates are now very similar to those obtained (where available) using the original 16×16 pixels.

The results for the digits dataset and the KL digits dataset are very similar so are treated together. Most algorithms perform a few percent better on the KL digits dataset. The KL digits dataset is the closest to being normal. This could be predicted beforehand, as it is a linear transformation of the attributes that, by the Central Limit Theorem, would be closer to normal than the original. Because there are very many attributes in each linear combination, the KL digits dataset is very close to normal (skewness = 0.1802, kurtosis = 2.9200) as against the exact normal values of (skewness = 0, kurtosis = 3.0).

In both Digits datasets dataset k-NN comes top and RBF and "ALLOC80" also do fairly well – in fact ALLOC80 failed and an equivalent kernel method, with smoothing parameter asymptotically chosen, was used. These three algorithms are all closely related. Kohonen also does well in the Digits dataset (but for some reason failed on KL digits); Kohonen has some similarities with k-NN type algorithms. The success of such algorithms suggests that the attributes are equally scaled and equally important. Quadisc also does well, coming second in both datasets. The KL version of digits appears to be well suited to Quadisc: there is a substantial difference in variances (SD_ratio = 1.9657), while at the same time the distributions are not too far from multivariate normality with kurtosis of order 3.

Backprop and LVQ do quite well on the 4×4 digits dataset, bearing out the oft-repeated claim in the neural net literature that neural networks are very well suited to pattern recognition problems (e.g. Hecht-Nelson, 1989).

The Decision Tree algorithms do not do very well on these digits datasets. The tree sizes are typically in the region of 700–1000 nodes.

9.3.3   Vehicle silhouettes (Vehicle)

Fig. 9.2: Vehicle silhouettes prior to high level feature extraction. These are clockwise from top left: Double decker bus, Opel Manta 400, Saab 9000 and Chevrolet van.

A problem in object recognition is to find a method of distinguishing 3D objects within a 2D image by application of an ensemble of shape feature extractors to the 2D silhouettes of the objects. This data was originally gathered at the Turing Institute in 1986-87 by J.P. Siebert. Four "Corgi" model vehicles were used for the experiment: a double decker bus, Chevrolet van, Saab 9000 and an Opel Manta 400. This particular combination of vehicles was chosen with the expectation that the bus, van and either one of the cars would be readily distinguishable, but it would be more difficult to distinguish between the cars. The vehicles were rotated and a number of image silhouettes were obtained from a variety of orientations and angles. All images were captured with a spatial resolution of 128 $\times$

128 pixels quantised to 64 grey levels.

These images were cleaned up, binarised and subsequently processed to produce 18 variables intended to characterise shape. For example, circularity, radius ratio, compactness, scaled variance along major and minor axes, etc. A total of 946 examples were obtained but 100 were retained in case of dispute, so the trials reported here used only 846 examples and the algorithms were run using 9-fold cross-validation to obtain error rates, given in Table 9.6

Table 9.6: Results for the vehicle dataset (4 classes, 18 attributes, 846 observations, 9-fold cross-validation).

Algorithm	Max. Storage	Time (sec.) Train	Time (sec.) Test	Error Rate Train	Error Rate Test	Rank
Discrim	231	16.3	3.0	0.202	0.216	6
Quadisc	593	250.9	28.6	0.085	0.150	1
Logdisc	685	757.9	8.3	0.167	0.192	4
SMART	105	2502.5	0.7	0.062	0.217	7
ALLOC80	227	30.0	10.0	0.000	0.173	3
k-NN	104	163.8	22.7	0.000	0.275	11
CASTLE	80	13.1	1.8	0.545	0.505	22
CART	158	24.4	0.8	0.284	0.235	8
IndCART	296	113.3	0.4	0.047	0.298	16
NewID	*	18.0	1.0	0.030	0.298	16
AC^2	776	3135.0	121.0	*	0.296	15
Baytree	71	27.1	0.5	0.079	0.271	10
NaiveBay	56	5.4	0.6	0.519	0.558	23
CN2	*	100.0	1.0	0.018	0.314	19
C4.5[3]	*	174.0	2.0	0.065	0.266	9
ITrule	307	985.3	*	*	0.324	20
Cal5	171	23.3	0.5	0.068	0.279	12
Kohonen	1441	5962.0	50.4	0.115	0.340	21
DIPOL92	64	150.6	8.2	0.079	0.151	2
Backprop	186	14411.2	3.7	0.168	0.207	5
RBF	716	1735.9	11.8	0.098	0.307	18
LVQ	77	229.1	2.8	0.171	0.287	14
Cascade	238	289.0	1.0	0.263	0.280	13
Default	*	*	*	0.750	0.750	24

One would expect this dataset to be non-linear since the attributes depend on the angle at which the vehicle is viewed. Therefore they are likely to have a sinusoidal dependence, although this dependence was masked by issuing the dataset in permuted order. Quadisc does very well, and this is due to the highly non-linear behaviour of this data. One would have expected the Backprop algorithm to perform well on this dataset since, it is claimed, Backprop can successfully model the non-linear aspects of a dataset. However, Backprop is not straightforward to run. Unlike discriminant analysis, which requires no choice of free parameters, Backprop requires essentially two free parameters - the number of hidden nodes and the training time. Neither of these is straightforward to decide. This figure for Backprop was obtained using 5 hidden nodes and a training time of four hours for the training time in each of the nine cycles of cross-validation. However, one can say that the sheer effort and time taken to optimise the performance for Backprop is a major disadvantage compared to Quadisc which can achieve a much better result with a lot less effort. DIPOL92 does nearly as well as Quadisc. As compared with Backprop it performs better and is quicker to run. It determines the number of nodes (hyperplanes, neurons) and the initial weights by a reasonable procedure at the beginning and doesn't use an additional layer of hidden units but instead a symbolic level. The poor performance of CASTLE is explained by the fact that the attributes are highly correlated. In consequence the relationship between class and attributes is not built strongly into the polytree. The same explanation accounts for the poor performance of Naive Bayes. k-NN, which performed so well on the raw digits dataset, does not do so well here. This is probably because in the case of the digits the attributes were all commensurate and carried equal weight. In the vehicle dataset the attributes all have different meanings and it is not clear how to build an appropriate distance measure.

The attributes for the vehicle dataset, unlike the other image analysis, were generated using image analysis tools and were not simply based on brightness levels. This suggests that the attributes are less likely to be equally scaled and equally important. This is confirmed by the lower performances of k-NN, LVQ and Radial Basis functions, which treat all attributes equally and have a built in mechanism for normalising, which is often not optimal. ALLOC80 did not perform well here, and so an alternative kernel method was used which allowed for correlations between the attributes, and this appeared to be more robust than the other three algorithms although it still fails to learn the difference between the cars. The original Siebert (1987) paper showed machine learning performing better than k-NN, but there is not much support for this in our results. The tree sizes for AC^2 and Cal5 were 116 and 156 nodes, respectively.

The high value of fract2 = 0.8189 (see Table 9.30) might indicate that linear discrimination could be based on just two discriminants. This may relate to the fact that the two cars are not easily distinguishable, so might be treated as one (reducing dimensionality of the mean vectors to 3D). However, although the fraction of discriminating power for the third discriminant is low (1 - 0.8189), it is still statistically significant, so cannot be discarded without a small loss of discrimination.

9.3.4   Letter recognition (Letter)

The dataset was constructed by David J. Slate, Odesta Corporation, Evanston, IL 60201. The objective here is to classify each of a large number of black and white rectangular pixel displays as one of the 26 capital letters of the English alphabet. (One-shot train and test was used for the classification.) The character images produced were based on 20 different fonts and each letter within these fonts was randomly distorted to produce a file of 20 000 unique images. For each image, 16 numerical attributes were calculated using edge counts and measures of statistical moments which were scaled and discretised into a range of integer values from 0 to 15.

Perfect classification performance is unlikely to be possible with this dataset. One of the fonts used, Gothic Roman, appears very different from the others.

Table 9.7: Results for the letters dataset (26 classes, 16 attributes, (train, test) = (15 000, 5000) observations).

Algorithm	Max. Storage	Time (sec.) Train	Test	Error Rate Train	Test	Rank
Discrim	78	325.6	84.0	0.297	0.302	18
Quadisc	80	3736.2	1222.7	0.101	0.113	4
Logdisc	316	5061.6	38.7	0.234	0.234	12
SMART	881	400919.0	184.0	0.287	0.295	17
ALLOC80	758	39574.7	*	0.065	0.064	1
k-NN	200	14.8	2135.4	0.000	0.068	2
CASTLE	1577	9455.3	2933.4	0.237	0.245	13
CART	FD	FD	FD	FD	FD	
IndCART	3600	1098.2	1020.2	0.010	0.130	8
NewID	376	1056.0	2.0	0.000	0.128	7
AC^2	2033	2529.0	92.0	0.000	0.245	13
Baytree	2516	275.5	7.1	0.015	0.124	6
NaiveBay	1464	74.6	17.9	0.516	0.529	20
CN2	*	40458.3	52.2	0.021	0.115	5
C4.5	1042	309.0	292.0	0.042	0.132	9
ITrule	593	22325.4	69.1	0.585	0.594	21
Cal5	1554	1033.4	8.2	0.158	0.253	16
Kohonen	1204	*	*	0.218	0.252	15
DIPOL92	189	1303.4	79.5	0.167	0.176	10
Backprop	154	277445.0	22.0	0.323	0.327	19
RBF	418	*	*	0.220	0.233	11
LVQ	377	1487.4	47.8	0.057	0.079	3
Default	*	*	*	0.955	0.960	22

Quadisc is the best of the classical statistical algorithms on this dataset. This is perhaps not surprising since the measures data gives some support to the assumptions underlying the method. Discrim does not perform well although the logistic version is a significant improvement. SMART is used here with a 22 term model and its poor performance is surprising. A number of the attributes are non-linear combinations of some others and SMART might have been expected to model this well. ALLOC80 achieves the best performance of all with k-NN close behind. In this dataset all the attributes are pre-scaled and all appear to be important so good performance from k-NN is to be expected. CASTLE constructs a polytree with only one attribute contributing to the classification which is too restrictive with this dataset. Naive Bayes assumes conditional independence and this is certainly not satisfied for a number of the attributes. NewID and AC^2 were only trained on 3000 examples drawn from the full training set and that in part explains their rather uninspiring performance. NewID builds a huge tree containing over 1760 nodes while the AC^2 tree is about half the size. This difference probably explains some of the difference in their respective results. Cal5 and C4.5 also build complex trees while CN2 generates 448 rules in order to classify the training set. ITrule is the poorest algorithm on this dataset.

Generally we would not expect ITrule to perform well on datasets where many of the attributes contributed to the classification as it is severely constrained in the complexity of the rules it can construct. Of the neural network algorithms, Kohonen and LVQ would be expected to perform well for the same reasons as k-NN. Seen in that light, the Kohonen result is a little disappointing.

In a previous study Frey & Slate (1991) investigated the use of an adaptive classifier system and achieved a best error rate of just under 20%.

9.3.5   Chromosomes (Chrom)

Table 9.8: Results for the chromosome dataset (24 classes, 16 attributes, (train, test) = (20 000, 20 000) observations).

Algorithm	Max. Storage	Time (sec.) Train	Time (sec.) Test	Error Rate Train	Error Rate Test	Rank
Discrim	1586	830.0	357.0	0.073	0.107	3
Quadisc	1809	1986.3	1607.0	0.046	0.084	1
Logdisc	1925	20392.8	291.4	0.079	0.131	8
SMART	1164	307515.4	92.9	0.082	0.128	7
ALLOC80	1325	184435.0	*	0.192	0.253	18
k-NN	1097	20.1	14140.6	0.000	0.123	5
CASTLE	279	230.2	96.2	0.129	0.178	15
CART	FD	FD	FD	FD	FD	
IndCART	3768	2860.3	2763.8	0.007	0.173	11
NewID	1283	552.0	17.0	0.000	0.176	14
AC^2	1444	1998.0	138.0	0.000	0.234	16
Baytree	2840	1369.5	29.7	0.034	0.164	10
NaiveBay	1812	107.8	61.0	0.260	0.324	19
CN2	1415	9192.6	131.9	0.010	0.150	9
C4.5	589	1055.3	*	0.038	0.175	13
ITrule	637	34348.0	30.0	0.681	0.697	20
Cal5	1071	564.5	31.5	0.142	0.244	17
Kohonen	1605	*	*	0.109	0.174	12
DIPOL92	213	961.8	258.2	0.049	0.091	2
Backprop	FD	FD	FD	FD	FD	
RBF	471	*	*	0.087	0.129	6
LVQ	373	1065.5	*	0.067	0.121	4
Default	*	*	*	0.956	0.956	21

This data was obtained via the MRC Human Genetics Unit, Edinburgh from the routine amniotic 2668 cell data set (courtesy C. Lundsteen, Righospitalet, Copenhagen). In our trials we used only 16 features (and 40 000 examples) which are a subset of a larger database which has 30 features and nearly 80 000 examples. The subset was selected to reduce the scale of the problem, and selecting the features defined as level 1 (measured directly from the chromosome image) and level 2 (measures requiring the axis, e.g. length, to be specified). We omitted observations with an "unknown" class as well as features with level 3 (requiring both axis and profile and knowledge of the chromosome polarity) and level 4 (requiring both the axis and both the polarity and the centrometre location). Classification was done using one-shot train-and-test.

The result for ALLOC80 is very poor, and the reason for this is not clear. An alternative kernel classifier (using a Cauchy kernel, to avoid numerical difficulties) gave an error rate of 10.67% which is much better. Although quadratic discriminants do best here, there is reason to believe that its error rate is perhaps not optimal as there is clear evidence of non-normality in the distribution of the attributes.

The best of Decision Tree results is obtained by CN2 which has 301 rules. C4.5 and AC^2 have 856 and 626 terminal nodes, respectively, and yet obtain very differnt error rates. By contrast NewID has 2967 terminal nodes, but does about as well as C4.5.

Further details of this dataset can be found in Piper & Granum (1989) who have done extensive experiments on selection and measurement of variables. For the dataset which resembled the one above most closely, they achieved an error rate of 9.2%.

9.3.6   Landsat satellite image (SatIm)

The original Landsat data for this database was generated from data purchased from NASA by the Australian Centre for Remote Sensing, and used for research at the University of New South Wales. The sample database was generated taking a small section (82 rows and 100 columns) from the original data. The classification for each pixel was performed on the basis of an actual site visit by Ms. Karen Hall, when working for Professor John A. Richards, at the Centre for Remote Sensing. The database is a (tiny) sub-area of a scene, consisting of 82×100 pixels, each pixel covering an area on the ground of approximately 80*80 metres. The information given for each pixel consists of the class value and the intensities in four spectral bands (from the green, red, and infra-red regions of the spectrum).

The original data are presented graphically in Figure 9.3. The first four plots (top row and bottom left) show the intensities in four spectral bands: Spectral bands 1 and 2 are in the green and red regions of the visible spectrum, while spectral bands 3 and 4 are in the infra-red (darkest shadings represent greatest intensity). The middle bottom diagram shows the land use, with shadings representing the seven original classes in the order: red soil, cotton crop, vegetation stubble, mixture (all types present), grey soil, damp grey soil and very damp grey soil, with red as lightest and very damp grey as darkest shading. Also shown (bottom right) are the classes as predicted by linear discriminants. Note that the most accurate predictions are for cotton crop (rectangular region bottom left of picture), and that the predicted boundary damp-vary damp grey soil (L-shape top left of picture) is not well positioned.

So that information from the neighbourhood of a pixel might contribute to the classification of that pixel, the spectra of the eight neighbours of a pixel were included as attributes together with the four spectra of that pixel. Each line of data corresponds to a 3×3 square neighbourhood of pixels completely contained within the 82×100 sub-area. Thus each line contains the four spectral bands of each of the 9 pixels in the 3×3 neighbourhood and the class of the central pixel which was one of: red soil, cotton crop, grey soil, damp grey soil, soil with vegetation stubble, very damp grey soil. The "mixed-pixels", of which there were 8.6%, were removed for our purposes, so that there are only six classes in this dataset.

The examples were randomised and certain lines were deleted so that simple reconstruction of the original image was not possible. The data were divided into a train set and

Spectral band 1   Spectral band 2   Spectral band 3

Spectral band 4   Land use (Actual)   Land use (Predicted)

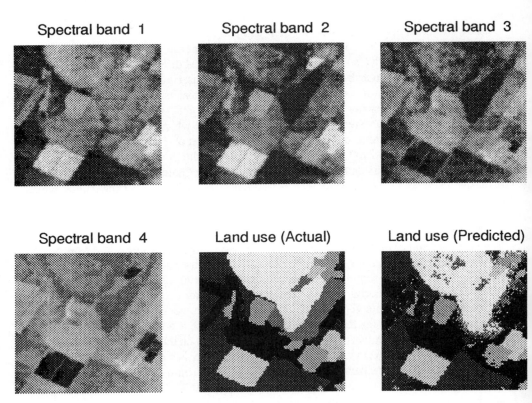

Fig. 9.3: Satellite image dataset. Spectral band intensities as seen from a satellite for a small (8.2*6.6 km) region of Australia. Also given are the actual land use as determined by on-site visit and the estimated classes as given by linear discriminants.

a test set with 4435 examples in the train set and 2000 in the test set and the error rates are given in Table 9.9.

In the satellite image dataset k-NN performs best. Not surprisingly, radial basis functions, LVQ and "ALLOC80" also do fairly well as these three algorithms are closely related. [In fact, ALLOC80 failed on this dataset, so an equivalent method, using an asymptotically chosen bandwidth, was used.] Their success suggests that all the attributes are equally scaled and equally important. There appears to be little to choose between any of the other algorithms, except that Naive Bayes does badly (and its close relative CASTLE also does relatively badly).

The Decision Tree algorithms perform at about the same level, with CART giving the best result using 66 nodes. Cal5 and AC^2 used trees with 156 and 116 nodes, respectively, which suggests more pruning is desired for these algorithms.

This dataset has the highest correlation between attributes (corr.abs = 0.5977). This may partly explain the failure of Naive Bayes (assumes attributes are conditionally independent), and CASTLE (confused if several attributes contain equal amounts of information). Note that only three canonical discriminants are sufficient to separate all six class means (fract3

Table 9.9: Results for the satellite image dataset (6 classes, 36 attributes, (train, test) = (4435, 2000) observations).

Algorithm	Maximum Storage	Time (sec.) Train	Test	Error Rate Train	Test	Rank
Discrim	254	67.8	11.9	0.149	0.171	19
Quadisc	364	157.0	52.9	0.106	0.155	14
Logdisc	1205	4414.1	41.2	0.119	0.163	17
SMART	244	27376.2	10.8	0.123	0.159	16
ALLOC80	244	63840.2	28756.5	0.036	0.132	5
k-NN	180	2104.9	944.1	0.089	0.094	1
CASTLE	*	75.0	80.0	0.186	0.194	21
CART	253	329.9	14.2	0.079	0.138	6
IndCART	819	2109.2	9.2	0.023	0.138	6
NewID	1800	226.0	53.0	0.067	0.150	10
AC^2	*	8244.0	17403.0	*	0.157	15
Baytree	161	247.8	10.2	0.020	0.147	9
NaiveBay	133	75.1	16.5	0.308	0.287	22
CN2	682	1664.0	35.8	0.010	0.150	10
C4.5^4	1150	434.0	1.0	0.040	0.150	10
ITrule	FD	FD	FD	FD	FD	
Cal5	412	764.0	7.2	0.125	0.151	13
Kohonen	*	12627.0	129.0	0.101	0.179	20
DIPOL92	293	764.3	110.7	0.051	0.111	3
Backprop	469	72494.5	52.6	0.112	0.139	8
RBF	195	564.2	74.1	0.111	0.121	4
LVQ	227	1273.2	44.2	0.048	0.105	2
Cascade	1210	7180.0	1.0	0.112	0.163	17
Default	*	*	*	0.758	0.769	23

= 0.9691). This may be interpreted as evidence of seriation, with the three classes "grey soil", "damp grey soil" and "very damp grey soil" forming a continuum. Equally, this result can be interpreted as indicating that the original four attributes may be successfully reduced to three with no loss of information. Here "information" should be interpreted as mean square distance between classes, or equivalently, as the entropy of a normal distribution.

The examples were created using a 3×3 neighbourhood so it is no surprise that there is a very large correlation amongst the 36 variables. The results from CASTLE suggest that only three of the variables for the centre pixel are necessary to classify the observation. However, other algorithms found a significant improvement when information from the neighbouring pixels was used.

9.3.7   Image segmentation (Segm)

The instances were drawn randomly from a database of 7 outdoor colour images. These were hand segmented to create a classification for every pixel as one of brickface, sky, foliage, cement, window, path, grass. There were 19 attributes appropriate for each 3×3 region, for example summary measures of contrast in the vertical and horizontal directions.

Table 9.10: Results for the image segmentation dataset (7 classes, 11 attributes, 2310 observations, 10-fold cross-validation).

Algorithm	Max. Storage	Time (sec.) Train	Test	Error Rate Train	Test	Rank
Discrim	365	73.6	6.6	0.112	0.116	19
Quadisc	395	49.7	15.5	0.155	0.157	20
Logdisc	535	301.8	8.4	0.098	0.109	17
SMART	144	13883.9	0.5	0.039	0.052	11
ALLOC80	124	15274.3	*	0.033	0.030	1
k-NN	171	5.0	28.0	0.000	0.077	16
CASTLE	142	465.4	38.3	0.108	0.112	18
CART	175	79.0	2.3	0.005	0.040	6
IndCART	744	1410.5	1325.1	0.012	0.045	9
NewID	*	386.0	2.0	0.000	0.034	4
AC^2	7830	18173.0	479.0	0.000	0.031	2
Baytree	676	677.3	26.9	0.000	0.033	3
NaiveBay	564	516.4	29.0	0.260	0.265	21
CN2	174	114.2	2.7	0.003	0.043	8
C4.5	57	142.0	1.3	0.013	0.040	6
ITrule	139	545.7	19.9	0.445	0.455	22
Cal5	373	247.1	13.7	0.042	0.062	13
Kohonen	233	11333.2	8.5	0.046	0.067	14
DIPOL92	91	503.0	25.0	0.021	0.039	5
Backprop	148	88467.2	0.4	0.028	0.054	12
RBF	381	65.0	11.0	0.047	0.069	15
LVQ	123	368.2	6.4	0.019	0.046	10
Default	*	*	*	0.760	0.760	23

Average error rates were obtained via 10-fold cross-validation, and are given in Table 9.10.

AC^2 did very well here and used an average of 52 nodes in its decision trees. It is interesting here that ALLOC80 does so much better than k-NN. The reason for this is that ALLOC80 has a variable selection option which was initially run on the data, and only 5 of the original attributes were finally used. When 14 variables were used the error rate increased to 21%. Indeed a similar attribute selection procedure increased the performance of k-NN to a very similar error rate. This discrepancy raises the whole issue of pre-processing the data before algorithms are run, and the substantial difference this can make. It is clear that there will still be a place for intelligent analysis alongside any black-box techniques for quite some time!

9.3.8 Cut

This dataset was supplied by a StatLog partner for whom it is commercially confidential. The dataset was constructed during an investigation into the problem of segmenting individual characters from joined written text. Figure 9.4 shows an example of the word "Eins" (German for One). Each example consists of a number of measurements made on the text relative to a potential cut point along with a decision on whether to cut the text at that

Fig. 9.4: The German word "Eins" with an indication of where it should be cut to separate the individual letters.

point or not. As supplied, the dataset contained examples with 50 real valued attributes. In an attempt to assess the performance of algorithms relative to the dimensionality of the problem, a second dataset was constructed from the original using the "best" 20 attributes selected by stepwise regression on the whole dataset. This was the only processing carried out on this dataset. The original and reduced datasets were tested. In both cases training sets of 11220 examples and test sets of 7480 were used in a single train-and-test procedure to assess accuracy.

Although individual results differ between the datasets, the ranking of methods is broadly the same and so we shall consider all the results together. The default rule in both cases would give an error rate of around 6% but since Kohonen, the only unsupervised method in the project, achieves an error rate of 5% for both datasets it seems reasonable to choose this value as our performance threshold.

This is a dataset on which k–nearest neighbour might be expected to do well; all attributes are continuous with little correlation, and this proves to be the case. Indeed, with a variable selection option k-NN obtained an error rate of only 2.5%. Conversely, the fact that k-NN does well indicates that many variables contribute to the classification. ALLOC80 approaches k-NN performance by undersmoothing leading to overfitting on the training set. While this may prove to be an effective strategy with large and representative training sets, it is not recommended in general. Quadisc, CASTLE and Naive Bayes perform poorly on both datasets because, in each case, assumptions underlying the method do not match the data.

Quadisc assumes multi–variate normality and unequal covariance matrices and neither of these assumptions is supported by the data measures. CASTLE achieves default performance using only one variable, in line with the assumption implicit in the method that only a small number of variables will determine the class. Naive Bayes assumes conditional independence amongst the attributes and this is unlikely to hold for a dataset of this type.

Machine learning algorithms generally perform well although with wide variation in tree sizes. Baytree and IndCART achieve low error rates at the expense of building trees containing more than 3000 nodes. C4.5 performs almost as well, though building a tree containing 159 terminal nodes. Cal5 produces a very parsimonious tree, containing only 26 nodes for the Cut20 dataset, which is very easy to understand. AC^2 and NewID build trees

Table 9.11: Comparative results for the Cut20 dataset (2 classes, 20 attributes, (train, test) = (11 220, 7480) observations).

Algorithm	Max. Storage	Time (sec.) Train	Test	Error Rate Train	Test	Rank
Discrim	71	115.5	22.7	0.052	0.050	15
Quadisc	75	394.8	214.2	0.090	0.088	22
Logdisc	1547	587.0	101.2	0.046	0.046	13
SMART	743	21100.5	21.8	0.047	0.047	14
ALLOC80	302	32552.2	*	0.033	0.037	4
k-NN	190	54810.7	6052.0	0.031	0.036	2
CASTLE	175	1006.0	368.5	0.060	0.061	17
CART	FD	FD	FD	FD	FD	
IndCART	1884	*	*	0.002	0.040	6
NewID	1166	1445.0	3.0	0.000	0.039	5
AC^2	915	917.0	48.0	0.000	0.063	19
Baytree	1676	145.3	25.9	0.002	0.034	1
NaiveBay	1352	83.6	27.6	0.074	0.077	20
CN2	9740	5390.0	470.0	0.000	0.042	8
C4.5	2436	293.0	28.0	0.010	0.036	2
ITrule	630	11011.0	50.9	0.083	0.082	21
Cal5	188	455.5	23.4	0.043	0.045	11
Kohonen	1046	*	*	0.046	0.050	15
DIPOL92	379	506.0	36.1	0.043	0.045	11
Backprop	144	88532.0	7.0	0.037	0.043	9
RBF	901	6041.0	400.0	0.042	0.044	10
LVQ	291	1379.0	86.9	0.029	0.041	7
Default	*	*	*	0.059	0.061	17

with 38 and 339 nodes, respectively. ITrule, like CASTLE, cannot deal with continuous attributes directly and also discretises such variables before processing. The major reason for poor performance, though, is that tests were restricted to conjunctions of up to two attributes. CN2, which tested conjunctions of up to 5 attributes, achieved a much better error rate. AC^2 could not handle the full dataset and the results reported are for a 10% subsample.

It is interesting that almost all algorithms achieve a better result on Cut50 than Cut20. This suggests that the attributes excluded from the reduced dataset contain significant discriminatory power. Cal5 achieves its better performance by building a tree five times larger than that for Cut20. NewID and AC^2 both build significantly smaller trees (196 and 28 nodes) and classify more accurately with them. C4.5 uses a tree with 142 nodes with a slight improvement in accuracy. Similarly CN2 discovers a smaller set of rules for Cut50 which deliver improved performance. This general improvement in performance underlines the observation that what is "best" or "optimal" in linear regression terms may not be "best" for other algorithms.

Table 9.12: Results for the Cut50 dataset (2 classes, 50 attributes, (train, test) = (11 220, 7480) observations).

Algorithm	Max. Storage	Time (sec.) Train	Test	Error Rate Train	Test	Rank
Discrim	73	449.2	52.5	0.052	0.050	15
Quadisc	77	2230.7	1244.2	0.092	0.097	21
Logdisc	1579	1990.4	227.0	0.038	0.037	7
SMART	779	63182.0	50.4	0.035	0.039	12
ALLOC80	574	32552.2	*	0.030	0.034	3
k-NN	356	62553.6	6924.0	0.025	0.027	1
CASTLE	765	7777.6	1094.8	0.060	0.061	18
CART	FD	FD	FD	FD	FD	
IndCART	3172	2301.4	2265.4	0.004	0.037	7
NewID	1166	1565.0	2.0	0.000	0.038	10
AC^2	1812	1850.0	47.0	0.000	0.054	18
Baytree	2964	324.0	65.4	0.001	0.035	4
NaiveBay	2680	219.4	69.9	0.106	0.112	22
CN2	*	28600.0	501.0	0.000	0.030	2
C4.5	*	711.0	31.0	0.008	0.035	4
ITrule	642	61287.5	*	*	0.084	20
Cal5	508	1131.9	58.7	0.030	0.037	7
Kohonen	*	*	*	0.046	0.050	15
DIPOL92	884	1242.5	96.9	0.031	0.036	6
Backprop	146	18448.0	12.0	0.041	0.041	14
RBF	649	6393.0	1024.0	0.036	0.038	10
LVQ	476	2991.2	205.0	0.024	0.040	13
Default	*	*	*	0.059	0.061	17

9.4 DATASETS WITH COSTS

The following three datasets were all tackled using cross-validation. The "error rates" that have been used as a measure of performance are now replaced by average costs per observation (averaged over all cycles in cross-validation). The average cost is obtained for all algorithms by multiplying the confusion matrix by the cost matrix, summing the entries, and dividing by the number of observations. In the case of a cost matrix in which all errors have unit cost – normally referred to as "no cost matrix" – this measure of average cost is the same as the error rates quoted previously. Note that some algorithms did not implement the cost matrix, although in principle this would be straightforward. However, we still include all of the algorithms in the tables, partly for completeness but primarily to show the effect of ignoring the cost matrix. In general, those algorithms which do worse than the Default rule are those which do not incorporate costs into the decision making process.

9.4.1 Head injury (Head)

The data set is a series of 1000 patients with severe head injury collected prospectively by neurosurgeons between 1968 and 1976. This head injury study was initiated in the Institute of Neurological Sciences, Glasgow. After 4 years 2 Netherlands centres (Rotterdam and Groningen) joined the study, and late data came also from Los Angeles. The details of the data collection are given in Jennet *et al.* (1979).

The original purpose of the head injury study was to investigate the feasibility of predicting the degree of recovery which individual patients would attain, using data collected shortly after injury. Severely head injured patients require intensive and expensive treatment; even with such care almost half of them die and some survivors remain seriously disabled for life. Clinicians are concerned to recognise which patients have potential for recovery, so as to concentrate their endeavours on them. Outcome was categorised according to the Glasgow Outcome Scale, but the five categories described therein were reduced to three for the purpose of prediction. These were:

d/v dead or vegetative;

sev severe disability;

m/g moderate disability or good recovery.

Table 9.13 gives the different cost of various possible misclassifications.

Table 9.13: Misclassification costs for the head injury dataset. The column represents the predicted class, and the row the true class.

	d/v	sev	m/g
d/v	0	10	75
sev	10	0	90
m/g	750	100	0

The dataset had a very large number of missing values for patients (about 40%) and these were replaced with the median value for the appropriate class. This makes our version of the data considerably easier for classification than the original data, and has the merit that all procedures can be applied to the same dataset, but has the disadvantage that the resulting rules are unrealistic in that this replacement strategy is not possible for real data of unknown class. Nine fold cross-validation was used to estimate the average misclassification cost. The predictive variables are age and various indicators of the brain damage, as reflected in brain dysfunction. These are listed below. Indicators of brain dysfunction can vary considerably during the few days after injury. Measurements were therefore taken frequently, and for each indicant the best and worst states during each of a number of successive time periods were recorded. The data supplied were based on the best state during the first 24 hours after the onset of coma. The EMV score in the table is known in the medical literature as the Glasgow Coma Scale.

- Age, grouped into decades $0 - 9, 10 - 19, \ldots, 60 - 69, 70+$
- The sum of E, M and V scores, *i.e.* EMV score, *i.e.*

    Eye opening in response to stimulation (E)

    Motor response of best limb in response to stimulation (M)

    Verbal response to stimulation (V)

- Motor Response Pattern. An overall summary of the motor responses in all four limbs
- Change in neurological function over the first 24 hours

- Eye indicant. A summary of SEM, OCS and OVS, *i.e.*

    Spontaneous Eye Movements (SEM)

    Oculocephalics (OCS)

    Oculovestibulars (OVS)

- Pupil reaction to light

Table 9.14: Results for the head injury dataset (3 classes, 6 attributes, 900 observations, 9-fold cross-validation). Algorithms in italics have not incorporated costs.

Algorithm	Max. Storage	Time (sec.)		Average Costs		Rank
		Train	Test	Train	Test	
Discrim	200	12.6	3.1	19.76	19.89	3
Quadisc	642	36.6	32.0	17.83	20.06	4
Logdisc	1981	736.4	7.3	16.60	17.96	1
SMART	81	572.2	3.5	13.59	21.81	8
ALLOC80	191	1.4	38.3	18.9	31.90	13
k-NN	144	9.0	11.2	9.20	35.30	15
CASTLE	82	2.6	2.0	18.87	20.87	6
CART	154	17.6	0.8	19.84	20.38	5
IndCART	88	5.5	0.4	25.76	25.52	11
NewID	38	9.0	3.0	18.91	53.64	20
AC²	400	624.0	28.0	17.88	56.87	21
Baytree	73	2.5	0.3	10.94	22.69	9
NaiveBay	52	2.9	0.3	23.68	23.95	10
CN2	149	24.3	3.0	14.36	53.55	19
C4.5⁵	339	5.0	0.2	59.82	82.60	24
ITrule	97	6.5	*	*	37.61	16
Cal5	51	3.0	0.2	32.54	33.26	14
Kohonen	90	1772.0	3.0	35.6	70.70	23
DIPOL92	41	10.0	1.0	25.31	26.52	12
Backprop	518	312.5	31.9	18.23	21.53	7
RBF	150	17.4	5.1	53.37	63.10	22
LVQ	82	190.7	1.2	29.30	46.58	18
Cascade	271	181.0	1.0	15.25	19.46	2
Default	*	*	*	44.10	44.10	17

SMART and DIPOL92 are the only algorithms that as standard can utilise costs directly in the training phase (we used in our results a modified version of Backprop that could utilise costs, but this is very experimental). However, although these two algorithms do reasonably well, they are not the best. Logistic regression does very well and so do Discrim and Quadisc

CART, IndCART, Bayes Tree and Cal5 are the only decision trees that used a cost matrix here, and hence the others have performed worse than the Default rule. CART and Cal5 both had trees of around 5-7 nodes, whereas AC^2 and NewID both had around 240 nodes. However, using error rate as a criterion we cannot judge whether these algorithms were under-pruning, since no cost matrix was used in the classifier. But, for interpretability, the smaller trees are preferred.

Titterington *et al.* (1981) compared several discrimination procedures on this data. Our dataset differs by replacing all missing values with the class median and so the results are not directly comparable.

9.4.2   Heart disease (Heart)

Table 9.15: Results for the heart disease dataset (2 classes, 13 attributes, 270 observations, 9-fold cross-validation). Algorithms in italics have not incorporated costs.

Algorithm	Max. Storage	Time (sec.) Train	Test	Average Costs Train	Test	Rank
Discrim	223	7.7	1.8	0.315	0.393	2
Quadisc	322	18.2	9.2	0.274	0.422	5
Logdisc	494	79.9	4.2	0.271	0.396	3
SMART	88	350.0	0.1	0.264	0.478	10
ALLOC80	95	31.2	5.2	0.394	0.407	4
k-NN	88	0.0	1.0	0.000	0.478	10
CASTLE	93	20.0	3.4	0.374	0.441	6
CART	142	4.1	0.8	0.463	0.452	8
IndCART	65	8.4	0.1	0.261	0.630	18
NewID	21	9.0	3.0	0.000	0.844	24
AC^2	209	243.0	7.0	0.000	0.744	20
Baytree	63	2.7	0.3	0.111	0.526	14
NaiveBay	50	1.5	1.0	0.351	0.374	1
CN2	125	19.2	4.7	0.206	0.767	21
$C4.5^6$	93	29.4	0.8	0.439	0.781	22
ITrule	102	5.1	*	*	0.515	13
Cal5	51	2.3	0.8	0.330	0.444	7
Kohonen	36	227.1	1.9	0.429	0.693	19
DIPOL92	53	18.0	0.3	0.429	0.507	12
Backprop	299	128.2	12.9	0.381	0.574	16
RBF	154	20.4	3.7	0.303	0.781	22
LVQ	54	76.6	1.0	0.140	0.600	17
Cascade	122	78.3	1.0	0.207	0.467	9
Default	*	*	*	0.560	0.560	15

This database comes from the Cleveland Clinic Foundation and was supplied by Robert Detrano, M.D., Ph.D. of the V.A. Medical Center, Long Beach, CA. It is part of the collection of databases at the University of California, Irvine collated by David Aha.

The purpose of the dataset is to predict the presence or absence of heart disease given the results of various medical tests carried out on a patient. This database contains 13 attributes, which have been extracted from a larger set of 75. The database originally contained 303 examples but 6 of these contained missing class values and so were discarded leaving 297. 27 of these were retained in case of dispute, leaving a final total of 270. There are two classes: presence and absence (of heart-disease). This is a reduction of the number of classes in the original dataset in which there were four different degrees of heart-disease. Table 9.16 gives the different costs of the possible misclassifications. Nine fold cross-validation was used to estimate the average misclassification cost. Naive Bayes performed best on the heart dataset. This may reflect the careful selection of attributes by the doctors. Of the decision trees, CART and Cal5 performed the best. Cal5 tuned the pruning parameter, and used an average of 8 nodes in the trees, whereas AC^2 used 45 nodes. However, AC^2 did not take the cost matrix into account, so the prefered pruning is still an open question.

This data has been studied in the literature before, but without taking any cost matrix into account and so the results are not comparable with those obtained here.

Table 9.16: Misclassification costs for the heart disease dataset. The columns represent the predicted class, and the rows the true class.

	absent	present
absent	0	1
present	5	0

9.4.3   German credit (Cr.Ger)

Table 9.17: Cost matrix for the German credit dataset. The columns are the predicted class and the rows the true class.

	good	bad
good	0	1
bad	5	0

The original dataset (provided by Professor Dr. Hans Hofmann, Universität Hamburg) contained some categorical/symbolic attributes. For algorithms that required numerical attributes, a version was produced with several indicator variables added. The attributes that were ordered categorical were coded as integer. This preprocessed dataset had 24 numerical attributes and 10-fold cross-validation was used for the classification, and for uniformity all algorithms used this preprocessed version. It is of interest that NewID did the trials with both the preprocessed version and the original data, and obtained nearly identical error rates (32.8% and 31.3%) but rather different tree sizes (179 and 306 nodes). The attributes of the original dataset include:

    status of existing current account,
    duration of current account,
    credit history,
    reason for loan request (e.g. new car, furniture),
    credit amount,
    savings account/bonds,
    length of employment,
    installment rate in percentage of disposable income,
    marital status and sex,
    length of time at presentresidence,
    age and
    job.

Results are given in Table 9.18. The providers of this dataset suggest the cost matrix of Table 9.17. It is interesting that only 10 algorithms do better than the Default. The results clearly demonstrate that some Decision Tree algorithms are at a disadvantage when costs are taken into account. That it is possible to include costs into decision trees, is demonstrated by the good results of Cal5 and CART (Breiman *et al.*, 1984). Cal5 achieved a good result with an average of only 2 nodes which would lead to very transparent rules. Of those algorithms that did not include costs, C4.5 used a tree with 49 nodes (with an error rate of 27.3%), whereas AC^2 and NewID used an average of over 300 nodes (with error rates of 29.4% and 32.8% respectively).

Table 9.18: Results for the German credit dataset (2 classes, 24 attributes, 1000 observations, 10-fold cross-validation). Algorithms in italics have not incorporated costs.

Algorithm	Maximum Storage	Time (sec.) Train	Test	Average Costs Train	Test	Rank
Discrim	556	50.1	7.3	0.509	0.535	1
Quadisc	534	53.6	8.2	0.431	0.619	9
Logdisc	391	56.0	6.7	0.499	0.538	2
SMART	935	6522.9	*	0.389	0.601	6
ALLOC80	103	9123.3	*	0.597	0.584	4
k-NN	286	2.4	9.0	0.000	0.694	10
CASTLE	93	109.9	9.5	0.582	0.583	3
CART	95	114.0	1.1	0.581	0.613	8
IndCART	668	337.5	248.0	0.069	0.761	14
NewID	118	12.8	15.2	0.000	0.925	19
AC^2	771	9668.0	232.0	0.000	0.878	17
Baytree	79	7.4	0.4	0.126	0.778	15
NaiveBay	460	26.0	5.3	0.600	0.703	12
CN2	320	116.8	3.1	0.000	0.856	16
C4.5	82	13.7	1.0	0.640	0.985	22
ITrule	69	32.5	3.0	*	0.879	18
Cal5	167	19.5	1.9	0.600	0.603	7
Kohonen	152	5897.2	5.3	0.689	1.160	23
DIPOL92	53	77.8	5.0	0.574	0.599	5
Backprop	148	2258.5	0.0	0.446	0.772	13
RBF	215	24.5	3.4	0.848	0.971	21
LVQ	97	322.7	4.7	0.229	0.963	20
Default	*	*	*	0.700	0.700	11

9.5 OTHER DATASETS

This section contains rather a "mixed bag" of datasets, mostly of an industrial application.

9.5.1 Shuttle control (Shuttle)

The dataset was provided by Jason Catlett who was then at the Basser Department of Computer Science, University of Sydney, N.S.W., Australia. The data originated from NASA and concern the position of radiators within the Space Shuttle. The problem appears to be noise-free in the sense that arbitrarily small error rates are possible given sufficient data.

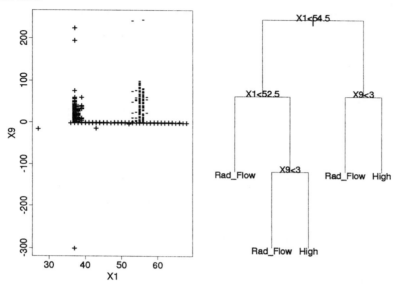

Fig. 9.5: Shuttle data: attributes 1 and 9 for the two classes Rad_Flow and High only. The symbols "+" and "-" denote the state Rad_Flow and High respectively. The 40856 examples are classified correctly by the decision tree in the right diagram.

The data was divided into a train set and a test set with 43500 examples in the train set and 14500 in the test set. A single train-and-test was used to calculate the accuracy. With samples of this size, it should be possible to obtain an accuracy of 99 - 99.9%. Approximately 80% of the data belong to class 1. At the other extreme, there are only 6 examples of class 6 in the learning set.

The shuttle dataset also departs widely from typical distribution assumptions. The attributes are numerical and appear to exhibit multimodality (we do not have a good statistical test to measure this). Some feeling for this dataset can be gained by looking at Figure 9.5. It shows that a rectangular box (with sides parallel to the axes) may be drawn to enclose all examples in the class "High", although the lower boundary of this box (X9 less than 3) is so close to examples of class "Rad_Flow" that this particular boundary cannot be clearly marked to the scale of Figure 9.5. In the whole dataset, the data seem to consist of isolated islands or clusters of points, each of which is pure (belongs to only one class), with one class comprising several such islands. However, neighbouring islands may be very close and yet come from different populations. The boundaries of the islands seem to be parallel with the coordinate axes. If this picture is correct, and the present data do not contradict it, as it is possible to classify the combined dataset with 100% accuracy using a decision tree, then it is of interest to ask which of our algorithms are *guaranteed* to arrive at the correct classification given an arbitrarily large learning dataset. In the following, we ignore practical matters such as training times, storage requirements etc., and concentrate on the limiting behaviour for an infinitely large training set.

Table 9.19: Results for the shuttle dataset with error rates are in % (7 classes, 9 attributes, (train, test) = (43 500, 14 500) observations).

Algorithm	Max. Storage	Time (sec.) Train	Time (sec.) Test	% Error Train	% Error Test	Rank
Discrim	1957	507.8	102.3	4.98	4.83	20
Quadisc	1583	708.6	176.6	6.35	6.72	21
Logdisc	1481	6945.5	106.2	3.94	3.83	18
SMART	636	110009.8	93.2	0.61	0.59	14
ALLOC80	636	55215.0	18333.0	0.95	0.83	15
k-NN	636	32531.3	10482.0	0.39	0.44	11
CASTLE	77	461.3	149.7	3.70	3.80	17
CART	176	79.0	2.3	0.04	0.08	5
IndCART	329	1151.9	16.2	0.04	0.09	6
NewID	1535	6180.0	*	0.00	0.01	1
AC^2	200	2553.0	2271.0	0.00	0.32	8
Baytree	368	240.0	16.8	0.00	0.02	2
NaiveBay	225	1029.5	22.4	4.60	4.50	19
CN2	1432	11160.0	*	0.00	0.03	3
C4.5[7]	3400	13742.4	11.1	0.04	0.10	7
ITrule	665	91969.7	*	*	0.41	9
Cal5	372	313.4	10.3	0.03	0.03	3
Kohonen	FD	FD	FD	FD	FD	
DIPOL92	674	2068.0	176.2	0.44	0.48	13
Backprop	144	5174.0	21.0	4.50	0.43	10
RBF	249	*	*	1.60	1.40	16
LVQ	650	2813.3	83.8	0.40	0.44	11
Default	*	*	*	21.59	20.84	22

Procedures which might therefore be expected to find a perfect rule for this dataset would seem to be: k-NN, Backprop and ALLOC80. ALLOC80 failed here, and the result obtained by another kernel method (using a *sphered* transformation of the data) was far from perfect. RBF should also be capable of perfect accuracy, but some changes would be required in the particular implementation used in the project (to avoid singularities). Using a variable selection method (selecting 6 of the attributes) k-NN achieved an error rate of 0.055%.

Decision trees will also find the perfect rule provided that the pruning parameter is properly set, but may not do so under all circumstances as it is occasionally necessary to override the splitting criterion (Breiman *et al.*, 1984) . Although a machine learning procedure may find a decision tree which classifies perfectly, it may not find the simplest representation. The tree of Figure 9.5, which was produced by the Splus procedure tree(), gets 100% accuracy with five terminal nodes, whereas it is easy to construct an equivalent tree with only three terminal nodes (see that the same structure occurs in both halves of the tree in Figure 9.5). It is possible to classify the full 58 000 examples with only 19 errors using a linear decision tree with nine terminal nodes. Since there are seven classes, this is a remarkably simple tree. This suggests that the data have been generated by a process that is governed by a *linear decision tree*, that is, a decision tree in which tests are applied sequentially, the result of each test being to allocate one section of the data to one class and to apply subsequent tests to the remaining section. As there are very few examples of class 6 in the whole 58 000 dataset, it would require enormous amounts of data to construct reliable classifiers for class 6. The actual trees produced by the algorithms are rather small, as expected: AC^2 has 13 nodes, and both Cal5 and CART have 21 nodes.

9.5.2 Diabetes (Diab)

This dataset was originally donated by Vincent Sigillito, Applied Physics Laboratory, Johns Hopkins University, Laurel, MD 20707 and was constructed by constrained selection from a larger database held by the National Institute of Diabetes and Digestive and Kidney Diseases. It is publicly available from the machine learning database at UCI (see Appendix A). All patients represented in this dataset are females at least 21 years old of Pima Indian heritage living near Phoenix, Arizona, USA.

The problem posed here is to predict whether a patient would test positive for diabetes according to World Health Organization criteria (*i.e.* if the patients' 2 hour post-load plasma glucose is at least 200 mg/dl.) given a number of physiological measurements and medical test results. The attribute details are given below:

number of times pregnant

plasma glucose concentration in an oral glucose tolerance test

diastolic blood pressure (mm/Hg)

triceps skin fold thickness (mm)

2-hour serum insulin (mu U/ml)

body mass index (kg/m^2)

diabetes pedigree function

age (years)

This is a two class problem with class value 1 being interpreted as "tested positive for diabetes". There are 500 examples of class 1 and 268 of class 2. Twelve-fold cross validation was used to estimate prediction accuracy.

The dataset is rather difficult to classify. The so-called "class" value is really a binarised form of another attribute which is itself highly indicative of certain types of diabetes but does not have a one-to-one correspondence with the medical condition of being diabetic.

No algorithm performs exceptionally well, although ALLOC80 and k-NN seem to be the poorest. Automatic smoothing parameter selection in ALLOC80 can make poor choices for datasets with discrete valued attributes and k-NN can have problems scaling such datasets. Overall though, it seems reasonable to conclude that the attributes do not predict the class well. Cal5 uses only 8 nodes in its decision tree, whereas NewId, which performs less well, has 119 nodes. AC^2 and C4.5 have 116 and 32 nodes, repectively and CN2 generates 52 rules, although there is not very much difference in the error rates here.

This dataset has been studied by Smith *et al.* (1988) using the ADAP algorithm. Using 576 examples as a training set, ADAP achieved an error rate of .24 on the remaining 192 instances.

Table 9.20: Results for the diabetes dataset (2 classes, 8 attributes, 768 observations, 12-fold cross-validation).

Algorithm	Max. Storage	Time (sec.) Train	Time (sec.) Test	Error Rate Train	Error Rate Test	Rank
Discrim	338	27.4	6.5	0.220	0.225	3
Quadisc	327	24.4	6.6	0.237	0.262	11
Logdisc	311	30.8	6.6	0.219	0.223	1
SMART	780	3762.0	*	0.177	0.232	4
ALLOC80	152	1374.1	*	0.288	0.301	21
k-NN	226	1.0	2.0	0.000	0.324	22
CASTLE	82	35.3	4.7	0.260	0.258	10
CART	144	29.6	0.8	0.227	0.255	9
IndCART	596	215.6	209.4	0.079	0.271	14
NewID	87	9.6	10.2	0.000	0.289	19
AC^2	373	4377.0	241.0	0.000	0.276	18
Baytree	68	10.4	0.3	0.008	0.271	14
NaiveBay	431	25.0	7.2	0.239	0.262	11
CN2	190	38.4	2.8	0.010	0.289	19
C4.5	61	11.5	0.9	0.131	0.270	13
ITrule	60	31.2	1.5	0.223	0.245	6
Cal5	137	236.7	0.1	0.232	0.250	8
Kohonen	62	1966.4	2.5	0.134	0.273	17
DIPOL92	52	35.8	0.8	0.220	0.224	2
Backprop	147	7171.0	0.1	0.198	0.248	7
RBF	179	4.8	0.1	0.218	0.243	5
LVQ	69	139.5	1.2	0.101	0.272	16
Default	*	*	*	0.350	0.350	23

9.5.3 DNA

This classification problem is drawn from the field of molecular biology. Splice junctions are points on a DNA sequence at which "superfluous" DNA is removed during protein creation. The problem posed here is to recognise, given a sequence of DNA, the boundaries between exons (the parts of the DNA sequence retained after splicing) and introns (the parts of the DNA that are spliced out). The dataset used in the project is a processed version of the Irvine Primate splice-junction database. Each of the 3186 examples in the database consists of a window of 60 nucleotides, each represented by one of four symbolic values (a,c,g,t), and the classification of the middle point in the window as one of; intron–extron boundary, extron–intron boundary or neither of these. Processing involved the removal of a small number of ambiguous examples (4), conversion of the original 60 symbolic attributes to 180 or 240 binary attributes and the conversion of symbolic class labels to numeric labels (see Section 7.4.3). The training set of 2000 was chosen randomly from the dataset and the remaining 1186 examples were used as the test set.

This is basically a partitioning problem and so we might expect, in advance, that Decision Tree algorithms should do well. The classes in this problem have a heirarchical

Table 9.21: Results for the DNA dataset (3 classes, 60/180/240 attributes, (train, test) = (2000, 1186) observations).

Algorithm	Max. Storage	Time (sec.)		Error Rate		Rank
		Train	Test	Train	Test	
Discrim	215	928.5	31.1	0.034	0.059	4
Quadisc	262	1581.1	808.6	0.000	0.059	4
Logdisc	1661	5057.4	76.2	0.008	0.061	6
SMART	247	79676.0	16.0	0.034	0.115	17
ALLOC80	188	14393.5	*	0.063	0.057	3
k-NN	247	2427.5	882.0	0.000	0.146	20
CASTLE	86	396.7	225.0	0.061	0.072	8
CART	283	615.0	8.6	0.075	0.085	11
IndCART	729	523.0	515.8	0.040	0.073	9
NewID	729	698.4	1.0	0.000	0.100	15
AC^2	9385	12378.0	87.0	0.000	0.100	15
Baytree	727	81.7	10.5	0.001	0.095	13
NaiveBay	727	51.8	14.8	0.052	0.068	7
CN2	10732	869.0	74.0	0.002	0.095	13
C4.5	1280	9.0	2.0	0.040	0.076	10
ITrule	282	2211.6	5.9	0.131	0.135	19
Cal5	755	1616.0	7.5	0.104	0.131	18
Kohonen	2592	*	*	0.104	0.339	21
DIPOL92	518	213.4	10.1	0.007	0.048	2
Backprop	161	4094.0	9.0	0.014	0.088	12
RBF	1129	*	*	0.015	0.041	1
LVQ	FD	FD	FD	FD	FD	
Default	*	*	*	0.475	0.492	22

structure; the primary decision is whether the centre point in the window is a splice-junction or not. If it is a splice-junction then the secondary classification is as to its type; intron-extron or extron-intron.

Unfortunately comparisons between algorithms are more difficult than usual with this dataset as a number of methods were tested with a restricted number of attributes; some were tested with attribute values converted to 180 binary values, and some to 240 binary values. CASTLE and CART only used the middle 90 binary variables. NewID, CN2 and C4.5 used the original 60 categorical variables and k-NN, Kohonen, LVQ, Backprop and RBF used the one-of-four coding. The classical statistical algorithms perform reasonable well achieving roughly 6% error rate. k-NN is probably hampered by the large number of binary attributes, but Naive Bayes does rather well helped by the fact that the attributes are independent.

Surprisingly, machine learning algorithms do not outperform classical statistical algorithms on this problem. CASTLE and CART were at a disadvantage using a smaller window although performing reasonably. IndCART used 180 attributes and improved on the CART error rate by around 1%. ITrule and Cal5 are the poorest performers in this group. ITrule, using only uni–variate and bi–variate tests, is too restricted and Cal5 is probably confused by the large number of attributes.

Of the neural network algorithms, Kohonen performs very poorly not helped by unequal class proportions in the dataset. DIPOL92 constructs an effective set of piecewise linear decision boundaries but overall, RBF is the most accurate algorithm using 720 centres. It is rather worrying here, that LVQ claimed an error rate of 0, and this result was unchanged when the test data had the classes permuted. No reason could be found for this phenomenon – presumably it was caused by the excessive number of attributes – but that the algorithm should "lie" with no explanation or warning is still a mystery. This problem did not occur with any other dataset.

In order to assess the importance of the window size in this problem, we can examine in a little more detail the performance of one of the machine learning algorithms. CN2 classified the training set using 113 rules involving tests on from 2 to 6 attributes and misclassifying 4 examples. Table 9.22 shows how frequently attributes in different ranges appeared in those 113 rules. From the table it appears that a window of size 20 contains the

Table 9.22: Frequency of occurrence of attributes in rules generated by CN2 for the DNA training set.

	1–10	11–20	21–30	31–40	41–50	51–60
class 1	17	10	12	59	7	2
class 2	17	28	78	21	13	11
class 3	6	8	57	55	4	3
total	40	46	147	135	24	16

most important variables. Attributes just after the middle of the window are most important in determining class 1 and those just before the middle are most important in determining class 2. For class 3, variables close to the middle on either side are equally important. Overall though, variables throughout the 60 attribute window do seem to contribute. The question of how many attributes to use in the window is vitally important for procedures that include many parameters - Quadisc gets much better results (error rate of 3.6% on the test set) if it is restricted to the middle 20 categorical attributes.

It is therefore of interest to note that decision tree procedures get almost the same accuracies on the original categorical data and the processed binary data. NewID, obtained an error rate of 9.95% on the preprocessed data (180 variables) and 9.20% on the original data (with categorical attributes). These accuracies are probably within what could be called experimental error, so it seems that NewID does about as well on either form of the dataset. There is a little more to the story however, as the University of Wisconsin ran several algorithms on this dataset. In Table 9.23 we quote their results alongside ours for nearest neighbour. In this problem, ID3 and NewID are probably equivalent, and the slight discrepancies in error rates achieved by ID3 at Wisconsin (10.5%) compared to NewID (9.95%) in this study are attributable to the different random samples used. This cannot be the explanation for the differences between the two nearest neighbour results: there appears to be an irreconcilable difference, perhaps due to preprocessing, perhaps due to "distance" being measured in a conditional (class dependent) manner.

Certainly, the Kohonen algorithm used here encountered a problem when defining distances in the attribute space. When using the coding of 180 attributes, the Euclidean distances between pairs were not the same (the squared distances were 2.0 for pairs $(A, C), (A, G), (C, G)$ but only 1.0 for the pairs involving T: $(A, T), (C, T), (G, T)$). Therefore Kohonen needs the coding of 240 attributes. This coding was also adopted by other algorithms using distance measures (k-NN, LVQ).

Table 9.23: DNA dataset error rates for each of the three classes: splice–junction is Intron–Extron (IE), Extron–Intron (EI) or Neither. All trials except the last were carried out by the University of Wisconsin, sometimes with local implementations of published algorithms, using ten-fold cross-validation on 1000 examples randomly selected from the complete set of 3190. The last trial was conducted with a training set of 2000 examples and a test set of 1186 examples.

Algorithm	Neither	EI	IE	Overall
KBANN	4.62	7.56	8.47	6.28
Backprop	5.29	5.74	10.75	6.69
PEBLS	6.86	8.18	7.55	7.36
PERCEPTRON	3.99	16.32	17.41	10.31
ID3	8.84	10.58	13.99	10.50
Cobweb	11.80	15.04	9.46	12.08
N Neighbour (Wisconsin)	31.11	11.65	9.09	20.94
N Neighbour (Leeds)	0.50	25.74	36.79	14.60

9.5.4   Technical (Tech)

Table 9.24: The four most common classes in the technical data, classified by the value of attribute **X52**.

Range of X52	A_{69}	A_{72}	A_{77}	A_{78}
< -0.085	0	1	0	180
-0.085, -0.055	260	0	0	0
-0.055, +0.055	0	324	0	0
+0.055, +0.085	0	0	1036	0
> +0.085	0	0	0	392

Very little is known about this dataset as the nature of the problem domain is secret. It is of commercial interest to Daimler-Benz AG, Germany. The dataset shows indications of some sort of preprocessing, probably by some decision-tree type process, before it was received. To give only one instance, consider only the four most common classes $(A_{69}, A_{72}, A_{77}, A_{78})$, and consider only one attribute (**X52**). By simply tabulating the values of attribute **X52** it becomes obvious that the classifications are being made according to symmetrically placed boundaries on **X52**, specifically the two boundaries at -0.055 and +0.055, and also the boundaries at -0.085 and +0.085. These boundaries divide the range of **X52** into five regions, and if we look at the classes contained in these regions we get the frequency table in Table 9.24. The symmetric nature of the boundaries suggests strongly that the classes have been *defined* by their attributes, and that the class definitions are only concerned with *inequalities* on the attributes. Needless to say, such a system is perfectly suited to decision trees , and we may remark, in passing, that the above table was discovered by a decision tree when applied to the reduced technical dataset with all 56 attributes but with only the four most common classes (in other words, the decision tree could classify the reduced dataset with 1 error in 2193 examples using only one attribute).

Table 9.25: Results for the technical dataset (91 classes, 56 attributes, (train, test) = (4500, 2580) observations).

Algorithm	Max. Storage	Time (sec.) Train	Test	Error Rate Train	Test	Rank
Discrim	365	421.3	200.8	0.368	0.391	15
Quadisc	334	19567.8	11011.6	0.405	0.495	17
Logdisc	354	18961.2	195.9	0.350	0.401	16
SMART	524	21563.7	56.8	0.356	0.366	14
ALLOC80	FD	FD	FD	FD	FD	
k-NN	213	5129.9	2457.0	0.007	0.204	9
CASTLE	FD	FD	FD	FD	FD	
CART	FD	FD	FD	FD	FD	
IndCART	3328	1418.6	1423.3	0.007	0.095	2
NewID	592	527.1	12.5	0.000	0.090	1
AC^2	7400	5028.0	273.0	0.006	0.102	3
Baytree	1096	175.5	9.8	0.019	0.174	6
NaiveBay	656	169.2	81.6	0.323	0.354	12
CN2	*	3980.0	465.0	0.048	0.123	5
C4.5	2876	384.0	96.0	0.050	0.120	4
ITrule	FD	FD	FD	FD	FD	
Cal5	842	2422.1	7.1	0.110	0.183	7
Kohonen	640	*	*	0.326	0.357	13
DIPOL92	941	7226.0	1235.0	0.080	0.192	8
Backprop	FD	FD	FD	FD	FD	
RBF	510	1264.0	323.0	0.304	0.324	11
LVQ	559	2443.2	87.3	0.196	0.261	10
Default	*	*	*	0.770	0.777	18

The dataset consists of 7080 examples with 56 attributes and 91 classes. The attributes are all believed to be real: however, the majority of attribute values are zero. This may be the numerical value "0" or more likely "not relevant", "not measured" or "not applicable". One-shot train and test was used to calculate the accuracy.

The results for this dataset seem quite poor although all are significantly better than the default error rate of 0.777. Several algorithms failed to run on the dataset as they could not cope with the large number of classes. The decision tree algorithms IndCART, NewID and AC^2 gave the best results in terms of error rates. This reflects the nature of the preprocessing which made the dataset more suited to decision trees algorithms. However, the output produced by the tree algorithms is (not surprisingly) difficult to interpret – NewID has a tree with 590 terminal nodes, C4.5 has 258 nodes, Cal5 has 507 nodes and AC^2 has 589 nodes. Statistical algorithms gave much poorer results with Quadisc giving the highest error rate of all. They appear to over-train slightly as a result of too many parameters.

9.5.5 Belgian power (Belg)

Table 9.26: Results for the Belgian Power I (2 classes, 28 attributes, (train, test) = (1250, 1250) observations).

Algorithm	Max. Storage	Time (sec.) Train	Time (sec.) Test	Error Rate Train	Error Rate Test	Rank
Discrim	588	73.8	27.8	0.022	0.025	6
Quadisc	592	85.2	40.5	0.036	0.052	18
Logdisc	465	130.4	27.1	0.002	0.007	2
SMART	98	7804.1	15.6	0.003	0.006	1
ALLOC80	125	3676.2	*	0.026	0.044	16
k-NN	86	1.0	137.0	0.000	0.059	21
CASTLE	279	230.2	96.2	0.029	0.047	17
CART	170	135.1	8.5	0.009	0.034	11
IndCART	293	86.5	85.4	0.007	0.034	11
NewID	846	142.0	1.0	0.017	0.027	7
AC^2	222	1442.0	79.0	0.000	0.034	11
Baytree	289	24.7	6.7	0.000	0.030	9
NaiveBay	276	17.4	7.6	0.046	0.062	22
CN2	345	272.2	16.9	0.000	0.032	10
C4.5	77	66.0	11.6	0.010	0.040	15
ITrule	293	1906.2	41.1	0.043	0.065	23
Cal5	62	13.9	7.2	0.025	0.029	8
Kohonen	216	7380.6	54.9	0.026	0.056	20
DIPOL92	49	43.0	11.9	0.015	0.018	4
Backprop	146	478.0	2.0	0.011	0.017	3
RBF	*	121.4	29.3	0.021	0.034	11
LVQ	115	977.7	32.0	0.002	0.054	19
Cascade	391	806.0	1.0	0.005	0.019	5
Default	*	*	*	0.363	0.362	24

The object of this dataset is to find a fast and reliable indicator of instability in large scale power systems. The dataset is confidential to StatLog and belongs to T. van Cutsem and L. Wehenkel, University of Liège, Institut Montefiore, Sart-Tilman, B-4000 Liège, Belgium.

The emergency control of voltage stability is still in its infancy but one important aspect of this control is the early detection of critical states in order to reliably trigger automatic corrective actions. This dataset has been constructed by simulating up to five minutes of the system behaviour. Basically, a case is labelled stable if all voltages controlled by On-Load Tap Changers are successfully brought back to their set-point values. Otherwise, the system becomes unstable.

There are 2500 examples of stable and unstable states each with 28 attributes which involve measurements of voltage magnitudes, active and reactive power flows and injections. Statistical algorithms cannot be run on datasets which have linearly dependent attributes and there are 7 such attributes (X18,X19,X20,X21,X23,X27,X28) in the Belgian Power dataset. These have to be removed when running the classical statistical algorithms. No other form of pre-processing was done to this dataset. Train and test sets have 1250

Kohonen Map - Belgian Power data

```
2  2  2  2  2  2  2  1  1  1  1  1  2  2  2  2  2  2  2  2
2  2  2  2  2  2  1  2  1  1  1  1  2  1  2  2  2  2  2  2
2  2  2  2  2  2  2  2  1  1  1  1  2  2  2  2  2  2  2  2
2  2  2  2  2  2  2  2  1  1  1  2  2  2  2  2  2  2  2  2
2  2  2  2  2  2  2  2  2  1  1  2  2  2  2  2  2  2  2  2
2  2  2  2  2  2  2  2  2  2  2  2  1  1  1  2  2  2  2  2
2  2  2  2  1  2  2  2  2  2  1  1  1  1  1  1  2  1  2
2  2  2  2  1  2  2  2  2  2  2  1  1  1  1  1  1  1  1
1  1  2  2  2  2  2  2  2  2  1  1  1  1  1  1  1  1  1
1  1  2  2  2  2  2  2  1  1  1  1  1  1  1  1  1  1  1
1  1  1  1  2  2  2  2  2  1  1  1  1  1  1  1  1  1  1
1  1  1  1  1  2  1  2  2  1  1  1  1  1  1  1  1  1  1
1  1  1  1  1  1  1  1  1  1  1  1  1  1  1  1  1  1  1
1  1  1  1  1  1  1  1  1  1  1  1  1  1  1  1  1  1  1
1  1  1  1  1  1  1  1  1  1  1  1  1  1  1  1  1  1  1
1  1  1  1  1  1  1  1  1  1  1  1  1  1  1  1  1  1  1
1  1  1  1  1  1  1  1  1  1  1  1  1  1  1  1  1  1  1
1  1  1  1  1  1  1  1  1  1  1  1  1  1  1  1  1  1  1
1  1  1  1  1  1  1  1  1  1  1  1  1  1  1  1  1  1  1
1  1  1  1  1  1  1  1  1  1  1  1  1  1  1  1  1  1  1
```

Fig. 9.6: Kohonen map of the Belgian Power data, showing potential clustering. Both classes 1 and 2 appear to have two distinct clusters.

examples each and single train-and-test is used for the classification.

The statistical algorithms SMART and Logdisc produced results which are significantly better than the other algorithms tested on this dataset. Logdisc is approximately 50 times quicker at training than SMART and still produced an error rate of less than 1%. DIPOL92 also gives a fairly low error rate and is not time consuming to run. k-NN was confused by irrelevant attributes, and a variable selection option reduced the error rate to 3.4%. The Kohonen map of this data may help to understand this dataset. The clustering apparent in Fig. 9.5.5 shows, for example, that there may be two distinct types of "stable state" (denoted by 2). The decision trees did not do so well here. It is interesting that the smallest tree was produced by Cal5, with 9 nodes, and the largest tree was produced by NewID with 129 nodes, and yet the error rates are very similar at 2.9% and 2.7%, respectively.

Information about class clusters can be incorporated directly into the DIPOL92 model and helps to produce more accurate results. There is a more technical description of this dataset in van Cutsem *et al.* (1991).

9.5.6   Belgian power II (BelgII)

This dataset is drawn from a larger simulation than the one which produced the Belgian Power dataset. The objective remains to find a fast and reliable indicator of instability in large scale power systems. This dataset is also confidential and belongs to the University

Table 9.27: Results for the Belgian Power II dataset (2 classes, 57 attributes, (train, test) = (2000, 1000) observations).

Algorithm	Max. Storage	Time (sec.) Train	Test	Error Rate Train	Test	Rank
Discrim	75	107.5	9.3	0.048	0.041	15
Quadisc	75	516.8	211.8	0.015	0.035	13
Logdisc	1087	336.0	43.6	0.031	0.028	12
SMART	882	11421.3	3.1	0.010	0.013	1
ALLOC80	185	6238.4	*	0.057	0.045	16
k-NN	129	408.5	103.4	0.000	0.052	17
CASTLE	80	9.5	4.3	0.062	0.064	18
CART	232	467.9	11.8	0.022	0.022	7
IndCART	1036	349.5	335.2	0.004	0.014	2
NewID	624	131.0	0.5	0.000	0.017	4
AC^2	3707	3864.0	92.0	0.000	0.019	6
Baytree	968	83.7	11.8	0.000	0.014	2
NaiveBay	852	54.9	12.5	0.087	0.089	23
CN2	4708	967.0	28.0	0.000	0.025	9
C4.5	1404	184.0	18.0	0.008	0.018	5
ITrule	291	9024.1	17.9	0.080	0.081	21
Cal5	103	62.1	9.8	0.037	0.026	10
Kohonen	585	*	*	0.061	0.084	22
DIPOL92	154	95.4	13.1	0.030	0.026	10
Backprop	148	4315.0	1.0	0.021	0.022	7
RBF	*	*	*	0.037	0.035	13
LVQ	194	1704.0	50.8	0.018	0.065	19
Default	*	*	*	0.076	0.070	20

of Liège and Electricitè de France. The training set consists of 2000 examples with 57 attributes. The test set contains 1000 examples and there are two classes. No pre-processing was done and one-shot train-and-test was used to calculate the accuracy.

As for the previous Belgian Power dataset, SMART comes out top in terms of test error rate (although it takes far longer to run than the other algorithms considered here). Logdisc hasn't done so well on this larger dataset. k-NN was again confused by irrelevant attributes, and a variable selection option reduced the error rate to 2.2%. The machine learning algorithms IndCART, NewID, AC^2, Baytree and C4.5 give consistently good results. The tree sizes here were more similar with AC^2 using 36 nodes, C4.5 25 nodes, and NewID using 37 nodes. Naive Bayes is worst and along with Kohonen and ITrule give poorer results than the default rule for the test set error rate (0.074).

There is a detailed description of this dataset and related results in Wehenkel et al. (1993) .

9.5.7   Machine faults (Faults)

Due to the confidential nature of the problem, very little is known about this dataset. It was donated to the project by the software company ISoft, Chemin de Moulon, F-91190

Table 9.28: Results for the Machine Faults dataset (3 classes, 45 attributes, 570 observations, 10-fold cross-validation).

Algorithm	Max. Storage	Time (sec.) Train	Time (sec.) Test	Error Rate Train	Error Rate Test	Rank
Discrim	457	51.1	6.8	0.140	0.204	3
Quadisc	299	46.0	8.4	0.107	0.293	8
Logdisc	406	67.6	6.2	0.122	0.221	4
SMART	105	13521.0	*	0.101	0.339	17
ALLOC80	129	802.4	*	0.341	0.339	17
k-NN	87	260.7	5.2	0.376	0.375	20
CASTLE	176	350.3	17.3	0.254	0.318	12
CART	164	90.6	0.9	0.244	0.318	12
IndCART	672	36.7	37.2	0.156	0.335	16
NewID	*	*	*	0.000	0.304	10
AC^2	826	265.0	9.0	0.000	0.174	1
Baytree	596	8.6	1.8	0.003	0.283	7
NaiveBay	484	3.3	0.4	0.232	0.274	6
CN2	1600	69.2	7.8	0.000	0.354	19
C4.5	700	6.3	1.7	0.125	0.305	11
ITrule	75	42.1	1.8	0.331	0.330	15
Cal5	197	472.8	1.2	0.231	0.297	9
Kohonen	188	*	*	0.193	0.472	22
DIPOL92	52	54.0	10.0	0.120	0.191	2
Backprop	147	3724.6	0.0	0.028	0.228	5
RBF	332	58.6	12.0	0.102	0.320	14
LVQ	72	90.6	2.3	0.019	0.444	21
Default	*	*	*	0.610	0.610	23

Gif sur Yvette, France. The only information known about the dataset is that it involves the financial aspect of mechanical maintenance and repair. The aim is to evaluate the cost of repairing damaged entities. The original dataset had multiple attribute values and a few errors. This was processed to split the 15 attributes into 45. The original train and test sets supplied by ISoft were concatenated and the examples permuted randomly to form a dataset with 570 examples. The pre-processing of hierarchical data is discussed further in Section 7.4.5. There are 45 numerical attributes and 3 classes and classification was done using 10-fold cross-validation.

This is the only hierarchical dataset studied here. Compared with the other algorithms, AC^2 gives the best error rate. The AC^2 trials were done on the original dataset whereas the other algorithms on the project used a transformed dataset because they cannot handle datasets expressed in the knowledge representation language of AC^2. In other words, this dataset was preprocessed in order that other algorithms could handle the dataset. This preprocessing was done without loss of information on the attributes, but the hierarchy between attributes was destroyed. The dataset of this application has been designed to run with AC^2, thus all the knowledge entered has been used by the program. This explains (in part) the performance of AC^2 and underlines the importance of structuring the knowledge for an application. Although this result is of interest, it was not strictly a fair comparison, since AC^2 used domain-specific knowledge which the other algorithms did not (and for the most part, could not). In addition, it should be pointed out that the cross-validation procedure used with AC^2 involved a different splitting method that preserved the class proportions, so this will also bias the result somewhat. The size of the tree produced by AC^2 is 340 nodes, whereas Cal5 and NewID used trees with 33 nodes and 111 nodes, respectively.

Kohonen gives the poorest result which is surprising as this neural net algorithm should do better on datasets with nearly equal class numbers. It is interesting to compare this with the results for k-NN. The algorithm should work well on all datasets on which any algorithm similar to the nearest–neighbour algorithm (or a classical cluster analysis) works well. The fact the k-NN performs badly on this dataset suggests that Kohonen will too.

9.5.8   Tsetse fly distribution (Tsetse)

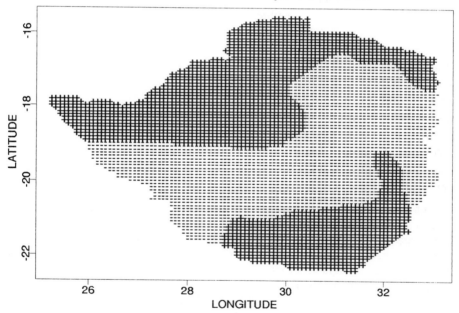

Fig. 9.7: Tsetse map: The symbols "+" and "-" denote the presence and absence of tsetse flies respectively.

Tsetse flies are one of the most prevalent insect hosts spreading disease (namely tripanoso-miasis) from cattle to humans in Africa. In order to limit the spread of disease it is of interest to predict the distribution of flies and types of environment to which they are best suited.

The tsetse dataset contains interpolated data contributed by CSIRO Division of For-restry, Australia (Booth et al., 1990) and was donated by Trevor H. Booth, PO Box 4008,

Queen Victoria Terrace, Canberra, ACT 2600, Australia.

Tsetse files were eradicated from most of Zimbabwe but a map of presence/absence was constructed before any eradication programme and this provides the classified examples. For a total of 4999 squares of side 7km, data has been collected from maps, climatic databases and remotely sensed information. The main interest is in the environmental conditions under which the tsetse fly thrives and the dataset used here consisted of 14 attributes related to this (shown below). The 2 classes are presence or absence of flies and the classification was done using one-shot train-and-test. The training set had 3500 examples and the test set had 1499. Both had roughly equal numbers in both classes.

All attribute values are numeric and indicated below. The original data had measurements of latitude and longitude as attributes which were used to construct the map. These attributes were dropped as the purpose is to identify the environmental conditions suitable for flies.

elevation

annual average NVDI vegetation index

NVDI vegetation index for February

NVDI vegetation index for September

max - min NVDI index

annual evaporation

annual rainfall

max of monthly mean temperature maxima

max of monthly mean temperature

mean of monthly means

min of monthly means minima

min of monthly means

max of monthly mean temperature maxima - min of monthly means minima

number of months with temperature < 15.3 degrees

The machine learning algorithms produce the best (CN2) and worst (ITrule) results for this dataset. The decision tree algorithms C4.5, CART, NewID and AC^2 all give rise to fairly accurate classification rules. The modern statistical algorithms, SMART, ALLOC80 and k-NN do significantly better than the classical statistical algorithms (Discrim, Quadisc and Logdisc). With a variable selection procedure k-NN obtains an error rate of 3.8%, again indicating some unhelpful attributes.

Similar work has been done on this dataset by Booth *et al.* (1990) and Ripley (1993) The dataset used by Ripley was slightly different in that the attributes were normalised to be in the range [0,1] over the whole dataset. Also, the train and test sets used in the classification were both samples of size 500 taken from the full dataset, which explains the less accurate results achieved. For example, linear discriminants had an error rate of 13.8%, an algorithm similar to SMART had 10.2%, 1-nearest neighbour had 8.4% and Backprop had 8.4%. The best results for LVQ was 9% and for tree algorithms an error rate of 10% was reduced to 9.6% on pruning.

However, the conclusions of both studies agree. The nearest neighbour and LVQ algorithms work well (although they provide no explanation of the structure in the dataset).

Table 9.29: Results for the tsetse dataset (2 classes, 14 attributes, (train, test) = (3500, 1499) observations).

Algorithm	Max. Storage	Time (sec.) Train	Time (sec.) Test	Error Rate Train	Error Rate Test	Rank
Discrim	69	25.8	3.6	0.120	0.122	20
Quadisc	73	58.5	19.7	0.092	0.098	17
Logdisc	599	139.7	21.9	0.116	0.117	18
SMART	179	7638.0	4.0	0.042	0.047	6
ALLOC80	138	1944.7	*	0.053	0.057	12
k-NN	99	3898.8	276.0	0.053	0.057	12
CASTLE	233	458.0	172.3	0.141	0.137	21
CART	182	63.5	3.8	0.006	0.041	5
IndCART	1071	*	*	0.009	0.039	3
NewID	207	49.0	1.0	0.000	0.040	4
AC^2	2365	2236.0	173.0	0.000	0.047	6
Baytree	979	21.9	2.6	0.001	0.037	2
NaiveBay	811	13.5	2.7	0.128	0.120	19
CN2	6104	468.0	21.0	0.000	0.036	1
C4.5	840	32.0	4.0	0.015	0.049	8
ITrule	199	761.4	3.4	0.233	0.228	22
Cal5	123	49.6	2.4	0.041	0.055	11
Kohonen	*	*	*	0.055	0.075	16
DIPOL92	131	406.1	53.3	0.043	0.053	10
Backprop	144	1196.0	2.0	0.059	0.065	14
RBF	1239	*	*	0.043	0.052	9
LVQ	141	536.5	14.0	0.039	0.065	14
Default	*	*	*	0.492	0.488	23

That the tree-based methods provide a very good and interpretable fit can be seen from the results of AC^2, CART, Cal5 and NewID. Similar error rates were obtained for AC^2 (which used 128 nodes), C4.5 (which used 92 nodes) and NewID (which used 130 nodes). However, Cal5 used only 72 nodes, and achieved a slightly higher error rate, which possibly suggests over-pruning. CASTLE has a high error rate compared with the other algorithms – it appears to use only one attribute to construct the classification rule. The MLP result (Backprop) is directly comparable with the result achieved by Ripley (attribute values were normalised) and gave a slightly better result (error rate 1.9% lower). However, the overall conclusion is the same in that MLPs did about the same as LVQ and nearest-neighbour, both of which are much simpler to use.

9.6   STATISTICAL AND INFORMATION MEASURES

We give, in Tables 9.30 and 9.31, the statistical and information measures as described in Section 7.3.2 and 7.3.3 for all of the datasets. As the calculation of the measures involved substantial computations, some of the measures were calculated for reduced datasets. For example, the measures for KL-digits are based on the training examples only.

The following notes are made for a few of the datasets only and are not meant to be comprehensive. Rather, some instructive points are chosen for illustrating the important ideas contained in the measures.

9.6.1   KL-digits dataset

The dataset that looks closest to being normal is the Karhunen-Loeve version of digits. This could be predicted beforehand, as it is a linear transformation of the attributes that, by the Central Limit Theorem, would be closer to normal than the original. Because there are very many attributes in each linear combination, the KL-digits dataset is very close to normal with skewness = 0.1802, and kurtosis = 2.92, as against the exact normal values of skewness = 0 and kurtosis = 3.0.

Rather interestingly, the **multivariate** kurtosis statistic $kurt\_inv$ for KL digits show a very marked departure from multivariate normality (3.743), despite the fact that the univariate statistics are close to normal (e.g. kurtosis = 2.920). This is not too surprising: it is possible to take a linear transform from Karhunen-Loeve space back to the original highly non-normal dataset. This shows the practical desirability of using a multivariate version of kurtosis.

The KL version of digits appears to be well suited to quadratic discriminants: there is a substantial difference in variances (SD_ratio = 1.9657), while at the same time the distributions are not too far from multivariate normality with kurtosis of order 3. Also, and more importantly, there are sufficient examples that the many parameters of the quadratic discriminants can be estimated fairly accurately.

Also the KL version appears to have a greater difference in variances (SD_ratio=1.9657) than the raw digit data (SD_ratio = 1.5673). This is an artefact: the digits data used here is got by summing over a set of 4×4 pixels. The original digits data, with 256 attributes, had several attributes with zero variances in some classes, giving rise to an infinite value for SD_ratio.

The total of the individual mutual informations for the KL dataset is $40 \times 0.2029 = 8.116$, and this figure can be compared with the corresponding total for the 4x4 digit dataset, namely $16 \times 0.5049 = 8.078$. These datasets are ultimately derived from the same dataset, so it is no surprise that these totals are rather close. However, most algorithms found the KL attributes more informative about class (and so obtained reduced error rates).

9.6.2   Vehicle silhouettes

In the vehicle dataset, the high value of fract2 = 0.9139 might indicate that discrimination could be based on just two discriminants. This may relate to the fact that the two cars are not easily distinguishable, so might be treated as one (reducing dimensionality of the mean vectors to 3D). However, although the fraction of discriminating power for the third discriminant is low (1 - 0.9139), it is still statistically significant, so cannot be discarded without a small loss of discrimination.

This dataset also illustrates that using mean statistics may mask significant differences in behaviour between classes. For example, in the vehicle dataset, for some of the populations (vehicle types 1 and 2), Mardia's kurtosis statistic is not significant. However, for both vehicle types 1 and 2, the univariate statistics are very significantly low, indicating marked departure from normality. Mardia's statistic does not pick this up, partly because the

Table 9.30: Table of measures for datasets

	Cred.Man	Cr.Aust	Dig44	KL	Vehicle
N	20 000	690	18 000	18 000	846
p	7	14	16	40	18
k	2	2	10	10	4
Bin.att	0	4	0	0	0
Cost	0	0	0	0	0
SD	1.0975	1.2623	1.5673	1.9657	1.5392
corr.abs	0.1146	0.1024	0.2119	0.1093	0.4828
cancor1	0.6109	0.7713	0.8929	0.9207	0.8420
cancor2			0.8902	0.9056	0.8189
fract1	1.0000	1.0000	0.2031	0.1720	0.4696
fract2			0.4049	0.3385	0.9139
skewness	6.1012	1.9701	0.8562	0.1802	0.8282
kurtosis	93.1399	12.5538	5.1256	2.9200	5.1800
$H(C)$	0.2893	0.9912	3.3219	3.3219	1.9979
$\bar{H}(X)$	2.7416	2.3012	6.5452	5.5903	4.2472
$\bar{M}(C,X)$	0.0495	0.1130	0.5049	0.2029	0.3538

	Letter	Chrom	SatIm	Segm	CUT
N	20 000	40 000	6435	2310	18 700
p	16	16	36	11	20
k	26	24	6	7	2
Bin.att	0	0	0	0	0
Cost	0	0	0	0	0
SD	1.8795	1.3218	1.2970	4.0014	1.0320
corr.abs	0.2577	0.1885	0.5977	0.1425	0.2178
cancor1	0.8896	0.9884	0.9366	0.9760	0.5500
cancor2	0.8489	0.9191	0.9332	0.9623	
fract1	0.1680	0.1505	0.3586	0.3098	1.0000
fract2	0.3210	0.2807	0.7146	0.6110	
skewness	0.5698	0.4200	0.7316	2.9580	0.9012
kurtosis	3.5385	4.4024	4.1737	24.4813	3.5214
$H(C)$	4.6996	4.5603	2.4734	2.8072	0.3256
$\bar{H}(X)$	3.0940	5.6411	5.5759	3.0787	4.6908
$\bar{M}(C,X)$	0.5189	1.3149	0.9443	0.6672	0.0292

Table 9.31: Table of measures for datasets

	Head	Cr.Ger	Heart	Shuttle	Diab	DNA
N	900	1000	270	58 000	768	3186
p	6	24	13	9	8	180
k	3	2	2	7	2	3
Bin.att	1	9	5	0	0	180
Cost	1	1	1	0	0	0
SD	1.1231	1.0369	1.0612	1.6067	1.0377	1.5407
corr.abs	0.1217	0.0848	0.1236	0.3558	0.1439	0.0456
cancor1	0.7176	0.5044	0.7384	0.9668	0.5507	0.8729
cancor2	0.1057			0.6968		0.8300
fract1	0.9787	1.0000	1.0000	0.6252	1.0000	0.5252
fract2	1.0000			0.9499		1.0000
skewness	1.0071	1.6986	0.9560	4.4371	1.0586	2.5582
kurtosis	5.0408	7.7943	3.6494	160.3108	5.8270	29.5674
$H(C)$	1.3574	0.8813	0.9902	0.9653	0.9331	1.4725
$\bar{H}(X)$	1.9786	1.5031	1.6386	3.4271	4.5301	0.8072
$\bar{M}(C, X)$	0.1929	0.0187	0.0876	0.3348	0.1120	0.0218

	Tech	Belg	BelgII	Faults	Tsetse
N	7078	2500	3000	570	4999
p	56	28	57	45	14
k	91	2	2	3	2
Bin.att	0	0	0	43	0
Cost	0	0	0	0	0
SD	2.2442	1.5124	1.0638	1.1910	1.1316
corr.abs		0.3503	0.1216	0.0751	0.3676
cancor1	0.9165	0.8869	0.5286	0.8842	0.7792
cancor2	0.6818			0.3002	
fract1	0.5575	1.0000	1.0000	0.8966	1.0000
fract2	0.866			1.000	
skewness	6.7156	0.4334	1.1180	1.8972	0.6483
kurtosis	108.2963	2.6581	6.7738	6.9866	4.3322
$H(C)$	4.8787	0.9453	0.3879	1.5749	0.9998
$\bar{H}(X)$	0.3672	5.4853	3.8300	0.8717	3.8755
$\bar{M}(C, X)$	0.1815	0.3172	0.0421	0.0366	0.2850

number of attributes is fairly large in relation to the number of examples per class, and partly because Mardia's statistic is less efficient than the univariate statistics.

9.6.3   Head injury

Among the datasets with more than two classes, the clearest evidence of collinearity is in the head injury dataset. Here the second canonical correlation is not statistically different from zero, with a critical level of $\alpha = 0.074$.

It appears that a single linear discriminant is sufficient to discriminate between the classes (more precisely: a second linear discriminant does not improve discrimination). Therefore the head injury dataset is very close to linearity. This may also be observed from the value of fract1 = 0.979, implying that the three class means lie close to a straight line. In turn, this suggests that the class values reflect some underlying continuum of severity, so this is not a true discrimination problem. Note the similarity with Fisher's original use of discrimination as a means of ordering populations.

Perhaps this dataset would best be dealt with by a pure regression technique, either linear or logistic. If so, Manova gives the best set of scores for the three categories of injury as (0.681,-0.105,-0.725), indicating that the middle group is slightly nearer to category 3 than 1, but not significantly nearer.

It appears that there is not much difference between the covariance matrices for the three populations in the head dataset (SD_ratio = 1.1231), so the procedure quadratic discrimination is not expected to do much better than linear discrimination (and will probably do worse as it uses many more parameters).

9.6.4   Heart disease

The leading correlation coefficient cancor1 = 0.7384 in the heart dataset is not very high (bear in mind that it is correlation^2 that gives a measure of predictability). Therefore the discriminating power of the linear discriminant is only moderate. This ties up with the moderate success of linear discriminants for this dataset (cost for the training data of 0.32).

9.6.5   Satellite image dataset

The satellite image data is the only dataset for which there appears to be very large correlations between the attributes (corr.abs = 0.5977), although there may be some large correlations in the vehicle dataset (but not too many presumably) since here corr.abs = 0.4828.

Note that only three linear discriminants are sufficient to separate all six class means (fract3 = 0.9691). This may be interpreted as evidence of seriation, with the three classes "grey soil", "damp grey soil" and "very damp grey soil" forming a continuum. Equally, this result can be interpreted as indicating that the original 36 attributes may be successfully reduced to three with no loss of information. Here "information" should be interpreted as mean square distance between classes, or equivalently, as the entropy of a normal distribution.

9.6.6   Shuttle control

The class entropy $H(C)$ is 0.965 and this figure gives an effective number of classes of $2^{H(C)} = 1.952$, which is approximately 2. This can be interpreted as follows. Although there are six classes in the shuttle dataset, some class probabilities are very low indeed: so low, in fact, that the complexity of the classification problem is on a par with a two-class problem.

9.6.7   Technical

Although all attributes are nominally continuous, there are very many zeroes, so many that we can regard some of the attributes as nearly constant (and equal to zero). This is shown by the average attribute entropy $\bar{H}(X) = 0.379$, which is substantially less than one bit. The average mutual information $\bar{M}(C, X) = 0.185$ and this is about half of the information carried by each attribute, so that, although the attributes contain little information content, this information contains relatively little noise.

9.6.8   Belgian power II

The Belgian Power II dataset is a prime candidate for data compression as the ratio of noise to useful information is very high (NS.ratio = 137.9). Substantial reduction in the size of the dataset is possible without affecting the accuracy of any classification procedure. This does not mean that the dataset is "noisy" in the sense of not allowing good prediction. The better algorithms achieve an error rate of less than 2% on the existing dataset, and would achieve the same error rate on the condensed dataset. This is particularly true for the decision trees: typically they use only a small number of attributes.

10

Analysis of Results

P. B. Brazdil (1) and R. J. Henery (2)
(1) University of Porto[1] and (2) University of Strathclyde

10.1 INTRODUCTION

We analyse the results of the trials in this chapter using several methods:

- The section on Results by Subject Areas shows that Neural Network and Statistical methods do better in some areas and Machine Learning procedures in others. The idea is to give some indication of the subject areas where certain methods do best.

- Multidimensional Scaling is a method that can be used to point out similarities in both algorithms and datasets using the performance (error-rates) of every combination algorithm $\times$ dataset as a basis. The aim here is to understand the relationship between the various methods.

- We also describe a simple-minded attempt at exploring the relationship between pruning and accuracy of decision trees.

- A principal aim of StatLog was to relate performance of algorithms (usually interpreted as accuracy or error-rate) to characteristics or measures of datasets. Here the aim is to give objective measures describing a dataset and to predict how well any given algorithm will perform on that dataset. We discuss several ways in which this might be done. This includes an empirical study of performance related to statistical and information-theoretic measures of the datasets. In particular, one of the learning algorithms under study (C4.5) is used in an ingenious attempt to predict performance of all algorithms (including C4.5!) from the measures on a given dataset.

- The performance of an algorithm may be predicted by the performance of similar algorithms. If results are already available for a few yardstick methods, the hope is that the performance of other methods can be predicted from the yardstick results.

In presenting these analyses, we aim to give many different views of the results so that a reasonably complete (although perhaps not always coherent) picture can be presented of a very complex problem, namely, the problem of explaining why some algorithms do better

---

[1]*Address for correspondence*: Laboratory of AI and Computer Science (LIACC), University of Porto, R. Campo Alegre 823, 4100 Porto, Portugal

on some datasets and not so well on others. These differing analyses may give conflicting and perhaps irreconcilable conclusions. However, we are not yet at the stage where we can say that this or that analysis is the final and only word on the subject, so we present all the facts in the hope that the reader will be able to judge what is most relevant to the particular application at hand.

10.2   RESULTS BY SUBJECT AREAS

To begin with, the results of the trials will be discussed in subject areas. This is partly because this makes for easier description and interpretation, but, more importantly, because the performance of the various algorithms is much influenced by the particular application. Several datasets are closely related, and it is easier to spot differences when comparisons are made within the same dataset type. So we will discuss the results under four headings:

- Datasets Involving Costs
- Credit Risk Datasets
- Image Related Datasets
- Others

Of course, these headings are not necessarily disjoint: one of our datasets (German credit) was a credit dataset involving costs. The feature dominating performance of algorithms is costs, so the German credit dataset is listed under the Cost datasets.

We do not attempt to give any absolute assessment of accuracies, or average costs. But we have listed the algorithms in each heading by their average ranking within this heading. Algorithms at the top of the table do well, on average, and algorithms at the bottom do badly.

To illustrate how the ranking was calculated, consider the two (no-cost) credit datasets. Because, for example, Cal5 is ranked 1st in the Australian.credit and 4th in the credit management dataset, Cal5 has a total rank of 5, which is the smallest total of all, and Cal5 is therefore top of the listing in the Credit datasets. Similarly, DIPOL92 has a total rank of 7, and so is 2nd in the list.

Of course, other considerations, such as memory storage, time to learn etc., must not be forgotten. In this chapter, we take only error-rate or average cost into account.

10.2.1   Credit datasets

We have results for two credit datasets. In two of these, the problem is to predict the creditworthiness of applicants for credit, but they are all either coded or confidential to a greater or lesser extent. So, for example, we do not know the exact definition of "uncreditworthy" or "bad risk". Possible definitions are (i) "More than one month late with the first payment"; (ii) "More than two months late with the first payment"; or even (iii) "The (human) credit manager has already refused credit to this person".

- Credit Management. Credit management data from the UK (confidential).
- German. Credit risk data from Germany.
- Australian. Credit risk data from (Quinlan, 1993)

It may be that these classifications are defined by a human: if so, then the aim of the decision rule is to devise a procedure that mimics the human decision process as closely as possible. Machine Learning procedures are very good at this, and this probably reflects a natural tendency for human decisions to be made in a sequential manner. It is then correspondingly easy for a human to understand the Decision Tree methods as this best reflects the human decision process.

Costs of misclassification

In two of our credit datasets, we were unable to assess either the prior odds of good-bad or the relative costs of making the wrong decisions. However, in the German credit data, we were given an independent assessment that the relative cost of granting credit to a bad risk customer was 5 times that of turning down an application from a good risk customer, or $c(g, b)/c(b, g) = 5$, where $c(b, g)$ is the cost of misclassifying a bad credit risk as good and $c(g, b)$ is the cost of misclassifying a good credit risk as bad. (Implicitly, we assume that the proportions of good-bad risks in the training sample reflect those in the population). Also, in the credit management dataset, it was explicitly stated by the dataset provider that errors of either type were equally important - a statement that we interpreted to mean that the cost-ratio was unity.

On the other hand, the definition of "bad" risk may be defined by the lateness of payments, or non-payment. The task here is to assess the degree of risk. Most datasets of this nature lose much useful information by binarising some measure of badness. For example, a customer may be classed as a "bad" risk if the first repayment is more than one month late, whereas a more natural approach would be to predict the number of months before the first payment is made. The StatLog versions of Machine Learning methods were not generally well adapted to prediction problems however. Apart from anything else, prediction problems involve some cost function (usually but not necessarily quadratic): the important point is that some errors are more serious than others.

Generally in credit risk assessment, the cost of misclassification is a vital element. The classification of a bad credit risk as good usually costs more than classification of a good credit risk as bad. Unfortunately, credit institutes cannot give precise estimates of the cost of misclassification. On the other hand, many of the algorithms in this study cannot use a cost matrix in performing the classification task, although there have recently been some attempts to consider misclassification costs in learning algorithms such NewID and C4.5 (see Knoll, 1993). If we were to judge learning algorithms solely on the basis of average misclassification cost, this would penalise the ML algorithms. In some of the datasets therefore, we used the average error rate instead: this is equivalent to average misclassification cost in a very special case as we will now show.

Recall that $c(b, g)$ is the cost of misclassifying a bad credit risk as good and $c(g, b)$ is the cost of misclassifying a good credit risk as bad. Suppose also that $E(b)$ and $E(g)$ are the error rates in the classification of bad and good risks, respectively. Denoting the prior probabilities of good and bad risks by π_g and π_b, we can calculate the expected cost of misclassification as :

$$K = c(b, g)\pi_b E(b) + c(g, b)\pi_g E(g) \tag{10.1}$$

As mentioned above, in practice it is very difficult to find out the values of $c(b, g)$ and $c(g, b)$ (see for example Srinivisan & Sim, 1987). Because of this, it is often assumed that

$$\frac{c(b, g)}{c(g, b)} = \frac{\pi_g}{\pi_b} \tag{10.2}$$

Using assumption (10.2), one can get the expected misclassification cost K from equation
(10.1)

$$K = c(b, g)\pi_b[E(b) + E(g)] \tag{10.3}$$

In equation (10.3) the factor $c(b, g)\pi_b$ is the same for all algorithms, so one can use the
total error rate ϕ

$$\phi = E(b) + E(g)$$

as an equivalent evaluation criterion when comparing the performance of algorithms.

Results and conclusions

Table 10.1: Error rates for Credit Datasets ordered by their average rank over the datasets.

credit	Cr.Aus	Cr.Man
CAL5	0.131	0.023
DIPOL92	0.141	0.020
Logdisc	0.141	0.030
SMART	0.158	0.020
C4.5	0.155	0.022
IndCART	0.152	0.025
Bprop	0.154	0.023
Discrim	0.141	0.033
RBF	0.145	0.031
Baytree	0.171	0.028
ITrule	0.137	0.046
AC2	0.181	0.030
k-NN	0.181	0.031
Naivebay	0.151	0.043
CASTLE	0.148	0.047
ALLOC80	0.201	0.031
CART	0.145	
NewID	0.181	0.033
CN2	0.204	0.032
LVQ	0.197	0.040
Kohonen		0.043
Quadisc	0.207	0.050
Default	0.440	0.050

The table of error rates for the credit datasets is given in Table 10.1. In reading this table,
the reader should beware that:

- Not much can be inferred from only two cases *re* the suitability of this or that algorithm
  for credit datasets generally;

- In real credit applications, differential misclassification costs tend to loom large, if not
  explicitly then by implication.

It is noteworthy that three of the top six algorithms are decision trees (Cal5, C4.5 and
IndCART), while the algorithm in second place (DIPOL92) is akin to a neural network.
We may conclude that decision trees do reasonably well on credit datasets. This conclusion

would probably be strengthened if we had persuaded CART to run on the credit management dataset, as it is likely that the error rate for CART would be fairly similar to IndCART's value, and then CART would come above IndCART in this table. However, where values were missing, as is the case with CART, the result was assumed to be the default value - an admittedly very conservative procedure, so CART appears low down in Table 10.1.

By itself, the conclusion that decision trees do well on credit datasets, while giving some practical guidance on a specific application area, does not explain why decision trees should be successful here. A likely explanation is that both datasets are partitioning datasets. This is known to be true for the credit management dataset where a human classified the data on the basis of the attributes. We suspect that it holds for the other credit dataset also, in view of the following facts: (i) they are both credit datasets; (ii) they are near each other in the multidimensional scaling representation of all datasets; and (iii) they are similar in terms of number of attributes, number of classes, presence of categorical attributes etc. Part of the reason for their success in this subject area is undoubtedly that decision tree methods can cope more naturally with a large number of binary or categorical attributes (provided the number of categories is small). They also incorporate interaction terms as a matter of course. And, perhaps more significantly, they mirror the human decision process.

10.2.2   Image datasets

Image classification problems occur in a wide variety of contexts. In some applications, the entire image (or an object in the image) must be classified, whereas in other cases the classification proceeds on a pixel-by-pixel basis (possibly with extra spatial information). One of the first problems to be tackled was of LANDSAT data, where Switzer (1980, 1983) considered classification of each pixel in a spatial context. A similar dataset was used in our trials, whereby the attributes (but not the class) of neighbouring pixels was used to aid the classification (Section 9.3.6). A further image segmentation problem, of classifying each pixel is considered in Section 9.3.7. An alternative problem is to classify the entire image into one of several classes. An example of this is object recognition, for example classifying a hand-written character (Section 9.3.1), or a remotely sensed vehicle (Section 9.3.3). Another example in our trials is the classification of chromosomes (Section 9.3.5), based on a number of features extracted from an image.

There are different "levels" of image data. At the simplest level we can consider the grey values at each pixel as the set of variables to classify each pixel, or the whole image. Our trials suggest that the latter are not likely to work unless the image is rather small; for example classifying a hand-written number on the basis of 16×16 grey levels defeated most of our algorithms. The pixel data can be further processed to yield a sharper image, or other information which is still pixel-based, for example a gradient filter can be used to extract edges. A more promising approach to classify images is to extract and select appropriate features and the vehicle silhouette (Section 9.3.3) and chromosome (Section 9.3.5) datasets are of this type. The issue of extracting the right features is a harder problem. The temptation is to measure everything which may be useful but additional information which is not relevant may spoil the performance of a classifier. For example, the nearest neighbour method typically treats all variables with equal weight, and if some are of no value then very poor results can occur. Other algorithms are more robust to this pitfall.

For presentation purposes we will categorise each of the nine image datasets as being one of Segmentation or Object Recognition, and we give the results of the two types separately.

Results and conclusions: Object Recognition

Table 10.2: Error rates for Object Recognition Datasets. Algorithms are listed in order of their average ranking over the five datasets. Algorithms near the top tend to do well at object recognition.

object	KL	Digits	Vehic	Chrom	Letter
Quadisc	0.025	0.054	0.150	0.084	0.113
k-NN	0.020	0.047	0.275	0.123	0.070
DIPOL92	0.039	0.072	0.151	0.091	0.176
LVQ	0.026	0.061	0.287	0.121	0.079
ALLOC80	0.024	0.068	0.173	0.253	0.064
Logdiscr	0.051	0.086	0.192	0.131	0.234
Discrim	0.075	0.114	0.216	0.107	0.302
SMART	0.057	0.104	0.217	0.128	0.295
RBF	0.055	0.083	0.307	0.129	0.233
Baytree	0.163	0.140	0.271	0.164	0.124
Backprop	0.049	0.080	0.207		0.327
CN2	0.180	0.134	0.314	0.150	0.115
C4.5	0.180	0.149	0.266	0.175	0.132
NewID	0.162	0.150	0.298	0.176	0.128
IndCART	0.170	0.154	0.298	0.173	0.130
Cascade	0.075	0.065	0.280		
AC^2	0.168	0.155	0.296	0.234	0.245
Kohonen		0.075	0.340	0.174	0.252
CASTLE	0.135	0.170	0.505	0.178	0.245
Cal5	0.270	0.220	0.279	0.244	0.253
CART		0.160	0.235		
ITrule	0.216	0.222	0.324	0.697	0.594
NaiveBay	0.223	0.233	0.558	0.324	0.529
Default	0.900	0.900	0.750	0.960	0.960

Table 10.2 gives the error-rates for the five object recognition datasets. It is believed that this group contains pure discrimination datasets (digit, vehicle and letter recognition). On these datasets, standard statistical procedures and neural networks do well overall.

It would be wrong to draw general conclusions from only five datasets but we can make the following points. The proponents of backpropagation claim that it has a special ability to model non-linear behaviour. Some of these datasets have significant non-linearity and it is true that backpropagation does well. However, in the case of the digits it performs only marginally better than quadratic discriminants, which can also model non-linear behaviour, and in the case of the vehicles it performs significantly worse. When one considers the large amount of extra effort required to optimise and train backpropagation one must ask whether it really offers an advantage over more traditional algorithms. Ripley (1993) also raises some important points on the use and claims of Neural Net methods.

CASTLE performs poorly but this is probably because it is not primarily designed for discrimination. Its main advantage is that it gives an easily comprehensible picture of the structure of the data. It indicates which variables influence one another most strongly and can identify which subset of attributes are the most strongly connected to the decision class. However, it ignores weak connections and this is the reason for its poor performance, in that weak connections may still have an influence on the final decision class.

SMART and linear discriminants perform similarly on these datasets. Both of these work with linear combinations of the attributes, although SMART is more general in that it takes non-linear functions of these combinations. However, quadratic discriminants performs rather better which suggests that a better way to model non-linearity would be to input selected quadratic combinations of attributes to linear discriminants.

The nearest neighbour algorithm does well if all the variables are useful in classification and if there are no problems in choosing the right scaling. Raw pixel data such as the satellite data and the hand-written digits satisfy these criteria. If some of the variables are misleading or unhelpful then a variable selection procedure should precede classification. The algorithm used here was not efficient in cpu time, since no condensing was used. Results from Ripley (1993) indicate that condensing does not greatly affect the classification performance.

Paired Comparison on Digits Data: KL and the 4x4 digits data represent different preprocessed versions of one and the same original dataset. Not unexpectedly, there is a high correlation between the error-rates (0.944 with two missing values: CART and Kohonen on KL).

Of much more interest is the fact that the statistical and neural net procedures perform much better on the KL version than on the 4x4 version. On the other hand, Machine Learning methods perform rather poorly on the 4x4 version and do even worse on the KL version. It is rather difficult to account for this phenomenon. ML methods, by their nature, do not seem to cope with situations where the information is spread over a large number of variables. By construction, the Karhunen-Loeve dataset deliberately creates variables that are linear combinations of the original pixel gray levels, with the first variable containing "most" information, the second variable containing the maximum information orthogonal to the first, etc.. From one point of view therefore, the first 16 KL attributes contain more information than the complete set of 16 attributes in the 4x4 digit dataset (as the latter is a particular set of linear combinations of the original data), and the improvement in error rates of the statistical procedures is consistent with this interpretation.

Results and conclusions: Segmentation

Table 10.3 gives the error rates for the four segmentation problems. Machine Learning procedures do fairly well in segmentation datasets, and traditional statistical methods do very badly. The probable explanation is that these datasets originate as partitioning problems.

Paired Comparison of Cut20 and Cut50: The dataset Cut20 consists of the first 20 attributes in the Cut50 dataset ordered by importance in a stepwise regression procedure. One would therefore expect, and generally one observes, that performance deteriorates when the number of attributes is decreased (so that the information content is decreased). One exception to this rule is quadratic discrimination which does badly in the Cut20 dataset and even worse in the Cut50 data. This is the converse of the paired comparison in the digits

Table 10.3: Error rates for Segmentation Datasets. Algorithms are listed in order of their average ranking over the four datasets. Algorithms near the top tend to do well in image segmentation problems.

segment	Satim	Segm	Cut20	Cut50
ALLOC80	0.132	0.030	0.037	0.034
Baytree	0.147	0.033	0.034	0.035
k-NN	0.094	0.077	0.036	0.027
DIPOL92	0.111	0.039	0.045	0.036
C4.5	0.150	0.040	0.036	0.035
NewID	0.150	0.034	0.039	0.038
CN2	0.150	0.043	0.042	0.030
IndCART	0.138	0.045	0.040	0.037
LVQ	0.105	0.046	0.041	0.040
RBF	0.121	0.069	0.044	0.038
Backprop	0.139	0.054	0.043	0.041
Cal5	0.151	0.062	0.045	0.037
SMART	0.159	0.052	0.047	0.039
AC^2	0.157	0.031	0.063	0.054
Logdisc	0.163	0.109	0.046	0.037
CART	0.138	0.040		
Kohonen	0.179	0.067	0.050	0.050
Discrim	0.171	0.116	0.050	0.050
CASTLE	0.194	0.112	0.061	0.061
Quadisc	0.155	0.157	0.088	0.097
Default	0.760	0.857	0.060	0.060
NaiveBay	0.287	0.265	0.077	0.112
ITrule		0.455	0.082	0.084
Cascade	0.163			

dataset: it appears that algorithms that are already doing badly on the most informative set of attributes do even worse when the less informative attributes are added.

Similarly, Machine Learning methods do better on the Cut50 dataset, but there is a surprise: they use smaller decision trees to achieve greater accuracy. This must mean that some of the "less significant" attributes contribute to the discrimination by means of interactions (or non-linearities). Here the phrase "less significant" is used in a technical sense, referring to the least informative attributes in linear discriminants. Clearly attributes that have little information for linear discriminants may have considerable value for other procedures that are capable of incorporating interactions and non-linearities directly.

k-NN is best for images

Perhaps the most striking result in the images datasets is the performance of k-nearest neighbour, with four outright top places and two runners-up. It would seem that, in terms of error-rate, best results in image data are obtained by k-nearest neighbour.

10.2.3   Datasets with costs

There are two medical datasets and one credit dataset in this section. These are illustrative of the application areas where costs are important. There are two ways in which algorithms can incorporate costs into a decision rule: at the learning stage or during the test stage. Most statistical procedures are based on estimates of probabilities, and incorporate costs only at the final test stage (in evaluating the expected cost of misclassification). However, some procedures can incorporate costs into the learning stage. One simple way to do this might be to give extra weight to observations from classes with high costs of misclassification.

Results and conclusions

Table 10.4: Average costs for Datasets with Cost Matrices. Algorithms are listed in order of their average ranking over the three datasets. Algorithms near the bottom cannot cope with costs.

costs	Head	Heart	Cr.Ger
Discrim	19.890	0.393	0.535
Logdisc	17.960	0.396	0.538
CASTLE	20.870	0.441	0.583
Quadisc	20.060	0.422	0.619
ALLOC80	31.900	0.407	0.584
CART	20.380	0.452	0.613
NaiveBay	23.950	0.374	0.703
SMART	21.810	0.478	0.601
Cal5	33.260	0.444	0.603
DIPOL92	26.520	0.507	0.599
k-NN	35.300	0.478	0.694
Cascade	19.500	0.467	
Backprop	21.530	0.574	0.772
Baytree	22.690	0.526	0.778
IndCART	25.520	0.630	0.761
Default	44.100	0.560	0.700
ITrule	37.610	0.515	0.879
LVQ	46.580	0.600	0.963
CN2	53.550	0.767	0.856
AC^2	56.870	0.744	0.878
NewID	53.640	0.844	0.925
Kohonen		0.693	1.160
RBF	63.100	0.781	0.971
C4.5	82.600	0.781	0.985

The average costs of the various algorithms are given in Table 10.4. There are some surprises in this table, particularly relating to the default procedure and the performance of most Machine Learning and some of the Neural Network procedures. Overall, it would seem that the ML procedures do worse than the default (of granting credit to everyone, or declaring everyone to be seriously ill).

10.2.4   Other datasets

Table 10.5: Error rates for remaining datasets. The shuttle error rates are in %. Algorithms are listed in order of their average ranking over the eight datasets. Most of the problems in the table are partitioning problems, so it is fairly safe to say that algorithms near the top of the table are most suited to partitioning problems.

others	Belg	NewBel	Tset	Diab	DNA	Faults	Shutt	Tech
DIPOL92	.018	.026	.053	.224	.048	.191	.480	.192
Baytree	.030	.014	.037	.271	.095	.283	.020	.174
NewID	.027	.017	.040	.289	.100	.304	.010	.090
IndCART	.034	.014	.039	.271	.073	.335	.090	.095
AC^2	.034	.019	.047	.276	.100	.174	.320	.102
C4.5	.040	.018	.049	.270	.076	.305	.100	.120
Cal5	.029	.026	.055	.250	.131	.297	.030	.183
SMART	.006	.013	.047	.232	.141	.339	.590	.366
Logdisc	.007	.028	.117	.223	.061	.221	3.830	.401
CN2	.032	.025	.036	.289	.095	.354	.030	.123
CART	.034	.022	.041	.255	.085	.318	.080	
Backprop	.017	.022	.065	.248	.088	.228	.430	
RBF	.034	.035	.052	.243	.041	.320	1.400	.324
Discrim	.025	.041	.122	.225	.059	.204	4.830	.391
Quadisc	.052	.035	.098	.262	.059	.293	6.720	.495
ALLOC80	.044	.045	.057	.301	.057	.339	.830	
NaiveBay	.062	.089	.120	.262	.068	.274	4.500	.354
CASTLE	.047	.064	.137	.258	.072	.318	3.800	
k-NN	.059	.052	.057	.324	.155	.375	.440	.204
ITrule	.065	.081	.228	.245	.135	.330	.410	
LVQ	.054	.065	.065	.272		.444	.440	.261
Kohonen	.056	.084	.075	.273	.339	.472		.357
Default	.362	.074	.490	.350	.480	.610	21.400	.770

Of the remaining datasets, at least two (shuttle and technical) are pure partitioning problems, with boundaries characteristically parallel to the attribute axes, a fact that can be judged from plots of the attributes. Two are simulated datasets (Belgian and Belgian Power II), and can be described as somewhere between prediction and partitioning. The aim of the tsetse dataset can be precisely stated as partitioning a map into two regions, so as to reproduce a given partitioning as closely as possible. The tsetse dataset is also artificial insofar as some of the attributes have been manufactured (by an interpolation from a small amount of information). The Diabetes dataset is a prediction problem.

The nature of the other datasets (DNA, Machine Faults), *i.e.* whether we are dealing with partitioning, prediction or discrimination, is not known precisely.

Results and conclusions

Table 10.5 gives the error-rates for these eight datasets. It is perhaps inappropriate to draw general conclusions from such a mixed bag of datasets. However, it would appear, from the performance of the algorithms, that the datasets are best dealt with by Machine Learning or Neural Network procedures. How much relevance this has to practical problems is debatable however, as two are simulated and two are pure partitioning datasets.

10.3 TOP FIVE ALGORITHMS

In Table 10.6 we present the algorithms that came out top for each of the 22 datasets. Only the top five algorithms are quoted. The table is quoted for reference only, so that readers can see which algorithms do well on a particular dataset. The algorithms that make the top five most frequently are DIPOL92 (12 times), ALLOC80 (11), Discrim (9), Logdiscr and Quadisc (8), but not too much should be made of these figures as they depend very much on the mix of problems used.

Table 10.6: Top five algorithms for all datasets.

Dataset	First	Second	Third	Fourth	Fifth
KL	k-NN	ALLOC80	Quadisc	LVQ	DIPOL92
Dig44	k-NN	Quadisc	LVQ	Cascade	ALLOC80
Satim	k-NN	LVQ	DIPOL92	RBF	ALLOC80
Vehic	Quadisc	DIPOL92	ALLOC80	Logdiscr	Bprop
Head	Logdiscr	Cascade	Discrim	Quadisc	CART
Heart	Naivebay	Discrim	Logdiscr	ALLOC80	Quadisc
Belg	SMART	Logdiscr	Bprop	DIPOL92	Discrim
Segm	ALLOC80	AC2	Baytree	NewID	DIPOL92
Diab	Logdiscr	DIPOL92	Discrim	SMART	RBF
Cr.Ger	Discrim	Logdiscr	CASTLE	ALLOC80	DIPOL92
Chrom	Quadisc	DIPOL92	Discrim	LVQ	k-NN
Cr.Aus	CAL5	ITrule	Discrim	Logdiscr	DIPOL92
Shutt	NewID	Baytree	CN2	CAL5	CART
DNA	RBF	DIPOL92	ALLOC80	Discrim	Quadisc
Tech	NewID	IndCART	AC2	C4.5	CN2
NewBel	SMART	IndCART	Baytree	NewID	C4.5
ISoft	AC2	DIPOL92	Discrim	Logdiscr	Bprop
Tset	CN2	Baytree	IndCART	NewID	CART
cut20	Baytree	k-NN	C4.5	ALLOC80	NewID
cut50	k-NN	CN2	ALLOC80	Baytree	C4.5
Cr.Man	SMART	DIPOL92	C4.5	CAL5	Bprop
letter	ALLOC80	k-NN	LVQ	Quadisc	CN2

Table 10.7 gives the same information as Table 10.6, but here it is the type of algorithm (Statistical, Machine Learning or Neural Net) that is quoted.

In the Head injury dataset, the top five algorithms are all Statistical, whereas the top five are all Machine Learning for the Shuttle and Technical datasets. Between these two extremes, there is a variety. Table 10.8 orders the datasets by the number of Machine Learning, Statistical or Neural Network algorithms that are in the top five.

From inspection of the frequencies in Table 10.8, it appears that Neural Networks and Statistical procedures do well on the same kind of datasets. In other words, Neural Nets tend to do well when statistical procedures do well and vice versa. As an objective measure of this tendency, a correspondence analysis can be used. Correspondence analysis attempts

Table 10.7: Top five algorithms for all datasets, by type: Machine Learning (ML); Statistics (Stat); and Neural Net (NN).

Dataset	First	Second	Third	Fourth	Fifth
KL	Stat	Stat	Stat	NN	NN
Dig44	Stat	Stat	NN	NN	Stat
Satim	Stat	NN	NN	NN	Stat
Vehic	Stat	NN	Stat	Stat	NN
Head	Stat	NN	Stat	Stat	ML
Heart	Stat	Stat	Stat	Stat	Stat
Belg	Stat	Stat	NN	NN	Stat
Segm	Stat	ML	ML	ML	NN
Diab	Stat	NN	Stat	Stat	NN
Cr.Ger	Stat	Stat	Stat	Stat	NN
Chrom	Stat	NN	Stat	NN	Stat
Cr.Aus	ML	ML	Stat	Stat	NN
Shutt	ML	ML	ML	ML	ML
DNA	NN	NN	Stat	Stat	Stat
Tech	ML	ML	ML	ML	ML
NewBel	Stat	ML	ML	ML	ML
ISoft	ML	NN	Stat	Stat	NN
Tset	ML	ML	ML	ML	ML
cut20	ML	Stat	ML	Stat	ML
cut50	Stat	ML	Stat	ML	ML
Cr.Man	Stat	NN	ML	ML	NN
letter	Stat	Stat	NN	Stat	ML

to give scores to the rows (here datasets) and columns (here procedure types) of an array with positive entries in such a way that the scores are mutually consistent and maximally correlated. For a description of correspondence analysis, see Hill (1982) and Mardia *et al.* (1979) . It turns out that the optimal scores for columns 2 and 3 (neural net and statistical procedures) are virtually identical, but these are quite different from the score of column 1 (the ML procedures). It would appear therefore that neural nets are more similar to statistical procedures than to ML. In passing we may note that the optimal scores that are given to the datasets may be used to give an ordering to the datasets, and this ordering can be understood as a measure of how suited the dataset is to ML procedures. If the same scores are allocated to neural net and statistical procedures, the corresponding ordering of the datasets is exactly that given in the table, with datasets at the bottom being more of type ML.

10.3.1   Dominators

It is interesting to note that some algorithms always do better than the default (among the datasets we have looked at). There are nine such: Discrim, Logdisc, SMART, k-NN, ALLOC80, CART, Cal5, DIPOL92 and Cascade. These algorithms "dominate" the default strategy. Also, in the seven datasets on which Cascade was run, ITrule is dominated by Cascade. The only other case of an algorithm being dominated by others is Kohonen: it

Table 10.8: Datasets ordered by algorithm type. Datasets at the top are most suited to Statistical and Neural Net procedures: Datasets at the bottom most suited to Machine Learning.

Dataset	ML	NN	Stat
Heart	0	0	5
Cr.Ger	0	1	4
KL	0	2	3
Dig44	0	2	3
Vehic	0	2	3
Belg	0	2	3
Diab	0	2	3
Chrom	0	2	3
DNA	0	2	3
Satim	0	3	2
Head	1	1	3
letter	1	1	3
ISoft	1	2	2
Cr.Aus	2	1	2
Cr.Man	2	2	1
cut20	3	0	2
cut50	3	0	2
Segm	3	1	1
NewBel	4	0	1
Shutt	5	0	0
Tech	5	0	0
Tset	5	0	0

is dominated by DIPOL92, Cascade and LVQ. These comparisons do not include datasets where results is missing (NA), so we should really say: "Where results are available, Kohonen is always worse than DIPOL92 and LVQ". Since we only have results for 7 Cascade trials, the comparison Cascade-Kohonen is rather meaningless.

10.4   MULTIDIMENSIONAL SCALING

It would be possible to combine the results of all the trials to rank the algorithms by overall success rate or average success rate, but not without some rather arbitrary assumptions to equate error rates with costs. We do not attempt to give such an ordering, as we believe that this is not profitable. We prefer to give a more objective approach based on multidimensional scaling (an equivalent procedure would be correspondence analysis). In so doing, the aim is to demonstrate the close relationships between the algorithms, and, at the same time, the close similarities between many of the datasets. Multidimensional scaling has no background theory: it is an exploratory tool for suggesting relationships in data rather than testing pre-chosen hypotheses. There is no agreed criterion which tells us if the scaling is successful, although there are generally accepted guidelines.

10.4.1 Scaling of algorithms

To apply multidimensional scaling, the first problem, paradoxically, is to scale the variables. The idea is to scale the error-rates and average costs in such a way that each dataset carries equal weight. This is not easy. In each dataset, we rescaled so that the error-rate (or average cost) had a minimum of zero and a maximum of unity. Such a rescaling is arbitrary, and can only be justified a posteriori, insofar as the results confirm known relationships. Once the initial scaling has been done, distances between all pairs of algorithms must be computed. Distance was taken to be the Euclidean distance between the rescaled error-rates on the 22 datasets. This results in a distance matrix representing distances between all pairs of algorithms in 23-dimensional space. The distance matrix can then be decomposed, by an orthogonal decomposition, into distances in a reduced space. Most conveniently, the dimensions of the reduced space are chosen to be two, so that the algorithms can be represented as points in a 2-dimensional plot. This plot is given in Figure 10.1.

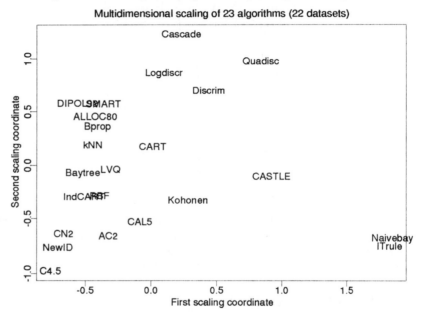

Fig. 10.1: Multidimensional scaling representation of algorithms in the 22-dimensional space (each dimension is an error rate or average cost measured on a given dataset). Points near to each other in this 2-D plot are not necessarily close in 22-D.

Whether the 2-dimensional plot is a good picture of 22-dimensional space can be judged from a comparison of the set of distances in 2-D compared to the set of distances in 22-D. One simple way to measure the goodness of the representation is to compare the total squared distances. Let D_2 be the total of the squared distances taken over all pairs of points in the 2-dimensional plot, and let D_{22} be the total squared distances over all pairs of points in 22-dimensions. The "stress" σ is defined to be $1 - D_2/D_{22}$. For Figure 10.1 the "stress" figure is 0.266. Considering the number of initial dimensions is very high, this is a reasonably small "stress", although we should say that, conventionally, the "stress" is said to be small when less than 0.05. With a 3-dimensional representation, the stress factor would be 0.089, indicating that it would be more sensible to think of algorithms differing in at least 3-dimensions. A three-dimensional representation would raise the prospect of representing all results in terms of three scaling coordinates which might be interpretable as error-rates of three (perhaps notional) algorithms.

Because the stress figure is low relative to the number of dimensions, points near each other in Figure 10.1 probably represent algorithms that are similar in performance. For example, the Machine Learning methods CN2, NewID and IndCART are very close to each other, and in general, all the machine learning procedures are close in Figure 10.1. Before jumping to the conclusion that they are indeed similar, it is as well to check the tables of results (although the stress is low, it is not zero so the distances in Figure 10.1 are approximate only). Looking at the individual tables, the reader should see that, for example, CN2, NewID and IndCART tend to come at about the same place in every table apart from a few exceptions. So strong is this similarity, that one is tempted to say that marked deviations from this general pattern should be regarded with suspicion and should be double checked.

10.4.2   Hierarchical clustering of algorithms

Hierarchical Clustering - 23 algorithms (22 datasets)

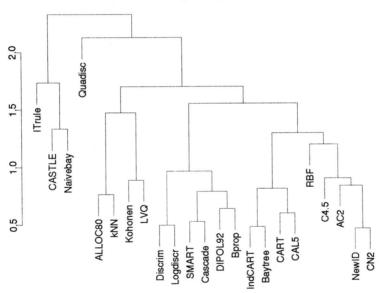

Fig. 10.2: Hierarchical clustering of algorithms using standardised error rates and costs.

There is another way to look at relationships between the algorithms based on the set of paired distances, namely by a hierarchical clustering of the algorithms. The resulting Figure 10.2 does indeed capture known similarities (linear and logistic discriminants are very close), and is very suggestive of other relationships.

It is to be expected that some of the similarities picked up by the clustering procedure will be accidental. In any case, algorithms should not be declared as similar on the basis of empirical evidence alone, and true understanding of the relationships will follow only when theoretical grounds are found for similarities in behaviour.

Finally, we should say something about some *dissimilarities*. There are some surprising "errors" in the clusterings of Figure 10.2. For example, CART and IndCART are attached to slightly different clusterings. This is a major surprise, and we do have ideas on why this is indeed true, but, nonetheless, CART and IndCART were grouped together in Tables 10.1-10.5 to facilitate comparisons between the two.

10.4.3   Scaling of datasets

The same set of re-scaled error rates may be used to give a 2-dimensional plot of datasets. From a formal point of view, the multidimensional scaling procedure is applied to the transpose of the matrix of re-scaled error rates. The default algorithm was excluded from this exercise as distances from this to the other algorithms were going to dominate the picture.

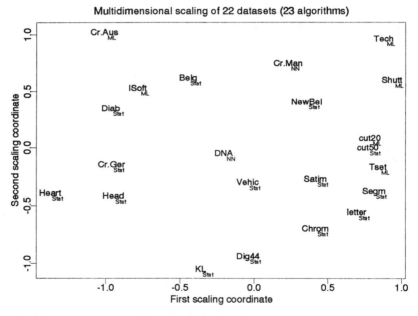

Fig. 10.3: Multidimensional scaling representation of the Datasets in 23-dimensional space (each dimension is an error rate and cost achieved by a particular algorithms). The symbols ML, NN and Stat below each dataset indicate which type of algorithm achieved the lowest error-rate or cost on that dataset. Datasets near to each other in this 2-D plot are not necessarily close in 23-D.

Figure 10.3 is a multidimensional scaling representation of the error rates and costs given in Tables 10.1-10.5. Each dataset in Tables 10.1-10.5 is described by a point in 23-dimensional space, the coordinates of which are the (scaled) error rates or costs of the various algorithms. To help visualise the relationships between the points (datasets), they have been projected down to 2-dimensions in such a way as to preserve their mutual distances as much as possible. This projection is fairly successful as the "stress" factor is only 0.149 (a value of 0.01 is regarded as excellent, a value of 0.05 is good). Again, a 3-dimensional representation might be more "acceptable" with a stress factor of 0.063. Such a 3-D representation could be interpreted as saying that datasets differ in three essentially orthogonal ways, and is suggestive of a description of datasets using just three measures. This idea is explored further in the next subsection.

Several interesting similarities are obvious from Figure 10.3. The Costs datasets are close to each other, as are the two types of image datasets. In addition, the credit datasets are all at the top of the diagram (except for the German credit data which involves costs). The two pathologically partitioned datasets Shuttle and Technical are together at the extreme top right of the diagram.

In view of these similarities, it is tempting to classify datasets of unknown origin by their proximities to other datasets of known provenance. For example, the Diabetes dataset is somewhere between a partitioning type dataset (cf. credit data) and a prediction type dataset (cf. head injury).

Interpretation of Scaling Coordinates

The plotting coordinates for the 2-dimensional description of datasets in Figure 10.3 are derived by orthogonal transformation of the original error rates/costs. These coordinates clearly represent distinctive features of the datasets as similar datasets are grouped together in the diagram. This suggests either that the scaling coordinates might be used as characteristics of the datasets, or, equivalently, might be related to characteristics of the datasets. This suggests that we look at these coordinates and try to relate them to the dataset measures that we defined in Chapter 7. For example, it turns out that the first scaling coordinate is positively correlated with the number of examples in the dataset. In Figure 10.3, this means that there is a tendency for the larger datasets to lie to the right of the diagram. The second scaling coordinate is correlated with the curious ratio kurtosis/q, where q is the number of classes. This implies that a dataset with small kurtosis and large number of classes will tend to lie in the bottom half of Figure 10.3. However, the correlations are quite weak, and in any case only relate to a subspace of two dimensions with a "stress" of 0.149, so we cannot say that these measures capture the essential differences between datasets.

10.4.4   Best algorithms for datasets

In Figure 10.3, each dataset has been labelled by the type of algorithm that does best on that particular dataset. For example, the algorithm AC^2 (of type ML) comes out top on the Faults dataset, so the dataset Faults has the label ML attached. Inspecting Figure 10.3, a very clear pattern emerges. Machine Learning procedures generally do best on datasets at the top or at the extreme right of the diagram. Statistical and Neural Network procedures do best on datasets in the lower half and to the left of the diagram. Of course, this pattern is very closely related to the fact that datasets from particular application areas are clustered together.

In the spirit of Correspondence Analysis, it would be possible to use the scaling coordinates of datasets or algorithms to come up with a mutually consistent set of coordinates that express the relationships between datasets and algorithms. This can be done, but there are too many missing values in the tables for the usual version of correspondence analysis (no missing values allowed).

10.4.5 Clustering of datasets

Starting from the distances in 23-dimensions, a standard clustering algorithm (using the furthest neighbour option) gives the clustering of Figure 10.4.

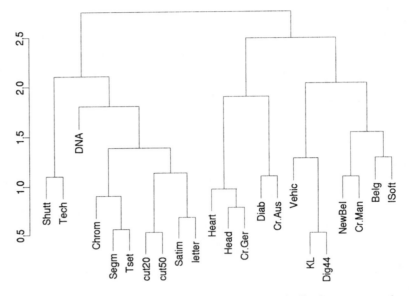

Fig. 10.4: Hierarchical clustering of datasets based on standardised error rates and costs.

10.5 PERFORMANCE RELATED TO MEASURES: THEORETICAL

There are very few theoretical indicators for algorithm accuracy. What little there are, make specific distributional assumptions, and the only question is whether these specific assumptions are valid. In such cases, it is possible to build checks into the algorithm that give an indication if the assumptions are valid.

10.5.1 Normal distributions

The statistical measures were defined in Section 7.3.2 with a view to monitoring the success of the two discriminant procedures that are associated with the normal distribution, namely linear and quadratic discriminants. Within the class of normal distributions, the measure SD_ratio provides a guide as to the relative suitability of linear and quadratic discrimination. If sample sizes are so large that covariance matrices can be accurately measured, it would be legitimate to use the quadratic version exclusively, as it reduces to the linear rule in the special case of equality of covariances. Practically speaking, the advice must be reversed: use linear discriminants unless the sample size is very large, the distribution is known to be nearly normal and the covariances are very different. So we consider now when to use quadratic discriminants. It should be noted that this advice is absolute in the sense that it is based only on measures related to the dataset.

10.5.2   Absolute performance: quadratic discriminants

In theory, quadratic discrimination is the best procedure to use when the data are normally distributed, especially so if the covariances differ. Because it makes very specific distributional assumptions, and so is very efficient for normal distributions, it is inadvisable to use quadratic discrimination for non-normal distributions (a common situation with parametric procedures - they are not robust to departures from the assumptions), and, because it uses many more parameters, it is also not advisable to use quadratic discrimination when the sample sizes are small. We will now relate these facts to our measures for the datasets.

The **ideal** dataset for quadratic discrimination would be a very large, normally distributed, dataset with widely differing covariance matrices. In terms of the measures, ideally we want β_1 = skewness = 0, β_2 = kurtosis = 3, and SD_ratio much greater than unity.

The **most normal** dataset in our study is the KL digits dataset, as β_1 = skewness = 0.18 (and this is small), β_2 = kurtosis = 2.92 (and this is near 3), and, most importantly, SD_ratio = 1.97 (and this is much greater than unity). This dataset is nearest ideal, so it is predictable that quadratic discrimination will achieve the lowest error rate. In fact, quadratic discriminants achieve an error rate of 2.5%, and this is only bettered by k-NN with an error rate of 2.0% and by ALLOC80 with an error rate of 2.4%.

At the other extreme, the **least normal** dataset is probably the shuttle dataset, with β_1 = skewness = 4.4 (very large)), β_2 = kurtosis = 160.3 (nowhere near 3), and, to make matters worse, the SD_ratio = 1.12 (and this is not much greater than unity). Therefore, we can predict that this is the least appropriate dataset for quadratic discrimination, and it is no surprise that quadratic discriminants achieve an error rate of 6.72%, which is worst of all our results for the shuttle dataset. The decision tree methods get error rates smaller than this by a factor of 100!

The important proviso should always be borne in mind that there must be enough data to estimate all parameters accurately.

10.5.3   Relative performance: Logdisc vs. DIPOL92

Another fruitful way of looking at the behaviour of algorithms is by making paired comparisons between closely related algorithms. This extremely useful device is best illustrated by comparing logistic discrimination (Logdisc) and DIPOL92. From their construction, we can see that DIPOL92 and logistic discrimination have exactly the same formal decision procedure in one special case, namely the case of two-class problems in which there is no clustering (*i.e.* both classes are "pure"). Where the two differ then, will be in multi-class problems (such as the digits or letters datasets) or in two-class problems in which the classes are impure (such as the Belgian Power dataset).

With this in mind, it is of interest to compare the performance of DIPOL92 *when it does not use clustering* with the performance of logistic discrimination, as is done in Table 10.9. The accuracies/average costs quoted for logistic discrimination are those in the main tables of Chapter 9. Those quoted for DIPOL92 are for the no-clustering version of DIPOL, and so are different, in general, from those in the main tables. Either in Table 10.9 or in the main tables, it is clear that sometimes one procedure is better and sometimes the other. From what is known about the algorithms, however, we should look at the two-class problems separately, and, if this is done, a pattern emerges. Indeed from Table 10.9, it

Table 10.9: Logistic Discriminants vs. DIPOL92 with no clustering.

Dataset	Logdisc	DIPOL92 (no clustering)	No. classes (q)
Belgian	0.0072	0.0184	2
Chromosome	0.1310	0.0917	24
Credit Aus	0.1406	0.1406	2
Credit Ger	0.5380	0.5440	2
Credit Man	0.0300	0.0292	2
Cut20	0.0460	0.0480	2
Cut50	0.0370	0.0490	2
DNA	0.0610	0.0490	3
Diabetes	0.2230	0.2380	2
Digit44	0.0860	0.0700	10
Faults	0.2210	0.2000	3
KL digit	0.0510	0.0400	10
Letter	0.2340	0.1770	26
New.Belg	0.0280	0.0380	2
Sat. image	0.1630	0.1480	6
Segmentation	0.1090	0.0510	7
Shuttle	0.0380	0.0530	7
Technical	0.4010	0.3530	91
Tsetse	0.1170	0.1210	2
Vehicle	0.1910	0.2070	4

seems that generally Logdisc is better than DIPOL92 for two-class problems. Knowing this, we can look back at the main tables and come to the following conclusions about the relative performance of Logdisc and DIPOL92.

Rules comparing Logdisc to DIPOL92
We can summarise our conclusions viz-a-viz logistic and DIPOL by the following rules, which amount to saying that DIPOL92 is usually better than Logdisc except for the cases stated.

- IF number of examples is small,

  - OR IF cost matrix involved,
  - OR IF number of classes = 2

    * AND if no distinct clusters within classes

- THEN Logdisc is better than DIPOL92
- ELSE DIPOL92 is better than Logdisc

10.5.4 Pruning of decision trees

This section looks at a small subset of the trials relating to decision tree methods. The specific aim is to illustrate how error rate (or cost) is related to the complexity (number of nodes) of the decision tree.

There is no obvious way of telling if the error-rate of a decision tree is near optimal, indeed the whole question of what is to be optimised is a very open one. In practice a

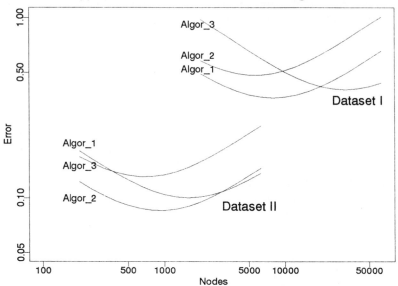

Fig. 10.5: Hypothetical dependence of error rates on number of end nodes (and so on pruning) for three algorithms on two datasets.

balance must be struck between conflicting criteria. One way of achieving a balance is the use of cost-complexity as a criterion, as is done by Breiman *et al.* (1984). This balances complexity of the tree against the error rate, and is used in their CART procedure as a criterion for pruning the decision tree. All the decision trees in this project incorporate some kind of pruning, and the extent of pruning is controlled by a parameter. Generally, a tree that is overpruned has too high an error rate because the decision tree does not represent the full structure of the dataset, and the tree is biased. On the other hand, a tree that is not pruned has too much random variation in the allocation of examples. In between these two extremes, there is usually an optimal amount of pruning. If an investigator is prepared to spend some time trying different values of this pruning parameter, and the error-rate is tested against an independent test set, the optimal amount of pruning can be found by plotting the error rate against the pruning parameter. Equivalently, the error-rate may be plotted against the number of end nodes. Usually, the error rate drops quite quickly to its minimum value as the number of nodes increases, increasing slowly as the nodes increase beyond the optimal value.

The number of end nodes is an important measure of the complexity of a decision tree. If the decision tree achieves something near the optimal error-rate, the number of end nodes is also measure of the complexity of the dataset. Although it is not to be expected that all decision trees will achieve their optimal error-rates with the same number of end-nodes, it seems reasonable that most decision trees will achieve their optimal error-rates when the number of end-nodes matches the complexity of the dataset.

Considerations like these lead us to expect that the error-rates of different algorithms on the same dataset will behave as sketched in Figure 10.5.

To achieve some kind of comparability between datasets, all the curves for one dataset can be moved horizontally and vertically *on the logarithmic scale*. This amounts to rescaling all the results on that dataset so that the global minimum error rate is unity and the number of nodes at the global minimum is unity.

When no attempt is made to optimise the amount of pruning, we resort to the following plausible argument to compare algorithms. Consider, for example, the Cut20 dataset. Four algorithms were tested, with very widely differing error rates and nodes, as shown in Table 10.10. As the lowest error rate is achieved by C4.5, make everything relative to C4.5, so that the relative number N/N_{opt} of nodes and relative error rates E/E_{opt} are given in Table 10.10 These standardised results for the Cut20 dataset are plotted in Figure 10.6, along

Table 10.10: Error rates and number of end nodes for four decision trees on the Cut20 dataset. Note that C4.5 achieves the lowest error rate, so we speculate that the optimal number of end nodes for decision trees is about 159.

Algorithm	No. end nodes	Error rate
AC^2	38	0.063
Cal5	14	0.045
C4.5	159	0.036
NewID	339	0.039

Table 10.11: Error rates and number of end nodes for four algorithms relative to the values for C4.5.

Algorithm	N/N_{opt}	E/E_{opt}
AC^2	0.239	1.750
Cal5	0.088	1.250
C4.5	1.000	1.000
NewID	2.132	1.083

with standardised results from 15 other datasets for which we had the relevant information, with the name of the algorithm as label. Of course, each dataset will give rise to at least one point with $N/N_{opt} = 1$ and $E/E_{opt} = 1$, but we are here concerned with the results that are not near this "optimal" point.

Note that Cal5 appears most frequently in the left of the Figure 10.6 (where it has less nodes than the "best" algorithm) and both NewID and AC^2 appear most frequently in the right of the diagram (where they have too many nodes). It would also appear that C4.5 is most likely to use the "best" number of nodes - and this is very indirect evidence that the amount of pruning used by C4.5 is correct on average, although this conclusion is based on a small number of datasets.

One would expect that a well-trained procedure should attain the optimal number of nodes on average, but it is clear that Cal5 is biased towards small numbers (this may be done deliberately to obtain trees with simple structure), whereas NewID and AC^2 are biased towards more complex trees. In the absence of information on the relative weights to be attached to complexity (number of nodes) or cost (error rate), we cannot say whether Cal5 has struck the right balance, but it does seem clear that NewID and AC^2 often use very

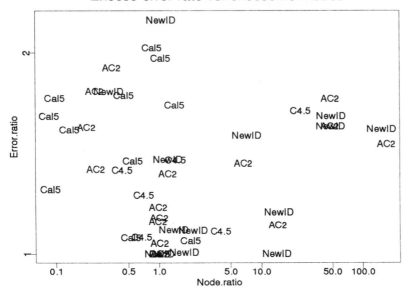

Fig. 10.6: Error rate and number of nodes for 16 datasets. Results for each dataset are scaled separately so that the algorithm with lowest error rate on that dataset has unit error rate and unit number of nodes.

complex structures with no compensation in reduced error rate.

10.6 RULE BASED ADVICE ON ALGORITHM APPLICATION

Many different statistical and machine learning algorithms have been developed in the past. If we are interested in applying these algorithms to concrete tasks we have to consider which learning algorithm is best suited for which problem. A satisfactory answer requires a certain know-how of this area, which can be acquired only with experience. We consider here if Machine Learning techniques themselves can be useful in organizing this knowledge, specifically the knowledge embedded in the empirical results of the StatLog trials. The aim is to relate the performance of algorithms to the characteristics of the datasets using only the empirical data. The process of generating a set of rules capable of relating these two concepts is referred to as *meta-level learning*.

10.6.1 Objectives

It appears that datasets can be characterised using certain features such as number of attributes, their types, amount of unknown values or other statistical parameters. It is reasonable to try to match the features of datasets with our past knowledge concerning the algorithms. If we select the algorithm that most closely matches the features of the dataset, then we increase the chances of obtaining useful results. The advantage is that not all algorithms need to be tried out. Those algorithms that do not match the data can be excluded, and so, a great deal of effort can be saved.

In order to achieve this aim, we need to determine which dataset features are relevant. After that, various instances of learning tasks can be examined with the aim of formulating a "theory" concerning the applicability of different machine learning and statistical algorithms.

The knowledge concerning which algorithm is applicable can be summarised in the form of rules stating that if the given dataset has certain characteristics then learning a particular algorithm may be applicable. Each rule can, in addition, be qualified using a certain measure indicating how reliable the rule is. Rules like this can be constructed manually, or with the help of machine learning methods on the basis of past cases. In this section we are concerned with this latter method. The process of constructing the rules represents a kind of *meta-level learning*.

As the number of tests was generally limited, few people have attempted to automate the formulation of a theory concerning the applicability of different algorithms. One exception was the work of Aha (1992) who represented this knowledge using the following rule schemas:

```
If the given dataset has characteristics C1...Cn,
Then
        try the learning algorithm Li
        in preference to learning algorithm Lj
```

One example of such a rule schema is:

```
If (# training instances < 737)  AND
   (# prototypes per class > 5.5)  AND
   (# relevant attributes > 8.5)
Then IB1 >> C4
```

where IB1 $>>$ C4 means that algorithm IB1 is predicted to have significantly higher accuracies than algorithm C4. Our approach differs from Aha's in several respects. The main difference is that we are not concerned with just a comparison between two algorithms, but rather a group of them.

Our aim is to obtain rules which would indicate when a particular algorithm works better than the rest. A number of interesting relationships have emerged. However, in order to have reliable results, we would need quite an extensive set of test results, certainly much more than the 22 datasets considered in this book.

As part of the overall aim of matching features of datasets with our past knowledge of algorithms, we need to determine which dataset features are relevant. This is not known *a priori*, so, for exploratory purposes, we used the reduced set of measures given in Table 10.12. This includes certain simple measures, such as number of examples, attributes and classes, and more complex statistical and information-based measures. Some measures represent derived quantities and include, for example, measures that are ratios of other measures. These and other measures are given in Sections 7.3.1 – 7.3.3.

10.6.2 Using test results in metalevel learning

Here we have used all of the available results - as listed in Chapter 9. The results for each dataset were analysed with the objective of determining which algorithms achieved *low error rates* (or *costs*). All algorithms with low error rates were considered *applicable* to

Table 10.12: Measures used in Metalevel Learning.

Measure	Definition
Simple	
N	Number of examples
p	Number of attributes
q	Number of Classes
Bin.att	Number of Binary Attributes
Cost	Cost matrix indicator
Statistical	
SD	Standard deviation ratio (geometric mean)
corr.abs	Mean absolute correlation of attributes
cancor1	First canonical correlation (7.3.2)
fract1	Fraction separability due to cancor1
skewness	Skewness - mean of $|E(X - \mu)^3| / \sigma^3$
kurtosis	Kurtosis - mean of $|E(X - \mu)^4| / \sigma^4$
Information theory	
$H(C)$	Entropy (complexity) of class
$\bar{H}(X)$	Mean entropy (complexity) of attributes
$\bar{M}(C, X)$	Mean mutual information of class and attributes
EN.attr	Equivalent number of attributes $H(C) / \bar{M}(C, X)$
NS.ratio	Noise-signal ratio $(\bar{H}(X) - \bar{M}(C, X)) / \bar{M}(C, X)$

this dataset. The other algorithms were considered *inapplicable*. This categorisation of the test results can be seen as a preparatory step for the metalevel learning task. Of course, the categorisation will permit us also to make prediction regarding which algorithms are applicable on a new dataset.

Of course, the question of whether the error rate is *high* or *low* is rather relative. The error rate of 15% may be excellent in some domains, while 5% may be bad in others. This problem is resolved using a method similar to *subset selection* in statistics. First, the best algorithm is identified according to the error rates. Then an acceptable margin of tolerance is calculated. All algorithms whose error rates fall within this margin are considered *applicable*, while the others are labelled as *inapplicable*. The level of tolerance can reasonably be defined in terms of the standard deviation of the error rate, but since each algorithm achieves a different error rate, the appropriate standard deviation will vary across algorithms.

To keep things simple, we will quote the standard deviations for the error rate of the "best" algorithm, *i.e.* that which achieves the lowest error rate. Denote the lowest error rate by ER. Then the standard deviation is defined by

$$EM = \sqrt{ER(1 - ER)/NT},$$

where NT is the number of examples in the test set. Then all algorithms whose error rates fall within the interval $(ER, ER + kEM)$ are considered *applicable*. Of course we still need to choose a value for k which determines the size of the interval. This affects the confidence that the truly best algorithm appears in the group considered. The larger the value of k, the higher the confidence that the best algorithm will be in this interval.

For example, let us consider the tests on the Segmentation dataset consisting of 2310 examples. The best algorithm appears to be ALLOC80 with the error rate of 3% ($ER = 0.03$). Then

$$EM = \sqrt{0.03(1 - 0.03)/2310} = 0.0035$$

which is 0.35%. In this example, we can say with high confidence that the best algorithms are in the group with error rates between 3% and $k \times 0.35\%$. If $k = 1$ the interval is relatively small $< 3\%, 3.35\% >$ and includes only two other algorithms (AC^2, BayesTree) apart from ALLOC80. All the algorithms that lie in this interval can be considered *applicable* to this dataset, and the others inapplicable. If we enlarge the margin, by considering larger values of k, we get a more relaxed notion of applicability (see Table 10.13).

Table 10.13: Classified Test Results on Image Segmentation Dataset for k=16.

Algorithm	Error	Class	Margin	
ALLOC80	.030	Appl	0.030	Margin for k=0
AC^2	.031	Appl		
BayesTree	.033	Appl		
			0.0335	Margin for k=1
NewID	.034	Appl		
			0.037	Margin for k=2
C4.5	.040	Appl		
CART	.040	Appl		
DIPOL92	.040	Appl		
CN2	.043	Appl		
			0.044	Margin for k=4
IndCART	.045	Appl		
LVQ	.046	Appl		
SMART	.052	Appl		
Backprop	.054	Appl		
			0.058	Margin for k=8
Cal5	.062	Appl		
Kohonen	.067	Appl		
RBF	.069	Appl		
k-NN	.077	Appl		
			0.086	Margin for k=16
Logdisc	.109	Non-Appl		
CASTLE	.112	Non-Appl		
Discrim	.116	Non-Appl		
Quadisc	.157	Non-Appl		
Bayes	.265	Non-Appl		
ITrule	.455	Non-Appl		
Default	.900	Non-Appl		

The decision as to where to draw the line (by choosing a value for k) is, of course, rather subjective. In this work we had to consider an additional constraint related to the purpose we had in mind. As our objective is to generate rules concerning applicability of algorithms we have opted for the more relaxed scheme of appplicability (k = 8 or 16), so as to have enough examples in each class (Appl, Non-Appl).

Some of the tests results analysed are not characterised using error rates, but rather *costs*. Consequently the notion of error margin discussed earlier has to be adapted to costs. The *standard error of the mean cost* can be calculated from the confusion matrices (obtained by testing), and the cost matrix. The values obtained for the leading algorithm in the three relevant datasets were:

Dataset	Algorithm	Mean cost	Standard error of mean
German credit	Discrim	0.525	0.0327
Heart disease	Discrim	0.415	0.0688
Head injury	Logdisc	18.644	1.3523

In the experiments reported later the error margin was simply set to the values 0.0327, 0.0688 and 1.3523 respectively, irrespective of the algorithm used.

Joining data relative to one algorithm

The problem of learning was divided into several phases. In each phase all the test results relative to just one particular algorithm (for example, CART) were joined, while all the other results (relative to other algorithms) were temporarily ignored. The purpose of this strategy was to simplify the class structure. For each algorithm we would have just two classes (Appl and Non-Appl). This strategy worked better than the obvious solution that included all available data for training. For example, when considering the CART algorithm and a margin of $k = 16$ we get the scheme illustrated in Figure 10.7. The classified test

CART-Appl,	Satim	CART-Non-Appl,	KL
CART-Appl,	Vehic	CART-Non-Appl,	Dig44
CART-Appl,	Head	CART-Non-Appl,	Chrom
CART-Appl,	Heart	CART-Non-Appl,	Shut
CART-Appl,	Belg	CART-Non-Appl,	Tech
CART-Appl,	Segm	CART-Non-Appl,	Cut
CART-Appl,	Diab	CART-Non-Appl,	Cr.Man
CART-Appl,	Cr.Ger	CART-Non-Appl,	Letter
CART-Appl,	Cr.Aust		
CART-Appl,	DNA		
CART-Appl,	BelgII		
CART-Appl,	Faults		
CART-Appl,	Tsetse		

Fig. 10.7: Classified test results relative to one particular algorithm (CART).

results are then modified as follows. The dataset name is simply substituted by a vector containing the corresponding dataset characteristics. Values which are not available or missing are simply represented by "?". This extended dataset is then used in the meta-level learning.

Choice of algorithm for learning

A question arises as to which algorithm we should use in the process of meta-level learning. We have decided to use C4.5 for the following reasons. First, as our results have demonstrated, this algorithm achieves quite good results overall. Secondly, the decision tree generated by C4.5 can be inspected and analysed. This is not the case with some statistical and neural learning algorithms.

So, for example, when C4.5 has been supplied with the partial test results relative to CART algorithm, it generated the decision tree in Figure 10.8. The figures that appear on

```
N  > 6435 : Non-Appl  (8.0)
N  <= 6435:
|   Skew <= 0.57 : Non-Appl  (2.0)
|   Skew > 0.57 :  Appl (12.0)
```

Fig. 10.8: Decision tree generated by C4.5 relative to CART.

the right hand side of each leaf are either of the form (N) or (N/E), where N represents the total number of examples satisfying the conditions of the associated branch, and E the number of examples of other classes that have been erroneously covered. If the data contains unknown values, the numbers N and E may be fractional.

It has been argued that rules are more legible than trees. The decision tree shown earlier can be transformed into a rule form using a very simple process, where each branch of a tree is simply transcribed as a rule. The applicability of CART can thus be characterised using the rules in Figure 10.9.

CART-Appl	$\leftarrow N \leq 6435$, Skew > 0.57
CART-Non-Appl	$\leftarrow N > 6435$
CART-Non-Appl	$\leftarrow N \leq 6435$, Skew ≤ 0.57

Fig. 10.9: Rules generated by C4.5 relative to CART.

Quinlan (1993) has argued that rules obtained from decision trees can be improved upon in various ways. For example, it is possible to eliminate conditions that are irrelevant, or even drop entire rules that are irrelevant or incorrect. In addition it is possible to reorder the rules according to certain criteria and introduce a default rule to cover the cases that have not been covered. The program C4.5 includes a command that permits the user to transform a decision tree into a such a rule set. The rules produced by the system are characterised using (pessimistic) error rate estimates.

As is shown in the next section, error rate (or its estimate) is not an ideal measure, however. This is particularly evident when dealing with continuous classes. This problem has motivated us to undertake a separate evaluation of all candidate rules and characterise them using a new measure. The aim is to identify those rules that appear to be most informative.

10.6.3   Characterizing predictive power

The rules concerning applicability of a particular algorithm were generated on the basis of only about 22 examples (each case represents the results of particular test on a particular dataset). Of these, only a part represented "positive examples", corresponding to the datasets on which the particular algorithm performed well. This is rather a modest number. Also, the set of dataset descriptors used may not be optimal. We could thus expect that the rules generated capture a mixture of relevant and fortuitous regularities.

In order to strengthen our confidence in the results we have decided to evaluate the rules generated. Our aim was to determine whether the rules could actually be used to make useful predictions concerning its applicability. We have adopted a leave-one-out procedure and applied it to datasets, such as the one shown in Table 10.13.

Following this procedure, we used all but one items in training, while the remaining item was used for testing. Of course, the set of rules generated in each pass could be slightly different, but the form of the rules was not our primary interest here. We were interested to verify how successful the rules were in predicting the applicability (or non-applicability) of the algorithm.

Let us analyse an example. Consider, for example, the problem of predicting the applicability of CART. This can be characterised using confusion matrices, such as the ones shown in Figure 10.10, showing results relative to the error margin k=16. Note that an extra (simulated) dataset has been used in the following calculations and tables, which is why the sum is now 22.

	Appl	Non-appl
Appl	11	2
Non-appl	1	8

Fig. 10.10: Evaluation of the meta-rules concerning applicability of CART. The rows represent the true class, and the columns the predicted class.

The confusion matrix shows that the rules generated were capable of correctly predicting the applicability of CART on an unseen dataset in 11 cases. Incorrect prediction was made only in 1 case. Similarly, if we consider non-applicability, we see that correct prediction is made in 8 cases, and incorrect one in 2. This gives a rather good overall success rate of 86%.

We notice that success rate is not an ideal measure, however. As the margin of applicability is extended (by making k larger), more cases will get classified as applicable. If we consider an extreme case, when the margin covers all algorithms, we will get an apparent success rate of 100%. Of course we are not interested in such a useless procedure!

This apparent paradox can be resolved by adopting the measure called information score (IS) (Kononenko & Bratko, 1991) in the evaluation. This measure takes into account prior probabilities. The information score associated with a definite positive classification is defined as $-\log P(C)$, where $P(C)$ represents the prior probability of class C. The information scores can be used to weigh all classifier answers. In our case we have two classes *Appl* and *Non-Appl*. The weights can be represented conveniently in the form of an information score matrix as shown in Figure 10.11.

	Appl	Non- Appl
Appl	$-\log P(Appl)$	$-\log(1 - P(Non\text{-}Appl))$
Non-Appl	$-\log(1 - P(Appl))$	$-\log P(Non\text{-} Appl)$

Fig. 10.11: Information Score Matrix. The rows represent the true class, and the columns the predicted class.

The information scores can be used to calculate the total information provided by a rule on the given dataset. This can be done simply by multiplying each element of the confusion matrix by the corresponding element of the information score matrix.

The quantities $P(Appl)$ and $P(Non\text{-}Appl)$ can be estimated from the appropriate frequencies. If we consider the frequency of *Appl* and *Non-Appl* for all algorithms (irrespective of the algorithm in question), we get a kind of absolute reference point. This enables us to make comparisons right across different algorithms.

For example, for the value of $\log P(Appl)$ we consider a dataset consisting of 506 cases (23 algorithms × 22 datasets). As it happens 307 cases fall into the class *Appl*. The information associated with $-\log P(Appl)$ is $-\log(307/506) = 0.721$. Similarly, the value of $-\log P(Non\text{-}Appl)$ is $-\log(199/506) = 1.346$.

We notice that due to the distribution of this data (given by a relatively large margin of applicability of $k = 16$), the examples of applicable cases are relatively common. Consequently, the information concerning applicability has a somewhat smaller weight (.721) than the information concerning non-applicability (1.346).

If we multiply the elements of the confusion matrix for CART by the corresponding elements of the information score matrix we get the matrix shown in Figure 10.12.

	Appl	Non-Appl
Appl	7.93	2.69
Non-Appl	0.72	10.77

Fig. 10.12: Adjusted confusion matrix for CART. The rows represent the true class, and the columns the predicted class.

This matrix is in a way similar to the confusion matrix shown earlier with the exception that the error counts have been weighted by the appropriate information scores. To obtain an estimate of the average information relative to one case, we need to divide all elements by the number of cases considered (*i.e. 22*). This way we get the scaled matrix in Figure 10.13.

	Appl	Non-Appl
Appl	0.360	0.122
Non-Appl	0.033	0.489

Fig. 10.13: Rescaled adjusted confusion matrix for CART.

This information provided by the classification of *Appl* is $0.360 - 0.033 = 0.327$ bits. The information provided by classification of *Non-Appl* is similarly $0.489 - 0.122 = 0.367$ bits.

This information obtained in the manner described can be compared to the information provided by a default rule. This can be calculated simply as follows. First we need to decide whether the algorithm should be applicable or non-applicable by default. This is quite simple. We just look for the classification which provides us with the highest information.

If we consider the previous example, the class *Appl* is the correct default for CART. This is because the information associated with this default is $(13 \times 0.721 - 9 \times 0.721)/22 = 0.131$ which is greater than the information associated with the converse rule (*i.e.* that

CART is *Non-Appl).*

How can we decide whether the rules involved in classification are actually useful? This is quite straightforward. A rule can be considered useful if it provides us with more information than the default. If we come back to our example, we see that the classification for *Appl* provides us with .327 bits, while the default classification provides only .131 bits. This indicates that the rules used in the classification are more informative than the default. In consequence, the actual rule should be kept and the default rule discarded.

10.6.4 Rules generated in metalevel learning

Figure 10.14 contains some rules generated using the method described. As we have not used a uniform notion of applicability throughout, each rule is qualified by additional information. The symbol $Appl_{\downarrow k}$ represents the concept of applicability derived on the basis of the best error rate. In case of $Appl_{\downarrow 16}$ the interval of applicability is (Best error rate, Best error rate + 16 STD's) and the interval of non-applicability is (Best error rate + 16 STD's, 1).

Each rule also shows the information score. This parameter gives an estimate of the usefulness of each rule. The rules presented could be supplemented by another set generated on the basis of the worst error rate (*i.e.* the error rate associated with the choice of most common class or worse). In the case of $Appl_{\uparrow 8}$ the interval of applicability is (Best error rate, Default error rate - 8 STD's) and the interval of non-applicability is (Default error rate - 8 STD's, 1).

The set of rules generated includes a number of "default rules" which can be easily recognised (they do not have any conditions on the right hand side of "←").

Each rule included shows also the normalised information score. This parameter gives an estimate of the usefulness of each rule. Only those rules that could be considered minimally useful (with information score > .300) have been included here. All rules for CART are also shown, as these were discussed earlier. In the implemented system we use a few more rules which are a bit less informative (with inf. scores down to .100).

Discussion

The problem of learning rules for all algorithms simultaneously is formidable. We want to obtain a sufficient number rules to qualify each algorithm. To limit the complexity of the problem we have considered one algorithm at a time. This facilitated the construction of rules. Considering that the problem is difficult, what confidence can we have that the rules generated are minimally sensible?

One possibility is to try to evaluate the rules, by checking whether they are capable of giving useful predictions. This is what we have done in one of the earlier sections. Note that measuring simply the success rate has the disadvantage that it does not distinguish between predictions that are easy to make, and those that are more difficult. This is why we have evaluated the rules by examining how informative they are in general.

For example, if we examine the rules for the applicability of CART we observe that the rules provide us with useful information if invoked. These measures indicate that the rules generated can indeed provide us with useful information.

Instead of evaluating rules in the way shown, we could present them to some expert to see if he would find them minimally sensible. On a quick glance the condition "N ≤ 6435"

Decision Tree and Rule Algorithms: *Inf. Score*

C4.5-Appl$_{\downarrow 16}$	$\leftarrow$	.477
NewID-Appl $_{\downarrow 16}$	$\leftarrow$	.609
AC^2-Non-Appl $_{\downarrow 8}$	$\leftarrow$	.447
CART-Appl $_{\downarrow 8}$	$\leftarrow N \leq 4999$, Kurtosis > 2.92	.186
CART-Appl $_{\downarrow 16}$	$\leftarrow N \leq 6435$, Skew > 0.57	.328
CART-Non-Appl $_{\downarrow 16}$	$\leftarrow N > 6435$	.367
IndCART-Appl $_{\downarrow 16}$	$\leftarrow$	.384
Cal5-Appl $_{\downarrow 16}$	$\leftarrow k \leq 7$	.524
CN2-Appl $_{\downarrow 16}$	$\leftarrow$	.702
ITrule-Non-Appl $_{\downarrow 8}$	$\leftarrow N > 768$	.549
ITrule-Non-Appl $_{\downarrow 16}$	$\leftarrow N > 1000$	.917

Statistical Algorithms:

Discrim-Appl $_{\downarrow 8}$	$\leftarrow N \leq 1000$	.247
Discrim-Non-Appl $_{\downarrow 8}$	$\leftarrow N > 1000$	.452
Discrim-Non-Appl $_{\downarrow 16}$	$\leftarrow k > 4$	.367
Quadisc-Appl $_{\downarrow 8}$	$\leftarrow N \leq 1000$	.309
Logdisc-Appl $_{\downarrow 8}$	$\leftarrow N \leq 3186$	.495
Logdisc-Non-Appl $_{\downarrow 16}$	$\leftarrow k > 4$	.367
ALLOC80-Appl $_{\downarrow 8}$	$\leftarrow$	.406
ALLOC80-Appl $_{\downarrow 16}$	$\leftarrow$	.797
k-NN-Appl $_{\downarrow 16}$	$\leftarrow$	.766
Bayes-Non-Appl $_{\downarrow 8}$	$\leftarrow$	.418
Bayes-Non-Appl $_{\downarrow 16}$	$\leftarrow$	.705
BayTree-Appl $_{\downarrow 16}$	$\leftarrow k \leq 7$	.557
BayTree-Non-Appl $_{\downarrow 16}$	$\leftarrow k > 7$	.305
CASTLE-Non-Appl $_{\downarrow 8}$	$\leftarrow N > 768$, Cost $= 0$	.420
CASTLE-Non-Appl $_{\downarrow 16}$	$\leftarrow$Bin.att $= 0$	.734

Neural Network Algorithms:

Dipol92-Appl $_{\downarrow 8}$	$\leftarrow$	.341
Dipol92-Appl $_{\downarrow 16}$	$\leftarrow$	.544
RBF-Non-Appl $_{\downarrow 8}$	$\leftarrow$	.401
LVQ-Appl $_{\downarrow 16}$	$\leftarrow$	.498
BackProp-Appl $_{\downarrow 8}$	$\leftarrow N \leq 3000$	.495
Kohonen-Non-Appl $_{\downarrow 8}$	$\leftarrow$	.641
Cascade-Non-Appl $_{\downarrow 8}$	$\leftarrow$	.706
Cascade-Non-Appl $_{\downarrow 16}$	$\leftarrow$	.866

Fig. 10.14: Some rules generated in Meta-Level Learning.

is a bit puzzling. Why should CART perform reasonably well, if the number of examples is less than this number?

Obviously, as the rules were generated on the basis of a relatively small number of examples, the rules could contain some fortuitous features. Of course, unless we have more data available it is difficult to point out which features are or are not relevant. However, it is necessary to note that the condition "N ≤ 6435" is not an absolute one. Rules should not be simply interpreted as - "The algorithm performs well if such and such condition is satisfied". The correct interpretation is something like - "The algorithm is likely to compete well under the conditions stated, provided no other more informative rule applies". This view helps also to understand better the rule for Discrim algorithm generated by the system.

$$\text{Discrim-Appl} \leftarrow N \leq 1000$$

The condition "N ≤ 1000" does not express all the conditions of applicability of algorithm Discrim, and could appear rather strange. However, the condition does make sense. Some algorithms have a faster learning rate than others. These algorithms compete well with others, provided the number of examples is small. The fast learning algorithms may however be overtaken by others later. Experiments with learning curves on the Satellite Image dataset show that the Discrim algorithm is among the first six algorithms in terms of error rate as long as the number of examples is relatively small (100, 200 etc.). This algorithm seems to pick up quickly what is relevant and so we could say, it competes well under these conditions. When the number of examples is larger, however, Discrim is overtaken by other algorithms. With the full training set of 6400 examples Discrim is in 19th place in the ranking. This is consistent with the rule generated by our system. The condition generated by the system is not so puzzling as it seems at first glance!

There is of course a well recognised problem that should be tackled. Many conditions contain numeric tests which are either true or false. It does not make sense to consider the Discrim algorithm applicable if the number of examples is less than 1000, and inapplicable, if this number is just a bit more. A more flexible approach is needed (for example using flexible matching).

10.6.5 Application Assistant

Rules generated in the way described permit us to give recommendations as to which classification algorithm could be used with a given dataset. This is done with the help of a kind of expert system called an Application Assistant (AplAs). This system contains a knowledge base which is interpreted by an interpreter. The knowledge base contains all the rules shown in the previous section. The interpreter is quite standard, but uses a particular method for resolution of conflicts.

We notice that the knowledge base may contain potentially conflicting rules. In general several rules may apply, some of which may recommend the use of a particular algorithm while others may be against it. Some people believe that knowledge bases should always be cleaned up so that such situations would not arise. This would amount to obliterating certain potentially useful information and so we prefer to deal with the problem in the following way.

For every algorithm we consider all the rules satisfying the conditions and sum all the information scores. The information scores associated with the recommendation to apply an algorithm are taken with a positive sign, the others with a negative one. For example, if we get a recommendation to apply an algorithm with an indication that this is apparently 0.5 bits worth, and if we also get an opposite recommendation (*i.e.* not to apply this algorithm) with an indication that this is 0.2 bits worth, we will go ahead with the recommendation, but decrease the information score accordingly (*i.e.* to 0.3 bits).

The output of this phase is a list of algorithms accompanied by their associated overall information scores. A positive score can be interpreted as an argument to apply the algorithm. A negative score can be interpreted as an argument against the application of the algorithm. Moreover, the higher the score, the more informative is the recommendation in general. The information score can be then considered as a strength of the recommendation.

The recommendations given are of course not perfect. They do not guarantee that the first algorithm in the recommendation ordering will have the best performance in reality. However, our results demonstrate that the algorithms accompanied by a strong recommendation do perform quite well in general. The opposite is also true. The algorithms that have not been recommended have a poorer performance in general. In other words, we observe that there is a reasonable degree of correlation between the recommendation and the actual test results. This is illustrated in Figure 10.15 which shows the recommendations generated for one particular dataset (Letters).

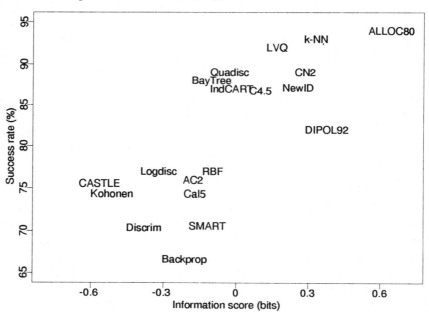

Fig. 10.15: Recommendations of the Application Assistant for the Letters dataset.

The recommendations were generated on the basis of a rules set similar to the one shown in Figure 10.14 (the rule set included just a few more rules with lower information scores).

The top part shows the algorithms with high success rates. The algorithms on the right are accompanied by a strong recommendation concerning applicability. We notice that several algorithms with high success rates apear there. The algorithm that is accompanied by the strongest reccomendation for this dataset is ALLOC80 (Information Score = 0.663 bits). This algorithm has also the highest success rate of 93.6 %. The second place in the ordering of algorithms recommended is k-NN shared by k-NN and DIPOL92. We note that k-NN is a very good choice, while DIPOL92 is not too bad either.

The correlation between the information score and success rate could, of course, be better. The algorithm CASTLE is given somewhat too much weight, while BayTree which is near the top is somewhat undervalued. The correlation could be improved, in the first place, by obtaining more test results. The results could also be improved by incorporating a better method for combining rules and the corresponding information scores. It would be beneficial to consider also other potentially useful sets of rules, including the ones generated on the basis of other values of k, or even different categorisation schemes. For example, all algorithms with a performance near the default rule could be considered non-applicable, while all others could be classified as applicable.

Despite the fact that there is room for possible improvements, the Application Assistant seems to produce promising results. The user can get a recommendation as to which algorithm could be used with a new dataset. Although the recommendation is not guaranteed always to give the best possible advice, it narrows down the user's choice.

10.6.6   Criticism of metalevel learning approach

Before accepting any rules, generated by C4.5 or otherwise, it is wise to check them against known theoretical and empirical facts. The rules generated in metalevel learning could contain spurious rules with no foundation in theory. If the rule-based approach has shortcomings, how should we proceed? Would it be better to use another classification scheme in place of the metalevel learning approach using C4.5? As there are insufficient data to construct the rules, the answer is probably to use an interactive method, capable of incorporating prior expert knowledge (background knowledge). As one simple example, if it is known that an algorithm can handle cost matrices, this could simply be provided to the system. As another example, the knowledge that the behaviour of NewID and AC^2 is likely to be similar could also be useful to the system. The rules for AC^2 could then be constructed from the rule for NewID, by adding suitable conditions concerning, for example the hierarchical structure of the attributes. Also, some algorithms have inbuilt checks on applicability, such as linear or quadratic discriminants, and these should be incorporated into the learnt rules.

10.6.7   Criticism of measures

Some of the statistical measures are in fact more complex in structure than the learning the rules. For example, the programming effort in calculating SD_ratio is greater than that in establishing the linear discriminant rule. Indeed, to find SD_ratio requires virtually all the quantities needed in finding the quadratic discriminant. This poses the question: if it is easier to run, say linear discriminants and NewID, why not run them and use the performance of these procedures as yardsticks by which to judge the performance of other algorithms? The similarities evident in the empirical results strongly suggest that the best predictor for logistic regression is linear discriminants (with logistic regression doing that little better on average), and AC^2 is very similar to NewID (if there is no hierarchy), and so on. This idea can be formalised as we indicate in the next section.

10.7 PREDICTION OF PERFORMANCE

What is required is a few simple yardstick methods, readily available (preferably in the public domain), that can be run quickly on the given dataset. We also need a set of rules that will predict the performance of all other algorithms from the yardstick results. As a first suggestion, consider Discrim, IndCART and k-NN. They contain a statistical, a decision-tree and a non-parametric method, so represent the main strands. The question is this: can they represent the full range of algorithms? In the terminology of multidimensional scaling: do they span the reduced space in which most algorithm results reside? The multi-dimensional scaling diagram in Figure 10.1 suggests that a three- or even two-dimensional subspace is sufficient to represent all results.

To give a few examples. Let *Discrim*, *k-NN* and *IndCART* represent the error rates achieved by the respective methods. To predict the accuracy of *Logdisc* from these three reference figures, we can use a multiple regression of *Logdisc* on the three variables *Discrim*, *k-NN* and *IndCART* (with no intercept term). After dropping non-significant terms from the regression, this produces the formula: $Logdisc = 0.79 Discrim$, with a squared correlation coefficient of 0.921. See Table 10.14 for a summary of the regression formulae for all the algorithms (excepting *Discrim*, *k-NN* and *IndCART* naturally).

Table 10.14: Predictors for error-rates based on Discrim, k-NN and IndCART.

Algorithm	Discrim	k-NN	IndCART	R-square	n trials
Quadisc	1.34			0.640	22
Logdisc	0.79			0.921	22
SMART	0.54			0.450	22
ALLOC80		0.80		0.846	21
CASTLE	1.12		0.56	0.874	21
CART			0.74	0.860	15
NewID			1.23	0.840	22
AC^2			1.12	0.723	22
Baytree			0.89	0.897	22
Naivebay	1.43		0.79	0.840	22
CN2		0.29	1.01	0.862	22
C4.5			1.17	0.752	22
ITrule	1.87			0.601	20
CAL5			0.97	0.709	22
Kohonen		1.24		0.672	18
DIPOL92	0.29			0.533	22
Bprop			0.53	0.679	20
Cascade	0.78			0.684	6
RBF			0.88	0.534	22
LVQ		1.05		0.821	21

The Discrim coefficient of 0.79 in the Logdisc example shows that Logdisc is generally about 21% more accurate than Discrim, and that the performance of the other two reference methods does not seem to help in the prediction. With an R-squared value of 0.921, we can be quite confident that Logdisc does better than Discrim. This result should be qualified with information on the number of attributes, normality of variables, etc, – and these are quantities that can be measured. In the context of deciding if further trials on additional algorithms are necessary, take the example of the shuttle dataset, and consider what action to recommend after discovering Discrim = 4.83%, IndCART = 0.09% and k-NN = 0.44%. It does not look as if the error rates of either Logdisc or SMART will get anywhere near IndCART's value, and the best prospect of improvement lies in the decision tree methods.

Consider DIPOL92 now. There appears to be no really good predictor, as the R-squared value is relatively small (0.533). This means that DIPOL92 is doing something outside the scope of the three reference algorithms. The best single predictor is: DIPOL92 = 0.29 Discrim, apparently indicating that DIPOL92 is usually much better than Discrim (although not so much better that it would challenge IndCART's good value for the shuttle dataset). This formula just cannot be true in general however: all we can say is that, for datasets around the size in StatLog, DIPOL92 has error rates about one third that of Discrim, but considerable fluctuation round this value is possible. If we have available the three reference results, the formula would suggest that DIPOL92 should be tried unless either k-NN or CART gets an accuracy much lower than a third of Discrim. Knowing the structure of DIPOL92 we can predict a good deal more however. When there are just two classes (and 9 of our datasets were 2-class problems), and if DIPOL92 does not use clustering, DIPOL92 is very similar indeed to logistic regression (they optimise on slightly different criteria). So the best predictor for DIPOL92 in 2-class problems with no obvious clustering will be Logdisc. At the other extreme, if many clusters are used in the initial stages of DIPOL92, then the performance is bound to approach that of, say, radial basis functions or LVQ.

Also, while on the subject of giving explanations for differences in behaviour, consider the performance of ALLOC80 compared to k-NN. From Table 10.14 it is clear that AL-LOC80 usually outperforms k-NN. The reason is probably due to the mechanism within ALLOC80 whereby irrelevant attributes are dropped, or perhaps because a surrogate was substituted for ALLOC80 when it performed badly. If such strategies were instituted for k-NN, it is probable that their performances would be even closer.

Finally, we should warn that such rules should be treated with great caution, as we have already suggested in connection with the rules derived by C4.5. It is especially dangerous to draw conclusions from incomplete data, as with CART for example, for the reason that a "Not Available" result is very likely associated with factors leading to high error rates, such as inability to cope with large numbers of categories, or large amounts of data. Empirical rules such as those we have put forward should be refined by the inclusion of other factors in the regression, these other factors being directly related to known properties of the algorithm. For example, to predict Quadisc, a term involving the measures SD_ratio would be required (if that is not too circular an argument).

10.7.1 ML on ML vs. regression

Two methods have been given above for predicting the performance of algorithms, based respectively on rule-based advice using dataset measures (ML on ML) and comparison with reference algorithms (regression). It is difficult to compare directly the success rates of the respective predictions, as the former is stated in terms of proportion of correct predictions and the latter in terms of squared correlation. We now give a simple method of comparing the predictability of performance from the two techniques. The R-squared value R^2 from regression and the C4.5 generated rule error rate ϵ can be compared by the following formula which is based on the assumption of equal numbers of *Non-Appl* and *Appl*:

$$R^2 = (1 - 2\epsilon)^2$$

As it should, this formula gives a correlation of $R = 0$ when the error rate is 0.5, as pure guesswork would get half the cases correct. To give an example in using this formula, the CART rules (k=16) had 3 errors in 22, with an error rate of

$$\epsilon = \frac{2}{22} = 0.1364$$

and an approximate R-square value of

$$R^2 = (1 - 2 \times 0.1364)^2 = 0.529$$

This is somewhat less than the value ($R^2 = 0.860$) obtained using the regression techniques of this section.

11

Conclusions

D. Michie (1), D. J. Spiegelhalter (2) and C. C.Taylor (3)
(1) University of Strathclyde, (2) MRC Biostatistics Unit, Cambridge and (3) University of Leeds[1]

11.1 INTRODUCTION

In this chapter we try to draw together the evidence of the comparative trials and subsequent analyses, comment on the experiences of the users of the algorithms, and suggest topics and areas which need further work. We begin with some comments on each of the methods. It should be noted here that our comments are often directed towards a specific implementation of a method rather than the method *per se*. In some instances the slowness or otherwise poor performance of an algorithm is due at least in part to the lack of sophistication of the program. In addition to the potential weakness of the programmer, there is the potential inexperience of the user. To give an example, the trials of AC^2 reported on previous chapters were based on a version programmed in LISP. A version is now available in the C language which cuts the CPU time by a factor of 10. In terms of error rates, observed differences in goodness of result can arise from

1. different suitabilities of the basic methods for given datasets
2. different sophistications of default procedures for parameter settings
3. different sophistication of the program user in selection of options and tuning of parameters
4. occurrence and effectiveness of pre-processing of the data by the user

The stronger a program in respect of 2, then the better buffered against shortcomings in 3. Alternatively, if there are no options to select or parameters to tune, then item 3 is not important.

We give a general view of the ease-of-use and the suitable applications of the algorithms. Some of the properties are subject to different interpretations. For example, in general a decision tree is considered to be less easy to understand than decision rules. However, both are much easier to understand than a regression formula which contains only coefficients, and some algorithms do not give any easily summarised rule at all (for example, k-NN).

---

[1] *Address for correspondence*: Department of Statistics, University of Leeds, Leeds LS2 9JT, U.K.

The remaining sections discuss more general issues that have been raised in the trials, such as time and memory requirements, the use of cost matrices and general warnings on the interpretation of our results.

11.1.1   User's guide to programs

Here we tabulate some measures to summarise each algorithm. Some are subjective quantities based on the user's perception of the programs used in StatLog, and may not hold for other implementations of the method. For example, many of the classical statistical algorithms can handle missing values, whereas those used in this project could not. This would necessitate a "front-end" to replace missing values before running the algorithm. Similarly, all of these programs should be able to incorporate costs into their classification procedure, yet some of them have not. In Table 11.1 we give information on various basic capabilities of each algorithm.

11.2   STATISTICAL ALGORITHMS

11.2.1   Discriminants

It can fairly be said that the performance of linear and quadratic discriminants was exactly as might be predicted on the basis of theory. When there was sufficient data, and the class covariance matrices quite dissimilar then quadratic discriminant did better, although at the expense of some computational costs. Several practical problems remain however:

1. the problem of deleting attributes if they do not contribute usefully to the discrimination between classes (see McLachlan, 1992)
2. the desirability of transforming the data; and the possibility of including some quadratic terms in the linear discriminant as a compromise between pure linear and quadratic discrimination. Much work needs to be done in this area.

We found that there was little practical difference in the performance of ordinary and logistic discrimination. This has been observed before - Fienberg (1980) quotes an example where the superiority of logistic regression over discriminant analysis is "slight" - and is related to the well-known fact that different link functions in generalised linear models often fit empirical data equally well, especially in the region near classification boundaries where the curvature of the probability surface may be negligible. McLachlan (1992) quotes several empirical studies in which the allocation performance of logistic regression was very similar to that of linear discriminants.

In view of the much greater computational burden required, the advice must be to use linear or quadratic discriminants for large datasets. The situation may well be different for small datasets.

11.2.2   ALLOC80

This algorithm was never intended for the size of datasets considered in this book, and it often failed on the larger datasets – with no adequate diagnostics. It can accept attribute data with both numeric and logical values and in this respect appears superior to the other statistical algorithms. The cross-validation methods for parameter selection are too cumbersome for these larger datasets, although in principle they should work. An outstanding problem here is to choose good smoothing parameters - this program uses a

Table 11.1: Users guide to the classification algorithms.

Algorithm	MV	Cost	Interp.	Compreh.	Params	User-fr.	Data
Discrim	N	T	3	4	4	Y	N
Quadisc	N	T	2	3	3	Y	N
Logdisc	N	T	3	4	4	Y	N
SMART	N	LT	1	2	1	N	NC
ALLOC80	N	LT	1	2	2	N	NC
k-NN	N	T	1	5	2	N	N
CASTLE	N	T	3	3	3	Y	NC
CART	Y	T	5	4	5	Y	NC
IndCART	Y	T	5	4	5	Y	NC
NewID	Y	N	5	4	4	Y	NC
AC^2	Y	N	5	4	4	Y	NCH
Baytree	Y	T	4	4	5	N	NC
NaiveBay	Y	T	3	4	4	Y	N
CN2	Y	N	5	4	4	Y	NC
C4.5	Y	N	5	4	4	Y	NC
ITrule	N	N	3	4	4	N	NC
Cal5	Y	LT	5	4	5	Y	NC
Kohonen	N	N	1	1	1	N	N
DIPOL92	N	LT	2	3	2	N	NC
Backprop	N	T	1	3	3	N	N
RBF	N	N	1	1	1	N	N
LVQ	N	N	1	1	1	N	N
Cascade	N	T	1	3	2	N	N

Key:

MV   whether the program accepts missing values

Cost   whether the program has a built-in facility to deal with a cost matrix at learning (L), testing (T) or not at all (N)

Interp.   whether the program gives an easily understood classifier (5 = very easy to interpret)

Compreh.   whether the principle of the method is easily understood (5 = very easy to grasp)

Params   whether the program has good user-guidelines or automatic selection of important parameters.

User-fr.   whether the program is user-friendly

Data   Type of data allowed in the attributes (N = numerical, C = categorical, H= hierarchical). However, note that categorical data can always be transormed to numerical.

multiplicative kernel, which may be rather inflexible if some of the attributes are highly correlated. Fukunaga (1990) suggests a "pre-whitening" of the data which is equivalent to using a multivariate normal kernel with parameters estimated from the sample covariance matrix. This method has shown promise in some of the datasets here, although it is not very robust, and of course still needs smoothing parameter choices.

ALLOC80 has a slightly lower error-rate than k-NN, and uses marginally less storage, but takes about twice as long in training and testing (and k-NN is already a very slow algorithm). However, since k-NN was always set to $k = 1$ this may not generally be true. Indeed, $k = 1$ is a special case of the kernel method so it should be expected to do better.

11.2.3 Nearest Neighbour

Although this method did very well on the whole, as expected it was slowest of all for the very large datasets. However, it is known (Hart, 1968) that substantial time saving can be effected, at the expense of some slight loss of accuracy, by using a condensed version of the training data. An area that requires further study is in fast data-based methods for choosing appropriate distance measures, variable selection and the appropriate number of neighbours. The program in these trials normally used just the nearest neighbour which is certainly not optimal. A simulation study on this problem was carried out by Enas & Choi (1986) . It is clear from many of the results that substantial improved accuracy can be obtained with careful choice of variables, but the current implementation is much too slow. Indeed, LVQ has about the same error-rate as k-NN, but is about 6 times faster, and uses about 25% less storage.

Where scaling of attributes is not important, such as in object recognition datasets, k-nearest neighbour is first in the trials. Yet the explanatory power of k-nearest neighbour might be said to be very small.

11.2.4 SMART

SMART is both a classification and regression type algorithm which is most easily used in batch mode. It is a very slow algorithm to train, but quite quick in the classification stage. The output is virtually incomprehensible to a non-statistician, but a graphical front-end could be written to improve the interpretability. See the example in Section 4.4.1. In addition there are some difficulties in choosing the number of terms to include in the model. This is a similar problem to choosing the smoothing parameter in kernel methods, or the number of neighbours in a nearest neighbour classifier. A major advantage SMART has over most of the other algorithms is that it accepts a cost matrix in its training as well as in its testing phase which, in principle, ought to make it much more suited for tackling problems where costs are important.

11.2.5 Naive Bayes

Naive Bayes can easily handle unknown or missing values. The main drawback of the algorithm is perhaps its "naïvety", *i.e.* it uses directly Bayes theorem to classify examples. In addition, for those not fluent with the statistical background there is generally little indication of why it has classified some examples in one class or the other.

Theory indicates, and our experience confirms, that Naive Bayes does best if the attributes are conditionally independent given the class. This seems to hold true for many medical datasets. One reason for this might be that doctors gather as many different ("independent") bits of relevant information as possible, but they do not include two attributes where one would do. For example, it could be that only one measure of high blood pressure (say diastolic) would be quoted although two (diastolic and systolic) would be available.

11.2.6 CASTLE

In essence CASTLE is a full Bayesian modelling algorithm, *i.e.* it builds a comprehensive probabilistic model of the events (in this case attributes) of the empirical data. It can be used to infer the probability of attributes as well as classes given the values of other attributes. The main reason for using CASTLE is that the polytree models the whole structure of the data, and no special role is given to the variable being predicted, viz. the class of the object. However instructive this may be, it is not the principal task in the above trials (which is to produce a classification procedure). So maybe there should be an option in CASTLE to produce a polytree which *classifies* rather than fits all the variables. To emphasise the point, it is easy to deflect the polytree algorithm by making it fit irrelevant bits of the tree (that are strongly related to each other but are irrelevant to classification). CASTLE can normally be used in both interactive and batch modes. It accepts any data described in probabilities and events, including descriptions of attributes-and-class pairs of data such as that used here. However, all attributes and classes must be discretised to categorical or logical data. The results of CASTLE are in the form of a (Bayesian) polytree that provides a graphical explanation of the probabilistic relationships between attributes and classes. Thus it is better in term of comprehensibility compared to some of the other statistical algorithms in its explanation of the probabilistic relationships between attributes and classes.

The performance of CASTLE should be related to how "tree-like" the dataset is. A major criticism of CASTLE is that there is no internal measure that tells us how closely the empirical data are fitted by the chosen polytree. We recommend that any future implementation of CASTLE incorporates such a "polytree" measure. It should be straightforward to build a goodness-of-fit measure into CASTLE based on a standard test.

As a classifier, CASTLE did best in the credit datasets where, generally, only a few attributes are important, but its most useful feature is the ability to produce simple models of the data. Unfortunately, simple models fitted only a few of our datasets.

11.3 DECISION TREES

There is a confusing diversity of Decision Tree algorithms, but they all seem to perform at about the same level. Five of the decision trees (AC^2, NewID, Cal5, C4.5, IndCART) considered in this book are similar in structure to the original ID3 algorithm, with partitions being made by splitting on an attribute, and with an entropy measure for the splits. There are no indications that this or that splitting criterion is best, but the case for using some kind of pruning is overwhelming, although, again, our results are too limited to say exactly how much pruning to use. It was hoped to relate the performance of a decision tree to some measures of complexity and pruning, specifically the average depth of the tree and the number of terminal nodes (leaves). In a sense CART's cost-complexity pruning automates this. Cal5 has generally much fewer nodes, so gives a simpler tree. AC^2 generally has many more nodes, and occasionally scores a success because of that. The fact that all the decision trees perform at the same accuracy with such different pruning procedures suggests that much work needs to be done on the question of how many nodes to use.

On the basis of our trials on the Tsetse fly data and the segmentation data, we speculate that Decision Tree methods will work well compared to classical statistical methods when the data are multimodal. Their success in the shuttle and technical datasets is due to the special structure of these datasets. In the case of the technical dataset observations were partly pre-classified by the use of a decision tree, and in the shuttle dataset we believe that this may also be so, although we have been unable to obtain confirmation from the data provider.

Among the decision trees, IndCART, CART and Cal5 method emerge as superior to others because they incorporate costs into decisions. Both CART and IndCART can deal with categorical variables, and CART has an important additional feature in that it has a systematic method for dealing with missing values. However, for the larger datasets the commercial package CART often failed where the IndCART implementation did not. In common with all other decision trees, CART, IndCART and Cal5 have the advantage of being distribution free.

11.3.1 AC^2 and NewID

NewID and AC^2 are direct descendants of ID3, and, empirically, their performance as classifiers is very close. The main reason for choosing AC^2 would be to use other aspects of the AC^2 package, for example, the interactive graphical package and the possibility of incorporating prior knowledge about the dataset, in particular certain forms of hierarchical structure; see Chapter 12. We looked at one dataset that was hierarchical in nature, in which AC^2 showed considerable advantage over other methods - see Section 9.5.7.

NewID is based on Ross Quinlan's original ID3 program which generates decision trees from examples. It is similar to CN2 in its interface and command system. Similar to CN2, NewID can be used in both interactive and batch mode. The interactive mode is its native mode; and to run in batch mode users need to write a Unix shell script as for CN2. NewID accepts attribute-value data sets with both logical and numeric data. NewID has a post-pruning facility that is used to deal with noise. It can also deal with unknown values. NewID outputs a confusion matrix. But this confusion matrix must be used with care because the matrix has an extra row and column for unclassified examples – some examples are not classified by the decision tree. It does not accept or incorporate a cost matrix.

AC^2 is an extension to ID3 style of decision tree classifiers to learn structures from a predefined hierarchy of attributes. Similarly to ID3 it uses an attribute-value based format for examples with both logical and numeric data. Because of its hierarchical representation it can also encode some relations between attribute values. It can be run in interactive mode and data can be edited visually under its user interface. AC^2 uses an internal format that is different from the usual format - mainly due to the need to express hierarchical attributes when there are such. But for non-hierarchical data, there is very limited requirement for data conversion. AC^2 can deal with unknown values in examples, and multi-valued attributes. It is also able to deal with knowledge concerning the studied domain, but with the exception of the Machine Faults dataset, this aspect was deliberately not studied in this book. The user interacts with AC^2 via a graphical interface. This interface consists of graphical editors, which enable the user to define the knowledge of the domain, to interactively build the example base and to go through the hierarchy of classes and the decision tree.

AC^2 produces decision trees which can be very large compared to the other decision tree algorithms. The trials reported here suggest that AC^2 is relatively slow. This older version used common LISP and has now been superseded by a C version, resulting in a much faster program.

11.3.2   C4.5

C4.5 is the direct descendent of ID3. It is run in batch mode for training with attribute-value data input. For testing, both interactive and batch modes are available. Both logical and numeric values can be used in the attributes; it needs a declaration for the types and range of attributes, and such information needs to be placed in a separate file. C4.5 is very easy to set up and run. In fact it is only a set of UNIX commands, which should be familiar to all UNIX users. There are very few parameters. Apart from the pruning criterion no major parameter adjustment is needed for most applications - in the trials reported here, the windowing facility was disabled. C4.5 produces a confusion matrix from classification results. However, it does not incorporate a cost matrix. C4.5 allows the users to adjust the degree of the tracing information displayed while the algorithm is running. This facility can satisfy both the users who do not need to know the internal operations of the algorithm and the users who need to monitor the intermidate steps of tree construction.

Note that C4.5 has a rule-generating module, which often improves the error rate and almost invariably the user-transparancy, but this was not used in the comparative trials reported in Chapter 9.

11.3.3   CART and IndCART

CART and IndCART are decision tree algorithms based on the work of Breiman *et al.* (1984). The StatLog version of CART is the commercial derivative of the original algorithm developed at Caltech. Both are classification and regression algorithms but they treat regression and unknown values in the data somewhat differently. In both systems there are very few parameters to adjust for new tasks.

The noise handling mechanism of the two algorithms are very similar. Both can also deal with unknown values, though in different ways. The algorithms both output a decision tree and a confusion matrix as output. But only CART incorporates costs (and it does so in both training and test phases). Note that CART failed to run in many of trials involving very large datasets.

11.3.4   Cal5

Cal5 is a numeric value decision tree classifier using statistical methods. Thus discrete values have to be changed into numeric ones. Cal5 is very easy to set up and run. It has a number of menus to guide the user to complete operations. However, there are a number of parameters, and for novice users the meanings of these parameters are not very easy to understand. The results from different parameter settings can be very different, but tuning of parameters is implemented in a semi-automatic manner.

The decision trees produced by Cal5 are usually quite small and are reasonably easy to understand compared to algorithms such as C4.5 when used with default settings of pruning parameters. Occasionally, from the point of view of minimising error rates, the tree is over-pruned, though of course the rules are then more transparent. Cal5 produces a confusion matrix and incorporates a cost matrix.

11.3.5   Bayes Tree

Our trials confirm the results reported in Buntine (1992): Bayes trees are generally slower in learning and testing, but perform at around the same accuracy as, say, C4.5 or NewID. However, it is not so similar to these two algorithms as one might expect, sometimes being substantially better (in the cost datasets), sometimes marginally better (in the segmented image datasets) and sometimes noticeably worse. Bayes tree also did surprisingly badly, for a decision tree, on the technical dataset. This is probably due to the relatively small sample sizes for a large number of the classes. Samples with very small *a priori* probabilities are allocated to the most frequent classes, as the dataset is not large enough for the *a priori* probabilities to be adapted by the empirical probabilities. Apart from the technical dataset, Bayes trees probably do well as a result of the explicit mechanism for "pruning" via smoothing class probabilities, and their success gives empirical justification for the at-first-sight-artificial model of tree probabilities.

11.4   RULE-BASED METHODS

11.4.1   CN2

The rule-based algorithm CN2 also belongs to the general class of recursive partitioning algorithms. Of the two possible variants, "ordered" and "unordered" rules, it appears that "unordered" rules give best results, and then the performance is practically indistinguishable from the decision trees, while at the same time offering gains in "mental fit" over decision trees. However, CN2 performed badly on the datasets involving costs, although this should not be difficult to fix. As a decision tree may be expressed in the form of rules (and vice-versa), there appears to be no practical reason for choosing rule-based methods except when the complexity of the data-domain demands some simplifying change of representation. This is not an aspect with which this book has been concerned.

CN2 can be used in both interactive and batch mode. The interactive mode is its native mode; and to run in batch mode users need to write a Unix shell script that gives the algorithm a sequence of instructions to run. The slight deviation from the other algorithms is that it needs a set of declarations that defines the types and range of attribute-values for each attribute. In general there is very little effort needed for data conversion.

CN2 is very easy to set up and run. In interactive mode, the operations are completely menu driven. After some familiarity it would be very easy to write a Unix shell script to run the algorithm in batch mode. There are a few parameters that the users will have to choose. However, there is only one parameter – rule types – which may have significant effect on the training results for most applications.

11.4.2   ITrule

Strictly speaking, ITrule is not a classification type algorithm, and was not designed for large datasets, or for problems with many classes. It is an exploratory tool, and is best regarded as a way of extracting isolated interesting facts (or rules) from a dataset. The facts (rules) are not meant to cover all examples. We may say that ITrule does not look for the "best set of rules" for classification (or for any other purpose). Rather it looks for a set of "best rules", each rule being very simple in form (usually restricted to conjunctions of two conditions), with the rules being selected as having high information content (in the sense of having high J-measure). Within these limitations, and also with the limitation of discretised variates, the search for the rules is exhaustive and therefore time-consuming. Therefore the number of rules found is usually limited to some "small" number, which can be as high as 5000 or more however. For use in classification problems, if the preset rules have been exhausted, a default rule must be applied, and it is probable that most errors are committed at this stage. In some datasets, ITrule may generate contradictory rules (*i.e.* rules with identical condition parts but different conclusions), and this may also contribute to a high error-rate. This last fact is connected with the asymmetric nature of the J-measure compared to the usual entropy measure. The algorithm does not incorporate a cost matrix facility, but it would appear a relatively simple task to incorporate costs as all rules are associated with a probability measure. (In multi-class problems approximate costs would need to be used, because each probability measure refers to the odds of observing a class or not).

11.5 NEURAL NETWORKS

With care, neural networks perform very well as measured by error rate. They seem to provide either the best or near to best predictive performance in nearly all cases – the notable exceptions are the datasets with cost matrices. In terms of computational burden, and the level of expertise required, they are much more complex than, say, the machine learning procedures. And there are still several unsolved problems, most notably the problems of how to incorporate costs into the learning phase and the optimal choice of architecture. One major weakness of neural nets is the lack of diagnostic help. If something goes wrong, it is difficult to pinpoint the difficulty from the mass of inter-related weights and connectivities in the net. Because the result of learning is a completed network with layers and nodes linked together with nonlinear functions whose relationship cannot easily be described in qualitative terms, neural networks are generally difficult to understand.

These algorithms are usually very demanding on the part of the user. He will have to be responsible for setting up the initial weights of the network, selecting the correct number of hidden layers and the number of nodes at each layer. Adjusting these parameters of learning is often a laborious task. In addition some of these algorithms are computationally inefficient. A notable exception here is LVQ which is relatively easy to set up and fast to run.

11.5.1 Backprop

This software package contains programs which implement Mult-Layer Perceptrons and Radial Basis Functions, as well as several neural network models which are not discussed here, including recurrent networks. It is reasonably versatile and flexible in that it can be used to train a variety of networks with a variety of methods using a variety of training data formats. However its functionality is not embellished with a friendly user interface, so its users need at least a cursory familiarity with UNIX and neural networks, and a significant block of time to peruse the documentation and work through the demonstrations.

The package is also modular, and extensible by anyone willing to write source code for new modules, based on existing templates and "hooks". One of the fundamental modules provides routines for manipulating matrices, submatrices, and linked lists of submatrices. It includes a set of macros written for the UNIX utility m4 which allows complicated array-handling routines to be written using relatively simple m4 source code, which in turn is translated into C source by m4. All memory management is handled dynamically.

There are several neural network modules, written as applications to the minimisation module. These include a special purpose 3-layer MLP, a fully-connected recurrent MLP, a fully-connected recurrent MLP with an unusual training algorithm (Silva & Almeida, 1990), and general MLP with architecture specified at runtime. There is also an RBF network which shares the I/O routines but does not use the minimiser.

There is a general feeling, especially among statisticians, that the multilayer perceptron is just a highly-parameterised form of non-linear regression. This is not our experience. In practice, the Backprop procedure lies somewhere between a regression technique and a decision tree, sometimes being closer to one and sometimes closer to the other. As a result, we cannot make general statements about the nature of the decision surfaces, but it would seem that they are not in any sense "local" (otherwise there would be a greater similarity with k-NN). Generally, the absence of diagnostic information and the inability to interpret the output is a great disadvantage.

11.5.2   Kohonen and LVQ

Kohonen's net is an implementation of the self-organising feature mapping algorithm based on the work of Kohonen (1989). Kohonen nets have an inherent parallel feature in the evaluation of links between "neurons". So this program is implemented, by Luebeck University of Germany, on a transputer with an IBM PC as the front-end for user interaction. This special hardware requirement thus differs from the norm and makes comparison of memory and CPU time rather difficult.

Kohonen nets are more general than a number of other neural net algorithms such as backpropagation. In a sense, it is a modelling tool that can be used to model the behaviour of a system with its input and output variables (attributes) all modelled as linked neuronal. In this respect, it is very similar to the statistical algorithm CASTLE – both can be used in wider areas of applications including classification and regression. In this book, however, we are primarily concerned with classification. The network can accept attribute-value data with numeric values only. This makes it necessary to convert logical or categorical attributes into numeric data.

In use there are very few indications as to how many nodes the system should have and how many times the examples should be repeatedly fed to the system for training. All such parameters can only be decided on a trial-and-error basis. Kohonen does not accept unknown values so data sets must have their missing attribute-values replaced by estimated values through some statistical methods. Similar to all neural networks, the output of the Kohonen net normally gives very little insight to users as to why the conclusions have been derived from the given input data. The weights on the links of the nodes in the net are not generally easy to explain from a viewpoint of human understanding.

LVQ is also based on a Kohonen net and the essential difference between these two programs is that LVQ uses **supervised** training, so it should be no surprise that in all the trials (with the exception of the DNA dataset) the results of LVQ are better than those of

Kohonen. So, the use of Kohonen should be limited to clustering or **unsupervised** learning, and LVQ should always be preferred for standard classification tasks. Unfortunately, LVQ has at least one "bug" that may give seriously misleading results, so the output should be checked carefully (beware reported error rates of zero!).

11.5.3   Radial basis function neural network

The radial basis function neural network (RBF for short) is similar to other neural net algorithms. But it uses a different error estimation and gradient descent function – *i.e.* the radial basis function. Similar to other neural net algorithms the results produced by RBF are very difficult to understand.

RBF uses a cross-validation technique to handle the noise. As the algorithm trains it continually tests on a small set called the "cross-validation set". When the error on this set starts to increase it stops training. Thus it can automatically decide when to stop training, which is a major advantage of this algorithm compared to other neural net algorithms. However it cannot cope with unknown values.

The algorithm is fairly well implemented so it is relatively easy to use compared to many neural network algorithms. Because it only has one parameter to adjust for each new application – the number of centres of the radial basis function – it is fairly easy to use.

11.5.4   DIPOL92

This algorithm has been included as a neural network, and is perhaps closest to MADA-LINE, but in fact it is rather a hybrid, and could also have been classified as a "non-parametric" statistical algorithm. It uses methods related to logistic regression in the first stage, except that it sets up a discriminating hyperplane between all pairs of classes, and then minimises an error function by gradient descent. In addition, an optional clustering procedure allows a class to be treated as several subclasses.

This is a new algorithm and the results are very encouraging. Although it never quite comes first in any one trial, it is very often second best, and its overall performance is excellent. It would be useful to quantify how much the success of DIPOL92 is due to the multi-way hyperplane treatment, and how much is due to the initial clustering, and it would also be useful to automate the selection of clusters (at present the number of subclasses is a user-defined parameter).

It is easy to use, and is intermediate between linear discriminants and multilayer perceptron in ease of interpretation. It strengthens the case for other hybrid algorithms to be explored.

11.6   MEMORY AND TIME

So far we have said very little about either memory requirements or CPU time to train and test on each dataset. On reason for this is that these can vary considerably from one implementation to another. We can, however, make a few comments.

11.6.1   Memory

In most of these large datasets, memory was not a problem. The exception to this was the full version of the hand-written digit dataset – see Section 9.3.1. This dataset had 256 variables and 10,000 examples and most algorithms (running on an 8 MB machine) could not handle it. However, such problems are likely to be rare in most applications. A problem with the interpretation of these figures is that they were obtained from the UNIX command

set time = (0 "%U %S %M")

and, for a simple FORTRAN program for example, the output is directly related to the dimension declarations. So an edited version could be cut to fit the given dataset and produce a "smaller memory requirement". A more sensible way to quantify memory would be in terms of the size of the data. For example, in the SAS manual (1985) it states that the memory required for nearest neighbour is $120p + 4p(p + 1) + n(8p + 16)$, *i.e.* for most situations, of order np. If similar results could be stated for all our algorithms this would make comparisons much more transparent, and also enable predictions for new datasets.

As far as our results are concerned, it is clear that the main difference in memory requirements will depend on whether the algorithm has to store all the data or can process it in pieces. The theory should determine this as well as the numbers, but it is clear that linear and quadratic discriminant classifiers are the most efficient here.

11.6.2   Time

Again, the results here are rather confusing. The times do not always measure the same thing, for example if there are parameters to select there are two options. User A may decide to just plug in the parameter(s) and suffer a slight loss in accuracy of the classifier. User B may decide to choose the parameters by cross-validation and reduce the error rate at the expense of a vastly inflated training time. It is clear then, that more explanation is required and a more thorough investigation to determine selection of parameters and the trade-off between time and error rate in individual circumstances. There are other anomalies: for example, SMART often quotes the smallest time to test, and the amount of computation required is a superset of that required for Discrim, which usually takes longer. So it appears that the interpretation of results will again be influenced by the implementation. It is of interest that SMART has the largest ratio of training to testing time in nearly all of the datasets. As with memory requirements, a statement that time is proportional to some function of the data size would be preferred. For example, the SAS manual quotes the time for the nearest neighbour classifier to test as proportional to tnp where t is the number of observations in the training data. The above warnings should make us cautious in drawing conclusions, in that some algorithms may not require parameter selection. However, if we sum the training and testing times, we can say generally that

- IndCART takes longer than CART
- Among the statistical algorithms, the "nonparametric" ones take longer, especially k-NN, SMART and ALLOC80
- Among the decision tree algorithms AC^2 and ITrule take longer
- Among the neural net algorithms, DIPOL92 is probably the quickest

11.7   GENERAL ISSUES

11.7.1   Cost matrices

If a cost matrix is involved, be warned that only CART, Cal5, the statistical procedures and some of the neural nets take costs into account at all. Even then, with the exception of

DIPOL92 and SMART, they do not use costs as part of the learning process. Of those algorithms which do not incorporate costs, many output a measure which can be interpreted as a probability, and costs could therefore be incorporated. This book has only considered three datasets which include costs partly for the very reason that some of the decision tree programs cannot cope with them. There is a clear need to have the option of incorporating a cost matrix into all classification algorithms, and in principle this should be a simple matter.

11.7.2   Interpretation of error rates

The previous chapter has already analysed the results from the trials and some sort of a pattern is emerging. It is hoped that one day we can find a set of measures which can be obtained from the data, and then using these measures alone we can predict with some degree of confidence which algorithms or methods will perform the best. There is some theory here, for example, the similarity of within-class covariance matrices will determine the relative performance of linear and quadratic discriminant functions and also the performance of these relative to decision tree methods (qualitative conditional dependencies will favour trees). However, from an empirical perspective there is still some way to go, both from the point of view of determining which measures are important, and how best to make the prediction. The attempts of the previous chapter show how this may be done, although more datasets are required before confidence can be attached to the conclusions.

The request for more datasets raises another issue: What kind of datasets? It is clear that we could obtain very biased results if we limit our view to certain types, and the question of what is representative is certainly unanswered. Section 2.1.3 outlines a number of different dataset types, and is likely that this consideration will play the most important rôle in determining the choice of algorithm.

The comparison of algorithms here is almost entirely of a "black-box" nature. So the recommendations as they stand are really only applicable to the "naïve" user. In the hands of an expert the performance of an algorithm can be radically different, and of course there is always the possibility of transforming or otherwise preprocessing the data. These considerations will often outweigh any choice of algorithm.

11.7.3   Structuring the results

Much of the analysis in the previous chapter depends on the scaling of the results. It is clear that to combine results across many datasets, care will need to be taken that they are treated equally. In Sections 10.4 and 10.7 the scaling was taken so that the error rates (or costs) for each dataset were mapped to the interval $[0, 1]$, whereas in Section 10.6 the scaling was done using an estimated standard error for the error rates (or costs). The different approaches makes the interpretation of the comparison in Section 10.7.1 rather difficult.

The pattern which emerges from the multidimensional scaling and associated hierarchical clustering of the algorithms is very encouraging. It is clear that there is a strong similarity between the construction and the performance of the algorithms. The hierarchical clustering of the datasets is not so convincing. However, the overall picture in Figure 10.3 confirms the breakdown of analysis by subject area (see Section 10.2) in that convex hulls which do not overlap can be drawn around the datasets of the specific subject areas.

An outlier here is the Tsetse fly data - which could also easily been placed in the category of "image datasets:segmentation", since the data are of a spatial nature, although it is not a standard image!

The analysis of Section 10.6 is a promising one, though there is not enough data to make strong conclusions or to take the rules too seriously. However, it might be better to predict performance on a continuous scale rather than the current approach which discretises the algorithms into "Applicable" and "Non-Applicable". Indeed, the choice of $k = 8$ or $k = 16$ (see Section 10.6.3) is very much larger than the more commonly used 2 or 3 standard errors in hypothesis testing.

The attempts to predict performance using the performance of "benchmark" algorithms (see Section 10.7) is highly dependent on the choice of datasets used. Also, it needs to be remembered that the coefficients reported in Table 10.14 are not absolute. They are again based on a transformation of all the results to the unit interval. So for example, the result that the error rate for ALLOC80 could be predicted by taking $0.8 \times$ the error rate for k-NN takes into account the error rates for all of the other algorithms. If we only consider this pair (k-NN and ALLOC80) then we get a coefficient of 0.9 but this is still influenced by one or two observations. An alternative is to consider the average percentage improvement of ALLOC80, which is 6.4%, but none of these possibilities takes account of the different sample sizes.

11.7.4   Removal of irrelevant attributes

There are many examples where the performance of algorithms may be improved by removing irrelevant attributes. A specific example is the DNA dataset, where the middle 20 of the 60 nominal attributes are by far the most relevant. If a decision tree, for example, is presented with this middle section of the data, it performs much better. The same is true of quadratic discriminants, and, this is a very general problem with black-box procedures. There are ways of removing variables in linear discriminants, for example, but these did not have much effect on accuracy, and this variable selection method does not extend to other algorithms.

11.7.5   Diagnostics and plotting

Very few procedures contain internal consistency checks. Even where they are available in principle, they have not been programmed into our implementations. For example, quadratic discrimination relies on multivariate normality, and there are tests for this, but they are programmed separately. Similarly CASTLE should be able to check if the assumption of polytree structure is a reasonable one, but this is not programmed in. The user must then rely on other ways of doing such checks. An important, but very much underused, method is simply to plot selected portions of the data, for example pairs of coordinates with the classes as labels. This often gives very important insights into the data. The manova procedure, multidimensional scaling, principal components and projection pursuit (SMART) all give useful ways in which multidimensional data can be plotted in two dimensions.

11.7.6   Exploratory data

If the object of the exercise is to explore the process underlying the classifications themselves, for example by finding out which variables are important or by gaining an insight into the structure of the classification process, then neural nets, k-nearest neighbour and ALLOC80 are unlikely to be much use. No matter what procedure is actually used, it is often best to prune radically, by keeping only two or three significant terms in a regression, or by using trees of depth two, or using only a small number of rules, in the hope that the important structure is retained. Less important structures can be added on later as greater accuracy is required. It should also be borne in mind that in exploratory work it is common to include anything at all that might conceivably be relevant, and that often the first task is to weed out the irrelevant information before the task of exploring structure can begin.

11.7.7   Special features

If a particular application has some special features such as missing values, hierarchical structure in the attributes, ordered classes, presence of known subgroups within classes (hierarchy of classes), etc. etc., this extra structure can be used in the classification process to improve performance and to improve understanding. Also, it is crucial to understand if the class values are in any sense random variables, or outcomes of a chance experiment, as this alters radically the approach that should be adopted.

The Procrustean approach of forcing all datasets into a common format, as we have done in the trials of this book for comparative purposes, is not recommended in general. The general rule is to use all the available external information, and not to throw it away.

11.7.8   From classification to knowledge organisation and synthesis

In Chapter 5 it was stressed that Machine Learning classifiers should possess a *mental fit* to the data, so that the learned concepts are meaningful to and evaluable by humans. On this criterion, the neural net algorithms are relatively opaque, whereas most of the statistical methods which do not have mental fit can at least determine which of the attributes are important. However, the specific black-box use of methods would (hopefully!) never take place, and it is worth looking forwards more speculatively to AI uses of classification methods.

For example, KARDIO's comprehensive treatise on ECG interpretation (Bratko *et al.*, 1989) does not contain a single rule of human authorship. Seen in this light, it becomes clear that classification and discrimination are not narrow fields within statistics or machine learning, but that the *art* of classification can generate substantial contributions to organise (and improve) human knowledge, – even, as in KARDIO, to manufacture new knowledge.

Another context in which knowledge derived from humans and data is synthesised is in the area of Bayesian expert systems (Spiegelhalter *et al.*, 1993), in which subjective judgments of model structure and conditional probabilities are formally combined with likelihoods derived from data by Bayes theorem: this provides a way for a system to smoothly adapt a model from being initially expert-based towards one derived from data. However, this representation of knowledge by causal nets is necessarily rather restricted because it does demand an exhaustive specification of the full joint distribution. However, such systems form a complete model of a process and are intended for more than simply classification. Indeed, they provide a unified structure for many complex stochastic problems, with connections to image processing, dynamic modelling and so on.

12

Knowledge Representation

Claude Sammut
University of New South Wales[1]

12.1 INTRODUCTION

In 1956, Bruner, Goodnow and Austin published their book *A Study of Thinking*, which became a landmark in psychology and would later have a major impact on machine learning. The experiments reported by Bruner, Goodnow and Austin were directed towards understanding a human's ability to categorise and how categories are learned.

> We begin with what seems a paradox. The world of experience of any normal man is composed of a tremendous array of discriminably different objects, events, people, impressions...But were we to utilise fully our capacity for registering the differences in things and to respond to each event encountered as unique, we would soon be overwhelmed by the complexity of our environment... The resolution of this seeming paradox ... is achieved by man's capacity to categorise. To categorise is to render discriminably different things equivalent, to group objects and events and people around us into classes... The process of categorizing involves ... an act of invention... If we have learned the class "house" as a concept, new exemplars can be readily recognised. The category becomes a tool for further use. The learning and utilisation of categories represents one of the most elementary and general forms of cognition by which man adjusts to his environment.

The first question that they had to deal with was that of representation: what is a concept? They assumed that objects and events could be described by a set of attributes and were concerned with how inferences could be drawn from attributes to class membership. Categories were considered to be of three types: conjunctive, disjunctive and relational.

> ...when one learns to categorise a subset of events in a certain way, one is doing more than simply learning to recognise instances encountered. One is also learning a rule that may be applied to new instances. The concept or category is basically, this "rule of grouping" and it is such rules that one constructs in forming and attaining concepts.

---

[1] *Address for correspondence*: School of Computer Science and Engineering, Artificial Intelligence Laboratory, University of New South Wales, PO Box 1, Kensington, NSW 2033, Australia

The notion of a rule as an abstract representation of a concept in the human mind came to be questioned by psychologists and there is still no good theory to explain how we store concepts. However, the same questions about the nature of representation arise in machine learning, for the choice of representation heavily determines the nature of a learning algorithm. Thus, one critical point of comparison among machine learning algorithms is the method of knowledge representation employed.

In this chapter we will discuss various methods of representation and compare them according to their power to express complex concepts and the effects of representation on the time and space costs of learning.

12.2 LEARNING, MEASUREMENT AND REPRESENTATION

A learning program is one that is capable of improving its performance through experience. Given a program, P, and some input, x, a normal program would yield the same result $P(x) = y$ after every application. However, a learning program can alter its initial state so that its performance is modified with each application. Thus, we can say $P(x|q) = y$. That is, y is the result of applying program P to input, x, given the initial state, q. The goal of learning is to construct a new initial, q', so that the program alters its behaviour to give a more accurate or quicker result. Thus, one way of thinking about what a learning program does is that it builds an increasingly accurate approximation to a mapping from input to output.

The most common learning task is that of acquiring a function which maps objects, that share common properties, to the same class value. This is the categorisation problem to which Bruner, Goodnow and Austin referred and much of our discussion will be concerned with categorisation.

Learning experience may be in the form of examples from a trainer or the results of trial and error. In either case, the program must be able to represent its observations of the world, and it must also be able to represent hypotheses about the patterns it may find in those observations. Thus, we will often refer to the *observation language* and the *hypothesis language*. The observation language describes the inputs and outputs of the program and the hypothesis language describes the internal state of the learning program, which corresponds to its theory of the concepts or patterns that exist in the data.

The input to a learning program consists of descriptions of objects from the universe and, in the case of supervised learning, an output value associated with the example. The universe can be an abstract one, such as the set of all natural numbers, or the universe may be a subset of the real-world. No matter which method of representation we choose, descriptions of objects in the real world must ultimately rely on measurements of some properties of those objects. These may be physical properties such as size, weight, colour, etc or they may be defined for objects, for example the length of time a person has been employed for the purpose of approving a loan. The accuracy and reliability of a learned concept depends heavily on the accuracy and reliability of the measurements.

A program is limited in the concepts that it can learn by the representational capabilities of both observation and hypothesis languages. For example, if an attribute/value list is used to represent examples for an induction program, the measurement of certain attributes and not others clearly places bounds on the kinds of patterns that the learner can find. The learner is said to be *biased* by its observation language. The hypothesis language also places constraints on what may and may not be learned. For example, in the language of attributes and values, relationships between objects are difficult to represent. Whereas, a more expressive language, such as first order logic, can easily be used to describe relationships.

Unfortunately, representational power comes at a price. Learning can be viewed as a search through the space of all sentences in a language for a sentence that best describes the data. The richer the language, the larger the search space. When the search space is small, it is possible to use "brute force" search methods. If the search space is very large, additional knowledge is required to reduce the search.

We will divide our attention among three different classes of machine learning algorithms that use distinctly different approaches to the problem of representation:

Instance-based learning algorithms learn concepts by storing prototypic instances of the concept and do not construct abstract representations at all.

Function approximation algorithms include connectionist and statistics methods. These algorithms are most closely related to traditional mathematical notions of approximation and interpolation and represent concepts as mathematical formulae.

Symbolic learning algorithms learn concepts by constructing a symbolic which describes a class of objects. We will consider algorithms that work with representations equivalent to propositional logic and first-order logic.

12.3   PROTOTYPES

The simplest form of learning is memorisation. When an object is observed or the solution to a problem is found, it is stored in memory for future use. Memory can be thought of as a look up table. When a new problem is encountered, memory is searched to find if the same problem has been solved before. If an exact match for the search is required, learning is slow and consumes very large amounts of memory. However, approximate matching allows a degree of generalisation that both speeds learning and saves memory.

For example, if we are shown an object and we want to know if it is a chair, then we compare the description of this new object with descriptions of "typical" chairs that we have encountered before. If the description of the new object is "close" to the description of one of the stored instances then we may call it a chair. Obviously, we must defined what we mean by "typical" and "close".

To better understand the issues involved in learning prototypes, we will briefly describe three experiments in *Instance-based learning* (IBL) by Aha, Kibler & Albert (1991). IBL learns to classify objects by being shown examples of objects, described by an attribute/value list, along with the class to which each example belongs.

12.3.1   Experiment 1

In the first experiment (IB1), to learn a concept simply required the program to store every example. When an unclassified object was presented for classification by the program, it used a simple Euclidean distance measure to determine the nearest neighbour of the object and the class given to it was the class of the neighbour.

This simple scheme works well, and is tolerant to some noise in the data. Its major disadvantage is that it requires a large amount of storage capacity.

12.3.2   Experiment 2

The second experiment (IB2) attempted to improve the space performance of IB1. In this case, when new instances of classes were presented to the program, the program attempted to classify them. Instances that were correctly classified were ignored and only incorrectly classified instances were stored to become part of the concept.

While this scheme reduced storage dramatically, it was less noise-tolerant than the first.

12.3.3   Experiment 3

The third experiment (IB3) used a more sophisticated method for evaluating instances to decide if they should be kept or not. IB3 is similar to IB2 with the following additions. IB3 maintains a record of the number of correct and incorrect classification attempts for each saved instance. This record summarised an instance's classification performance. IB3 uses a significance test to determine which instances are good classifiers and which ones are believed to be noisy. The latter are discarded from the concept description. This method strengthens noise tolerance, while keeping storage requirements down.

12.3.4   Discussion

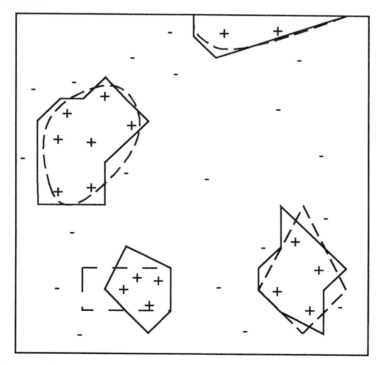

Fig. 12.1: The extension of an IBL concept is shown in solid lines. The dashed lines represent the target concept. A sample of positive and negative examples is shown. Adapted from Aha, Kibler and Albert (1991).

IB1 is strongly related to the k-nearest neighbour methods described in Section 4.3. Here k is 1. The main contribution of Aha, Kibler and Albert (1991) is the attempt to achieve satisfactory accuracy while using less storage. The algorithms presented in Chapter 4 assumed that all training data are available. Whereas IB2 and IB3 examine methods for "forgetting" instances that do not improve classification accuracy.

Figure 12.1 shows the boundaries of an imaginary concept in a two dimensions space. The dashed lines represent the boundaries of the target concept. The learning procedure attempts to approximate these boundaries by nearest neighbour matches. Note that the boundaries defined by the matching procedure are quite irregular. This can have its advantages when the target concept does not have a regular shape.

Learning by remembering typical examples of a concept has several other advantages. If an efficient indexing mechanism can be devised to find near matches, this representation can be very fast as a classifier since it reduces to a table look up. It does not require any sophisticated reasoning system and is very flexible. As we shall see later, representations that rely on abstractions of concepts can run into trouble with what appear to be simple concepts. For example, an abstract representation of a chair may consist of a description of the number legs, the height, etc. However, exceptions abound since anything that can be sat on can be thought of as a chair. Thus, abstractions must often be augmented by lists of exceptions. Instance-based representation does not suffer from this problem since it only consists exceptions and is designed to handle them efficiently.

One of the major disadvantages of this style of representation is that it is necessary to define a similarity metric for objects in the universe. This can often be difficult to do when the objects are quite complex.

Another disadvantage is that the representation is not human readable. In the previous section we made the distinction between an language of observation and a hypothesis language. When learning using prototypes, the language of observation may be an attribute/value representation. The hypothesis language is simply a set of attribute/value or *feature* vectors, representing the prototypes. While examples are often a useful means of communicating ideas, a very large set of examples can easily swamp the reader with unnecessary detail and fails to emphasis important features of a class. Thus a collection of typical instances may not convey much insight into the concept that has been learned.

12.4   FUNCTION APPROXIMATION

As we saw in Chapters 3, 4 and 6, statistical and connectionist approaches to machine learning are related to function approximation methods in mathematics. For the purposes of illustration let us assume that the learning task is one of classification. That is, we wish to find ways of grouping objects in a universe. In Figure 12.2 we have a universe of objects that belong to either of two classes "+" or "-".

By function approximation, we describe a surface that separates the objects into different regions. The simplest function is that of a line and linear regression methods and perceptrons are used to find linear discriminant functions.

Section 6.1 described the perceptron pattern classifier. Given a binary input vector, $\mathbf{x}$, a weight vector, $\mathbf{w}$, and a threshold value, T, if,

$$\sum_i w_i x_i > T$$

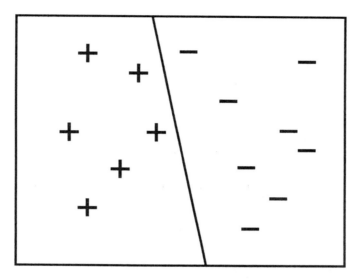

Fig. 12.2: A linear discrimination between two classes.

then the output is 1, indicating membership of a class, otherwise it is 0, indicating exclusion from the class. Clearly, $\mathbf{w} \cdot \mathbf{x} - T$ describes a hyperplane and the goal of perceptron learning is to find a weight vector, $\mathbf{w}$, that results in correct classification for all training examples.

The perceptron is an example of a *linear threshold unit* (LTU). A single LTU can only recognise one kind of pattern, provided that the input space is linearly separable. If we wish to recognise more than one pattern, several LTU's can be combined. In this case, instead of having a vector of weights, we have an array. The output will now be a vector:

$$\mathbf{u} = \mathbf{W}\mathbf{x}$$

where each element of u indicates membership of a class and each row in W is the set of weights for one LTU. This architecture is called a pattern associator.

LTU's can only produce linear discriminant functions and consequently, they are limited in the kinds of classes that can be learned. However, it was found that by cascading pattern associators, it is possible to approximate decision surfaces that are of a higher order than simple hyperplanes. In cascaded system, the outputs of one pattern associator are fed into the inputs of another, thus:

$$\mathbf{u} = \mathbf{W}(\mathbf{V}\mathbf{x})$$

To facilitate learning, a further modification must be made. Rather than using a simple threshold, as in the perceptron, multi-layer networks usually use a non-linear threshold such as a sigmoid function. Like perceptron learning, back-propagation attempts to reduce the errors between the output of the network and the desired result. Despite the non-linear threshold, multi-layer networks can still be thought of as describing a complex collection of hyperplanes that approximate the required decision surface.

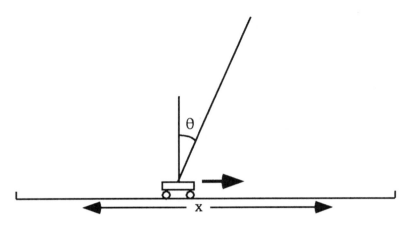

Fig. 12.3: A Pole Balancer.

12.4.1   Discussion

Function approximation methods can often produce quite accurate classifiers because they
are capable of constructing complex decision surfaces. The observation language for
algorithms of this class is usually a vector of numbers. Often preprocessing will convert
raw data into a suitable form. For example, Pomerleau (1989) accepts raw data from a
camera mounted on a moving vehicle and selects portions of the image to process for input
to a neural net that learns how to steer the vehicle. The knowledge acquired by such a
system is stored as weights in a matrix. Therefore, the hypothesis language is usually an
array of real numbers. Thus, the results of learning are not easily available for inspection by
a human reader. Moreover, the design of a network usually requires informed guesswork
on the part of the user in order to obtain satisfactory results. Although some effort has been
devoted to extracting meaning from networks, the still communicate little about the data.

   Connectionist learning algorithms are still computationally expensive. A critical factor
in their speed is the encoding of the inputs to the network. This is also critical to genetic
algorithms and we will illustrate that problem in the next section.

12.5   GENETIC ALGORITHMS

Genetic algorithms (Holland, 1975) perform a search for the solution to a problem by
generating candidate solutions from the space of all solutions and testing the performance
of the candidates. The search method is based on ideas from genetics and the size of
the search space is determined by the representation of the domain. An understanding of
genetic algorithms will be aided by an example.

   A very common problem in adaptive control is learning to balance a pole that is hinged
on a cart that can move in one dimension along a track of fixed length, as show in Figure
12.3. The control must use "bang-bang" control, that is, a force of fixed magnitude can be
applied to push the cart to the left or right.

   Before we can begin to learn how to control this system, it is necessary to represent
it somehow. We will use the BOXES method that was devised by Michie & Chambers

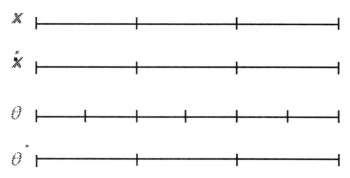

Fig. 12.4: Discretisation of pole balancer state space.

(1968). The measurements taken of the physical system are the angle of the pole, θ, and its angular velocity and the position of the cart, x, and its velocity. Rather than treat the four variables as continuous values, Michie and Chambers chose to discretise each dimension of the state space. One possible discretisation is shown in Figure 12.4.

This discretisation results in $3 \times 3 \times 6 \times 3 = 162$ "boxes" that partition the state space. Each box has associated with it an action setting which tells the controller that when the system is in that part of the state space, the controller should apply that action, which is a push to the left or a push to the right. Since there is a simple binary choice and there are 162 boxes, there are 2^{162} possible control strategies for the pole balancer.

The simplest kind of learning in this case, is to exhaustively search for the right combination. However, this is clearly impractical given the size of the search space. Instead, we can invoke a genetic search strategy that will reduce the amount of search considerably.

In genetic learning, we assume that there is a population of individuals, each one of which, represents a candidate problem solver for a given task. Like evolution, genetic algorithms test each individual from the population and only the fittest survive to reproduce for the next generation. The algorithm creates new generations until at least one individual is found that can solve the problem adequately.

Each problem solver is a *chromosome*. A position, or set of positions in a chromosome is called a *gene*. The possible values (from a fixed set of symbols) of a gene are known as *alleles*. In most genetic algorithm implementations the set of symbols is $\{0, 1\}$ and chromosome lengths are fixed. Most implementations also use fixed population sizes.

The most critical problem in applying a genetic algorithm is in finding a suitable encoding of the examples in the problem domain to a chromosome. A good choice of representation will make the search easy by limiting the search space, a poor choice will result in a large search space. For our pole balancing example, we will use a very simple encoding. A chromosome is a string of 162 boxes. Each box, or gene, can take values: 0 (meaning push left) or 1 (meaning push right). Choosing the size of the population can be tricky since a small population size provides an insufficient sample size over the space of solutions for a problem and large population requires a lot of evaluation and will be slow. In this example, 50 is a suitable population size.

Each iteration in a genetic algorithm is called a *generation*. Each chromosome in a population is used to solve a problem. Its performance is evaluated and the chromosome is given some rating of fitness. The population is also given an overall fitness rating based on the performance of its members. The fitness value indicates how close a chromosome or population is to the required solution. For pole balancing, the fitness value of a chromosome may be the number of time steps that the chromosome is able to keep the pole balanced for.

New sets of chromosomes are produced from one generation to the next. Reproduction takes place when selected chromosomes from one generation are recombined with others to form chromosomes for the next generation. The new ones are called *offspring*. Selection of chromosomes for reproduction is based on their fitness values. The average fitness of population may also be calculated at end of each generation. For pole balancing, individuals whose fitness is below average are replaced by reproduction of above average chromosomes. The strategy must be modified if two few or two many chromosomes survive. For example, at least 10% and at most 60% must survive.

Operators that recombine the selected chromosomes are called genetic operators. Two common operators are *crossover* and *mutation*. Crossover exchanges portions of a pair of chromosomes at a randomly chosen point called the crossover point. Some Implementations have more than one crossover point. For example, if there are two chromosomes, X and Y:

$$X = 1001\ 01011 \quad Y = 1110\ 10010$$

and the crossover point is 4, the resulting offspring are:

$$O_1 = 1001\ 10010 \quad O_2 = 1110\ 01011$$

Offspring produced by crossover cannot contain information that is not already in the population, so an additional operator, mutation, is required. Mutation generates an offspring by randomly changing the values of genes at one or more gene positions of a selected chromosome. For example, if the following chromosome,

$$Z = 100101011$$

is mutated at positions 2, 4 and 9, then the resulting offspring is:

$$O = 110001010$$

The number of offspring produced for each new generation depends on how members are introduced so as to maintain a fixed population size. In a *pure* replacement strategy, the whole population is replaced by a new one. In an *elitist strategy*, a proportion of the population survives to the next generation.

In pole balancing, all offspring are created by crossover (except when more the 60% will survive for more than three generations when the rate is reduced to only 0.75 being produced by crossover). Mutation is a background operator which helps to sustain exploration. Each offspring produced by crossover has a probability of 0.01 of being mutated before it enters the population. If more then 60% will survive, the mutation rate is increased to 0.25.

The number of offspring an individual can produce by crossover is proportional to its fitness:

$$\frac{fitness\ value}{population\ fitness} \times Number\ of\ children$$

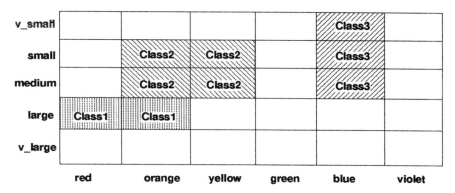

Fig. 12.5: Discrimination on attributes and values.

where the number of children is the total number of individuals to be replaced. Mates are chosen at random among the survivors.

The pole balancing experiments described above, were conducted by Odetayo (1988). This may not be the only way of encoding the problem for a genetic algorithm and so other solutions may be possible. However, this requires effort on the part of the user to devise a clever encoding.

12.6   PROPOSITIONAL LEARNING SYSTEMS

Rather than searching for discriminant functions, symbolic learning systems find expressions equivalent to sentences in some form of logic. For example, we may distinguish objects according to two attributes: size and colour. We may say that an object belongs to class 3 if its colour is red and its size is very small to medium. Following the notation of Michalski (1983), the classes in Figure 12.5 may be written as:

$$class1 \quad \leftarrow \quad size = large \land colour \in \{red, orange\}$$
$$class2 \quad \leftarrow \quad size \in \{small, medium\} \land colour \in \{orange, yellow\}$$
$$class3 \quad \leftarrow \quad size \in \{v\_small \dots medium\} \land colour = blue$$

Note that this kind of description partitions the universe into blocks, unlike the function approximation methods that find smooth surfaces to discriminate classes.

Interestingly, one of the popular early machine learning algorithms, Aq (Michalski, 1973), had its origins in switching theory. One of the concerns of switching theory is to find ways of minimising logic circuits, that is, simplifying the truth table description of the function of a circuit to a simple expression in Boolean logic. Many of the algorithms in switching theory take tables like Figure 12.5 and search for the best way of covering all of the entries in the table.

Aq, uses a *covering algorithm*, to build its concept description:

```
cover := {}
repeat
    select one positive example, e
    construct the set of all conjunctive expressions
        that cover e and no negative example in E-
```

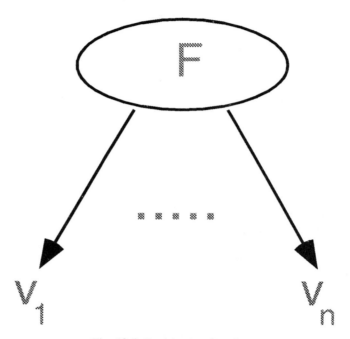

Fig. 12.6: Decision tree learning.

```
     choose the ''best'' expression, x, from this set
     add x as a new disjunct of the concept
     remove all positive examples covered by x
until there are no positive examples left
```

The "best" expression is usually some compromise between the desire to cover as many positive examples as possible and the desire to have as compact and readable a representation as possible. In designing Aq, Michalski was particularly concerned with the expressiveness of the concept description language.

A drawback of the Aq learning algorithm is that it does not use statistical information, present in the training sample, to guide induction. However, decision tree learning algorithms (Quinlan, 1993) do. The basic method of building a decision tree is summarised in Figure 12.6. An simple attribute/value representation is used and so, like Aq, decision trees are incapable of representing relational information. They are, however, very quick and easy to build.

- The algorithm operates over a set of training instances, C.
- If all instances in C are in class P, create a node P and stop. Otherwise select a feature, F and create a decision node.
- Partition the traning instances in C into subsets according to the values v_i of F.
- Apply the algorithm recursively to each if the subsets of C.

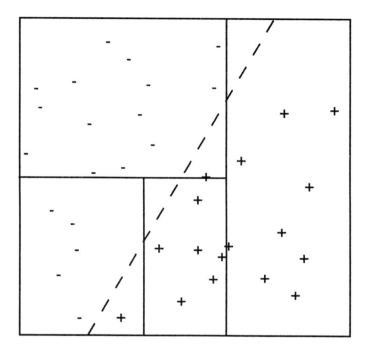

Fig. 12.7: The dashed line shows the real division of objects in the universe. The solid lines show a decision tree approximation.

Decision tree learning algorithms can be seen as methods for partitioning the universe into successively smaller rectangles with the goal that each rectangle only contains objects of one class. This is illustrated in Figure 12.7.

12.6.1 Discussion

Michalski has always argued in favour of rule-based representations over tree structured representations, on the grounds of readability. When the domain is complex, decision trees can become very "bushy" and difficult to understand, whereas rules tend to be modular and can be read in isolation of the rest of the knowledge-base constructed by induction. On the other hand, decision trees induction programs are usually very fast. A compromise is to use decision tree induction to build an initial tree and then derive rules from the tree thus transforming an efficient but opaque representation into a transparent one (Quinlan, 1987b).

It is instructive to compare the shapes that are produced by various learning systems when they partition the universe. Figure 12.7 demonstrates one weakness of decision tree and other symbolic classification. Since they approximate partitions with rectangles (if the universe is 2-dimensional) there is an inherent inaccuracy when dealing with domains with continuous attributes. Function approximation methods and IBL may be able to attain higher accuracy, but at the expense of transparency of the resulting theory. It is more difficult to make general comments about genetic algorithms since the encoding method

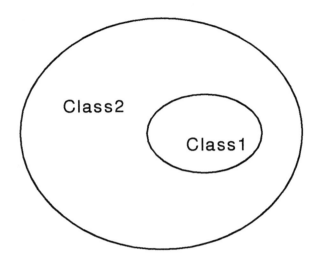

Fig. 12.8: Generalisation as set covering.

will affect both accuracy and readability.

As we have seen, useful insights into induction can be gained by visualising it as searching for a cover of objects in the universe. Unfortunately, there are limits to this geometric interpretation of learning. If we wish to learn concepts that describe complex objects and relationships between the objects, it becomes very difficult to visualise the universe. For this reason, it is often useful to rely on reasoning about the concept description language.

As we saw, the cover in Figure 12.5 can be expressed as clauses in propositional logic. We can establish a correspondence between sentences in the concept description language (the hypothesis language) and a diagrammatic representation of the concept. More importantly, we can create a correspondence between generalisation and specialisation operations on the sets of objects and generalisation and specialisation operations on the sentences of the language.

For example, Figure 12.8 shows two sets, labelled class 1 and class 2. It is clear that class 1 is a generalisation of class 2 since it includes a larger number of objects in the universe. We also call class 2 a specialisation of class 1. By convention, we say the description of class 1 is a generalisation of the description of class 2. Thus,

$$class1 \leftarrow size = large \qquad (12.1)$$

is a generalisation of

$$class2 \leftarrow size = large \wedge colour = red \qquad (12.2)$$

Once we have established the correspondence between sets of objects and their descriptions, it is often convenient to forget about the objects and only consider that we are working with expressions in a language. The reason is simple. Beyond a certain point of complexity, it is not possible to visualise sets, but it is relatively easy to apply simple transformations on sentences in a formal language. For example, Clause (12.2) can be generalised very easily to Clause (12.1) by dropping one of the conditions.

In the next section we will look at learning algorithms that deal with relational information. In this case, the emphasis on language is essential since geometric interpretations no longer provide us with any real insight into the operation of these algorithms.

12.7 RELATIONS AND BACKGROUND KNOWLEDGE

Inductions systems, as we have seen so far, might be described as "what you see is what you get". That is, the output class descriptions use the same vocabulary as the input examples. However, we will see in this section, that it is often useful to incorporate background knowledge into learning.

We use a simple example from Banerji (1980) to the use of background knowledge. There is a language for describing instances of a concept and another for describing concepts. Suppose we wish to represent the binary number, 10, by a left-recursive binary tree of digits "0" and "1":

```
[head: [head: 1; tail: nil]; tail: 0]
```

"head" and "tail" are the names of attributes. Their values follow the colon. The concepts of binary digit and binary number are defined as:

$$x \in digit \quad \equiv \quad x = 0 \lor x = 1$$
$$x \in num \quad \equiv \quad (tail(x) \in digit \land head(x) = nil)$$
$$\lor \quad (tail(x) \in digit \land head(x) \in num)$$

Thus, an object belongs to a particular class or concept if it satisfies the logical expression in the body of the description. Predicates in the expression may test the membership of an object in a previously learned concept.

Banerji always emphasised the importance of a description language that could "grow". That is, its descriptive power should increase as new concepts are learned. This can clearly be seen in the example above. Having learned to describe binary digits, the concept of digit becomes available for use in the description of more complex concepts such as binary number.

Extensibility is a natural and easily implemented feature of horn-clause logic. In addition, a description in horn-clause logic is a logic program and can be executed. For example, to recognise an object, a horn clause can be interpreted in a forward chaining manner. Suppose we have a set of clauses:

$$C_1 \quad \leftarrow \quad P_{11} \land P_{12} \tag{12.3}$$
$$C_2 \quad \leftarrow \quad P_{21} \land P_{22}C_1 \tag{12.4}$$

and an instance:

$$P_{11} \land P_{12} \land P_{21} \land P_{22} \tag{12.5}$$

Clause (12.3) recognises the first two terms in expression (12.5) reducing it to

$$P_{21} \land P_{22} \land C_1$$

Clause (12.4) reduces this to C_2. That is, clauses (12.3) and (12.4) recognise expression (12.5) as the description of an instance of concept C_2.

When clauses are executed in a backward chaining manner, they can either verify that the input object belongs to a concept or produce instances of concepts. In other words,

larger(hammer, feather).

denser(hammer, feather).

heavier(A, B) :– denser(A, B), larger(A, B).

:– heavier(hammer, feather).

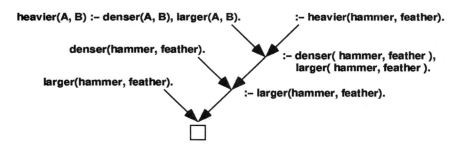

Fig. 12.9: A resolution proof tree from Muggleton & Feng (1990).

we attempt to prove an assertion is true with respect to a background theory. Resolution (Robinson, 1965) provides an efficient means of deriving a solution to a problem, giving a set of axioms which define the task environment. The algorithm takes two terms and resolves them into a most general unifier, as illustrated in Figure 12.9 by the execution of a simple Prolog program.

The box in the figure contains clauses that make up the theory, or knowledge base, and the question to be answered, namely, "is it true that a hammer is heavier than a feather"? A resolution proof is a proof by refutation. That is, answer the question, we assume that it is false and then see if the addition, to the theory, of this negative statement results in a contradiction.

The literals on the left hand side of a Prolog clause are positive. Those on the left hand side are negative. The proof procedure looks for *complimentary* literals in two clauses, *i.e.* literals of opposite sign that unify. In the example in Figure 12.9, $heavier(A, B)$ and $heaver(hammer, feather)$ unify to create the first resolvent:

$$denser(hammer, feather), heavier(hammer, feather)$$

A side effect of unification is to create variable substitutions $A/hammer, B/feather$. By continued application of resolution, we can eventually derive the empty clause, which indicates a contradiction.

Plotkin's (1970) work "originated with a suggestion of R.J. Popplestone that since unification is useful in automatic deduction by the resolution method, its dual might prove helpful for induction. The dual of the most general unifier of two literals is called the least general generalisation". At about the same time that Plotkin took up this idea, J.C. Reynolds was also developing the use of least general generalisations. Reynolds (1970) also recognised the connection between deductive theorem proving and inductive learning:

Robinson's Unification Algorithm allows the computation of the greatest common instance of any finite set of unifiable atomic formulas. This suggests the existence of a dual operation of "least common generalisation". It turns out that such an operation exists and can be computed by a simple algorithm.

The method of least general generalisations is based on subsumption. A clause C_1 subsumes, or is more general than, another clause C_2 if there is a substitution σ such that $C_2 \supseteq C_1 \sigma$.

The least general generalisation of

$$p(g(a), a) \tag{12.6}$$
$$and \quad p(g(b), b) \tag{12.7}$$
$$is \quad p(g(X), X) \tag{12.8}$$

Under the substitution $\{a/X\}$, (12.8) is equivalent to (12.6), and under the substitution $\{b/X\}$, (12.8) is equivalent to (12.7). Therefore, the least general generalisation of $p(g(a), a)$ and $p(g(b), b)$ is $p(g(X), X)$ and results in the inverse substitution $\{X/\{a, b\}\}$.

Buntine (1988) pointed out that simple subsumption is unable to take advantage of background information which may assist generalisation.

Suppose we are given two instances of a concept cuddly_pet,

$$cuddly\_pet(X) \quad \leftarrow \quad fluffy(X) \wedge dog(X) \tag{12.9}$$
$$cuddly\_pet(X) \quad \leftarrow \quad fluffy(X) \wedge cat(X) \tag{12.10}$$

Suppose we also know the following:

$$pet(X) \quad \leftarrow \quad dog(X) \tag{12.11}$$
$$pet(X) \quad \leftarrow \quad cat(X)$$

According to subsumption, the least general generalisation of (12.4) and (12.5) is:

$$cuddly\_pet(X) \leftarrow fluffy(X)$$

since unmatched literals are dropped from the clause. However, given the background knowledge, we can see that this is an over-generalisation. A better one is:

$$cuddly\_pet(X) \leftarrow fluffy(X) \wedge pet(X) \tag{12.12}$$

The moral being that a generalisation should only be done when the relevant background knowledge suggests it. So, observing (12.9), use clause (12.11) as a rewrite rule to produce a generalisation which is Clause (12.12). which also subsumes Clause (12.10).

Buntine drew on earlier work by Sammut (Sammut & Banerji, 1986) in constructing his generalised subsumption. Muggleton & Buntine (1998) took this approach a step further and realised that through the application of a few simple rules, they could invert resolution as Plotkin and Reynolds had wished. Here are two of the rewrite rules in propositional form:

Given a set of clauses, the body of one of which is completely contained in the bodies of the others, such as:

$$X \quad \leftarrow \quad A \wedge B \wedge C \wedge D \wedge E$$
$$Y \quad \leftarrow \quad A \wedge B \wedge C$$

the *absorption* operation results in:

$$X \leftarrow Y \wedge D \wedge E$$
$$Y \leftarrow A \wedge B \wedge C$$

Intra-construction takes a group of rules all having the same head, such as:

$$X \leftarrow B \wedge C \wedge D \wedge E$$
$$X \leftarrow A \wedge B \wedge D \wedge F$$

and replaces them with:

$$X \leftarrow B \wedge D \wedge Z$$
$$Z \leftarrow C \wedge E$$
$$Z \leftarrow A \wedge F$$

These two operations can be interpreted in terms of the proof tree shown in Figure 12.9. Resolution accepts two clauses and applies unification to find the maximal common unifier. In the diagram, two clauses at the top of a "V" are resolved to produce the resolvent at the apex of the "V". Absorption accepts the resolvent and one of the other two clauses to produce the third. Thus, it inverts the resolution step.

Intra-construction automatically creates a new term in its attempt to simplify descriptions. This is an essential feature of inverse resolution since there may be terms in a theory that are not explicitly shown in an example and may have to be invented by the learning program.

12.7.1 Discussion

These methods and others (Muggleton & Feng, 1990; Quinlan, 1990) have made relational learning quite efficient. Because the language of Horn-clause logic is more expressive than the other concept description languages we have seen, it is now possible to learn far more complex concepts than was previously possible. A particularly important application of this style of learning is knowledge discovery. There are now vast databases accumulating information on the genetic structure of human beings, aircraft accidents, company inventories, pharmaceuticals and countless more. Powerful induction programs that use expressive languages may be a vital aid in discovering useful patterns in all these data.

For example, the realities of drug design require descriptive powers that encompass stereo-spatial and other long-range relations between different parts of a molecule, and can generate, in effect, new theories. The pharmaceutical industry spends over $250 million for each new drug released onto the market. The greater part of this expenditure reflects today's unavoidably "scatter-gun" synthesis of compounds which *might* possess biological activity. Even a limited capability to construct predictive theories from data promises high returns.

The relational program Golem was applied to the drug design problem of modelling structure-activity relations (King *et al.*, 1992). Training data for the program was 44 trimethoprim analogues and their observed inhibition of E. coli dihydrofolate reductase. A further 11 compounds were used as unseen test data. Golem obtained rules that were statistically more accurate on the training data and also better on the test data than a Hansch linear regression model. Importantly, relational learning yields understandable rules that characterise the stereochemistry of the interaction of trimethoprim with dihydrofolate reductase observed crystallographically. In this domain, relational learning thus offers a new approach which complements other methods, directing the time-consuming process of the design of potent pharmacological agents from a lead compound, – variants of which need to be characterised for likely biological activity before committing resources to their synthesis.

12.8   CONCLUSIONS

We have now completed a rapid tour of a variety of learning algorithms and seen how the method of representing knowledge is crucial in the following ways:

- Knowledge representation determines the concepts that an algorithm can and cannot learn.
- Knowledge representation affects the speed of learning. Some representations lend themselves to more efficient implementation than others. Also, the more expressive the language, the larger is the search space.
- Knowledge representation determines the readability of the concept description. A representation that is opaque to the user may allow the program to learn, but a representation that is transparent also allows the user to learn.

Thus, when approaching a machine learning problem, the choice of knowledge representation formalism is just as important as the choice of learning algorithm.

13

Learning to Control Dynamic Systems

Tanja Urbančič (1) and Ivan Bratko (1,2)
(1) Jožef Stefan Institute[1] and (2) and University of Ljubljana

13.1 INTRODUCTION

The emphasis in controller design has shifted from the precision requirements towards the following objectives(Leitch & Francis, 1986; Enterline, 1988; Verbruggen and Åström, 1989; Åström, 1991; Sammut & Michie, 1991; AIRTC92, 1992):

- control without complete prior knowledge (to extend the range of automatic control applications),
- reliability, robustness and adaptivity (to provide successful performance in the real-world environment),
- transparency of solutions (to enable understanding and verification),
- generality (to facilitate the transfer of solutions to similar problems),
- realisation of specified characteristics of system response (to please customers).

These problems are tackled in different ways, for example by using expert systems (Dvorak, 1987), neural networks (Miller *et al.*, 1990; Hunt *et al.*, 1992), fuzzy control (Lee, 1990) and genetic algorithms (Renders & Nordvik, 1992). However, in the absence of a complete review and comparative evaluations, the decision about how to solve a problem at hand remains a difficult task and is often taken *ad hoc*. Leitch (1992) has introduced a step towards a systematisation that could provide some guidelines. However, most of the approaches provide only partial fulfilment of the objectives stated above. Taking into account also increasing complexity of modern systems together with real-time requirements, one must agree with Schoppers (1991), that designing control means looking for a suitable compromise. It should be tailored to the particular problem specifications, since some objectives are normally achieved at the cost of some others.

Another important research theme is concerned with the replication of human operators' subconscious skill. Experienced operators manage to control systems that are extremely difficult to be modelled and controlled by classical methods. Therefore, a "natural" choice would be to mimic such skilful operators. One way of doing this is by modelling the

---

[1]*Address for correspondence*: Jožef Stefan Institute, Univerza v Lubljani, 61111 Ljubljana, Slovenia

operator's strategy in the form of rules. The main problem is how to establish the appropriate
set of rules: While gaining skill, people often lose their awareness of what they are actually
doing. Their knowledge is implicit, meaning that it can be demonstrated and observed, but
hardly ever described explicitly in a way needed for the direct transfer into an automatic
controller. Although the problem is general, it is particularly tough in the case of control
of fast dynamic systems where subconscious actions are more or less the prevailing form
of performance.

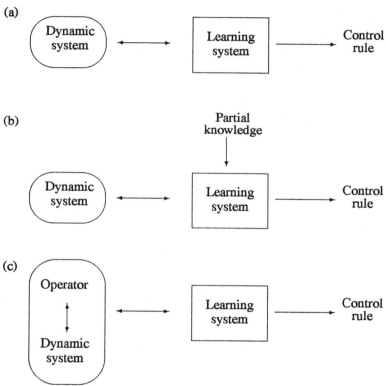

Fig. 13.1: Three modes of learning to control a dynamic system: (a) Learning from scratch,
(b) Exploiting partial knowledge, (c) Extracting human operator's skill.

The aim of this chapter is to show how the methods of machine learning can help
in the construction of controllers and in bridging the gap between the subcognitive skill
and its machine implementation. First successful attempts in learning control treated the
controlled system as a black box (for example Michie & Chambers, 1968), and a program
learnt to control it by trials. Due to the black box assumption, initial control decisions
are practically random, resulting in very poor performance in the first experiments. On
the basis of experimental evidence, control decisions are evaluated and possibly changed.
Learning takes place until a certain success criterion is met. Later on, this basic idea
was implemented in different ways, ranging from neural networks (for example Barto

et al., 1983; Anderson, 1987) to genetic algorithms (for example Odetayo & McGregor, 1989). Recently, the research concentrated on removing the deficiencies inherent to these methods, like the obscurity and unreliability of the learned control rules (Bain, 1990; Sammut & Michie, 1991; Sammut & Cribb, 1990) and time-consuming experimentation (Sammut, 1994) while still presuming no prior knowledge. Until recently, this kind of learning control has remained predominant. However, some of the mentioned deficiences are closely related to the black box assumption, which is hardly ever necessary in such a strict form. Therefore, the latest attempts take advantage of the existing knowledge, being explicit and formulated at the symbolic level (for example Urbančič & Bratko, 1992; Bratko, 1993; Varšek *et al.*, 1993), or implicit and observable just as operator's skill (Michie *et al.*, 1990; Sammut *et al.*, 1992; Camacho & Michie, 1992; Michie & Camacho, 1994).

The structure of the chapter follows this introductory discussion. We consider three modes of learning to control a system. The three modes, illustrated in Figure 13.1, are:

(a)   The learning system learns to control a dynamic system by trial and error, without any prior knowledge about the system to be controlled (learning from scratch).

(b)   As in (a), but the learning system exploits some partial explicit knowledge about the dynamic system.

(c)   The learning system observes a human operator and learns to replicate the operator's skill.

Experiments in learning to control are popularly carried out using the task of controlling the pole-and-cart system. In Section 13.2 we therefore describe this experimental domain. Sections 13.3 and 13.4 describe two approaches to learning from scratch: BOXES and genetic learning. In Section 13.5 the learning system exploits partial explicit knowledge. In Section 13.6 the learning system exploits the operator's skill.

13.2   EXPERIMENTAL DOMAIN

The main ideas presented in this chapter will be illustrated by using the pole balancing problem (Anderson & Miller, 1990) as a case study. So let us start with a description of this control task which has often been chosen to demonstrate both classical and nonconventional control techniques. Besides being an attractive benchmark, it also bears similarities with tasks of significant practical importance such as two-legged walking, and satellite attitude control (Sammut & Michie, 1991). The system consists of a rigid pole and a cart. The cart can move left and right on a bounded track. The pole is hinged to the top of the cart so that it can swing in the vertical plane. In the AI literature, the task is usually just to prevent the pole from falling and to keep the cart position within the specified limits, while the control regime is that of bang-bang. The control force has a fixed magnitude and all the controller can do is to change the force direction in regular time intervals.

Classical methods (for example Kwakernaak & Sivan, 1972) can be applied to controlling the system under several assumptions, including complete knowledge about the system, that is a differential equations model up to numerical values of its parameters. Alternative approaches tend to weaken these assumptions by constructing control rules in two essentially different ways: by learning from experience, and by qualitative reasoning. The first one will be presented in more detail later in this chapter. The second one will be described here only up to the level needed for comparison and understanding, giving a general idea about two solutions of this kind:

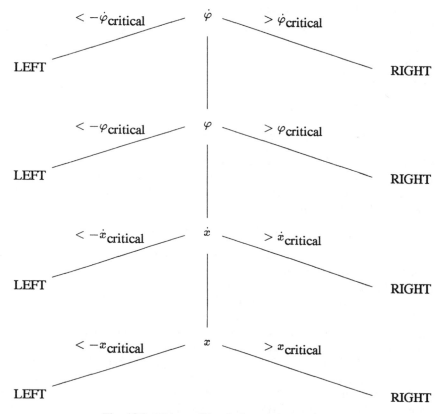

Fig. 13.2: Makarovič's rule for pole balancing.

- A solution, distinguished by its simplicity, was derived by Makarovič (1988) (see Figure 13.2). Rules of the same tree structure, but with the state variables ordered in different ways, were experimentally studied by Džeroski (1989). He showed that no less than seven permutations of state variables yielded successful control rules. We denote such rules as $\mathcal{M}(P)$, where P is a permutation of the variables, determining their top-down order.

- Another solution was inferred by Bratko (1991) from a very simple qualitative model of the inverted pendulum system. The derived control rule is described by the following relations:

$$\ddot{x}_{\text{goal}} = k_2 \left(k_1 \left(x_{\text{ref}} - x \right) - \dot{x} \right) \tag{13.1}$$

$$\varphi_{\text{ref}} = \frac{1}{g} \ddot{x}_{\text{goal}} \tag{13.2}$$

$$\ddot{\varphi}_{\text{goal}} = k_4 \left(k_3 \left(\varphi_{\text{ref}} - \varphi \right) - \dot{\varphi} \right) \tag{13.3}$$

$$F = -M_0^+ (\ddot{\varphi}_{\text{goal}}) \tag{13.4}$$

where x_{ref} and φ_{ref} denote reference values to be reached, $\ddot{x}_{\text{goal}}$ and $\ddot{\varphi}_{\text{goal}}$ denote goal values required for successful control, and M_0^+ denotes a monotonically increasing function passing through the point $(0, 0)$.

When the system is to be controlled under the bang-bang regime, control action A is determined by the sign of force F: **if** $F > 0$ **then** $A = pos$ **else** $A = neg$. Assuming $x_{ref} = 0$ and $k_4 > 0$ without loss of generality, Equations (13.1)–(13.4) can be simplified and normalised, resulting in

$$F = \text{sign}(p_1 x + p_2 \dot{x} + p_3 \varphi + \dot{\varphi}), \tag{13.5}$$

where $p_i, i = 1, \ldots, 3$ are numerical parameters.

Both Makarovič's and Bratko's rule successfully control the inverted pendulum, provided the appropriate values of the numerical parameters are chosen. Moreover, there exists a set of parameter values that makes Bratko's rule equivalent to the bang-bang variant of a classical control rule using the sign of pole-placement controller output (Džeroski, 1989).

13.3   LEARNING TO CONTROL FROM SCRATCH: BOXES

In learning approaches, trials are performed in order to gain experimental evidence about different control decisions. A trial starts with the system positioned in an initial state chosen from a specified region, and lasts until failure occurs or successful control is performed for a prescribed maximal period of time. Failure occurs when the cart position or pole inclination exceeds the given boundaries. The duration of a trial is called survival time. Learning is carried out by performing trials repeatedly until a certain success criterion is met. Typically, this criterion requires successful control within a trial to exceed a prescribed period of time. Initial control decisions are usually random. On the basis of experimental evidence, they are evaluated and possibly changed, thus improving control quality. This basic idea has been implemented in many different ways, for example in BOXES (Michie & Chambers, 1968), Adaptive Critic reinforcement method (Barto *et al.*, 1983), CART (Connell & Utgoff, 1987), multilayer connectionist approach (Anderson, 1987) and many others. Geva and Sitte (1993a) provide an exhaustive review. Here, two methods will be described in more detail: BOXES (Michie & Chambers, 1968) and genetic learning of control (Varšek *et al.*, 1993). The choice of methods presented here is subjective. It was guided by our aim to describe recent efforts in changing or upgrading the original ideas. We chose BOXES because it introduced a learning scheme that was inspirational to much further work.

13.3.1   BOXES

The BOXES program (Michie & Chambers, 1968) learns a state-action table, *i.e.* a set of rules that specify action to be applied to the system in a given state. Of course this would not be possible for the original, infinite state space. Therefore, the state space is divided into "boxes". A box is defined as the Cartesian product of the values of the system variables, where all the values belong to an interval from a predefined partition. A typical partition of the four dimensional state space into boxes distinguish 3 values of x, 3 of $\dot{x}$, 6 of φ and 3 of $\dot{\varphi}$, giving 162 boxes. All the points within a box are mapped to the same control decision. During one trial, the state-action table is fixed. When a failure is detected a trial ends. Decisions are evaluated with respect to the accumulated numeric information:

how many times the system entered a particular state, how successful it was after particular decisions, etc. The following information is accumulated for each box:

LL: "left life", weighted sum of survival times after left decision was taken in this state during previous trials,

RL: "right life", the same for the right decision,

LU: "left usage", weighted sum of the number of left decisions taken in this state during previous trials,

RU: "right usage", the same for right decisions,

$T_1, T_2, \ldots, T_N$: times (*i.e.* steps) at which the system enters this state during the current trial.

After a trial the program updates these figures. For the states in which decision "left" was taken, the new values are:

$$
\begin{aligned}
LL_{new} &= LL*DK + \sum_{i=1}^{N}(T_F - T_i) \\
LU_{new} &= LU*DK + N \\
RL_{new} &= RL*DK \\
RU_{new} &= RU*DK
\end{aligned}
$$

where the meaning of the parameters is as follows:

N: number of entries into the state during the run,

DK: constant that weighs recent experience relative to earlier experience ($DK \leq 1$),

T_F: finishing time of the trial.

Analogous updates are made for the states with decision "right".

For the whole system, GL ("global life") and GU ("global usage") are computed after each trial:

$$
\begin{aligned}
GL_{new} &= GL*DK + T_F \\
GU_{new} &= GU*DK + 1
\end{aligned}
$$

These values are used for a numeric evaluation of the success for both actions. The estimates are computed after a trial for each qualitative state:

$$
\begin{aligned}
V_{left} &= \frac{LL + K\,(GL/GU)}{LU + K} \\
V_{right} &= \frac{RL + K\,(GL/GU)}{RU + K}
\end{aligned}
$$

where K is constant that weighs global experience relative to local experience.

The program chooses the action with the higher estimate to be applied in the box during the next trial.

The performance of BOXES is generally described by the number of trials needed for first achieving 10 000 step survival. Figures vary considerably from paper to paper and are between 84 (Geva & Sitte, 1993b) and 557 (Sammut, 1994). Although interesting, these figures are not sufficient to validate the learning results. Reliability, robustness and characteristics of the controller performance are important as well and are discussed in many papers devoted to BOXES.

13.3.2   Refinements of BOXES

Sammut (1994) describes some recent refinements of the basic Michie-Chambers learning scheme. The central mechanism of learning in BOXES is the decision rule based on the "experience" of each box. The experience for each individual box is accumulated in the variables LL (left action lifetime), LU (left action usage), RL and RU (same for the right action). The Michie-Chambers rule determines the decision between left and right action depending on these variables. The rule is designed so that it combines two, possibly conflicting interests: exploitation and exploration. The first is to perform the action that in the past produced the best results (that is maximum lifetime), and the second is to *explore* the alternatives. The alternatives may in the future turn out in fact to be superior to what appears to be best at present.

The original Michie-Chambers formulas find a particular compromise between these two interests. The compromise can be adjusted by varying the parameters in the formulas.

Sammut (1994) describes a series of modifications of the original Michie-Chambers rule. The following elegant rule (named after Law & Sammut) experimentally performed the best in terms of learning rate and stability of learning:

if an action has not been tested then choose that action
else if $LL/LU^K > RL/RU^K$ then choose left
else if $RL/RU^K > LL/LU^K$ then choose right
else choose an action at random

K is a user defined parameter that adjusts the relative importance of exploitation and exploration. The lowest reasonable value for K is 1. This corresponds to pure exploitation without any desire to explore the untested. By increasing K, the system's mentality changes towards experimentalist. Then the system is willing to experiment with actions that from past experience look inferior.

A suitable compromise for K is needed for overall good performance. For the classical pole-and-cart problem, it was experimentally found that $K = 1.7$ is optimal. The learning rate is relatively stable for values of K between 1.4 and 1.8, and it degrades rapidly when K decreases below 1.4 or increases above 1.8. The following improvement of the Law & Sammut rule with respect to the Michie & Chambers rule was reported: on the average over 20 experiments, the original BOXES needed 557 trials to learn to control the system, whereas the Law & Sammut rule needed 75 trials (with $K = 1.7$). In trying to test the stability of the Law & Sammut rule, it was found that K was slightly, but not significantly, sensitive to small changes in the learning problem, such as changing the number of boxes from 162 to 225, or introducing asymmetry in the force (left push twice the right push).

Geva and Sitte (1993a) carried out exhaustive experiments concerning the same topic. With the appropriate parameter setting the BOXES method performed as well as the Adaptive Critic reinforcement learning (Barto *et al.*, 1983). They got an average of 52 trials out of 1000 learning experiments (standard deviation was 32).

13.4   LEARNING TO CONTROL FROM SCRATCH: GENETIC LEARNING

Genetic algorithms (GAs) are loosely based on Darwinian principles of evolution: repro-duction, genetic recombination, and the "survival of the fittest" (Holland, 1975; Goldberg, 1989). They maintain a set of candidate solutions called a population. Candidate solutions are usually represented as binary coded strings of fixed length. The initial population is generated at random. What happens during cycles called generations is as follows. Each member of the population is evaluated using a fitness function. After that, the population undergoes reproduction. Parents are chosen stochastically, but strings with a higher value of fitness function have higher probability of contributing an offspring. Genetic operators, such as crossover and mutation, are applied to parents to produce offspring. A subset of the population is replaced by the offspring, and the process continues on this new generation. Through recombination and selection, the evolution converges to highly fit population members representing near-optimal solutions to the considered problem.

When controllers are to be built without having an accurate mathematical model of the system to be controlled, two problems arise: first, how to *establish the structure* of the controller, and second, how to *choose numerical values* for the controller parameters. In the following, we present a three-stage framework proposed by Varšek *et al.* (©1993 IEEE). First, control rules, represented as tables, are obtained without prior knowledge about the system to be controlled. Next, *if-then* rules are synthesized by structuring information encoded in the tables, yielding comprehensible control knowledge. This control knowledge has adequate structure, but it may be non-operational because of inadequate settings of its numerical parameters. Control knowledge is finally made operational by fine-tuning numerical parameters that are part of this knowledge. The same fine-tuning mechanism can also be applied when available partial domain knowledge suffices to determine the structure of a control rule in advance.

In this approach, the control learning process is considered to be an instance of a combinatorial optimisation problem. In contrast to the previously described learning approach in BOXES, where the goal is to maximise survival time, here the goal is to maximise survival time, and, simultaneously, to minimise the discrepancy between the desired and actual system behaviour. This criterion is embodied in a cost function, called the *raw fitness function*, used to evaluate candidate control rules during the learning process. Raw fitness $f \in [0, 1]$ is calculated as follows:

$$f = \widehat{S}\,(1 - \widehat{Err})$$

$$\widehat{S} = \frac{1}{N} \sum_{k=1}^{N} \frac{S_k}{S_{\max}}$$

$$\widehat{Err} = \frac{1}{N} \sum_{k=1}^{N} \frac{Err_k}{S_k}$$

$$Err_k = \frac{1}{2} \sum_{i=1}^{S_k} (\frac{|x_i|}{x_{\max}} + \frac{|\varphi_i|}{\varphi_{\max}}), \quad k = 1 \dots N,$$

where $\widehat{S}$ is the normalised survival time, $\widehat{Err}$ is the normalised error, N is the number of trials performed to evaluate a candidate solution, S_k is the survival time in the k-th trial, $S_{\max}$ is the maximal duration of a trial, and Err_k is the cumulative error of the k-th trial.

After completing the learning process, solutions were thoroughly evaluated by performing 100 trials with maximal duration of a trial set to 1 000 000 steps, corresponding to over 5.5 hours of simulated time. Note that the maximal duration of a trial most frequently found in the AI literature is 200 seconds.

Phase 1: Obtaining control without prior knowledge

During this phase, BOXES-like decision rules were learned. For each of the pole-cart variables x, $\dot{x}$, φ and $\dot{\varphi}$, the domain is partitioned into three labelled intervals neg, $zero$ and pos. Each decision rule is then represented as a four-dimensional array, where each entry represents a control action. In addition, two partitioning thresholds are required for each system variable. Candidate solutions, comprising a decision rule along with the corresponding thresholds, are represented as binary strings.

To calculate a fitness value for each individual, 25 trials were carried out with the maximal duration of a trial set to 5000 steps. Populations of size 100 were observed for 60 generations. The experiment was repeated ten times. On average, after about 30 generations, individuals representing rules better than Makarovič's $\mathcal{M}(\dot{\varphi}, \varphi, \dot{x}, x)$ rule were discovered.

Phase 2: Inducing rule structure

To automatically synthesize comprehensible rules obtained during Phase 1, an inductive learning technique was employed. A derivative of the CN2 algorithm (Clark & Niblett, 1988), named Ginesys PC (Karalič & Gams, 1989), was used to compress the GA-induced BOXES-like rules into the *if-then* form. The learning domain for the compression phase was described in terms of four attributes and the class. The attribute values were interval labels for the pole-cart variables x, $\dot{x}$, φ and $\dot{\varphi}$, and the class represented the corresponding action (*i.e.* positive or negative control force).

The obtained rules are very close in form to Makarovič's rule. From the rules shown by Džeroski (1989) to successfully control the pole-cart system, rules $\mathcal{M}(\varphi, \dot{\varphi}, x, \dot{x})$, $\mathcal{M}(\dot{\varphi}, \varphi, x, \dot{x})$, and $\mathcal{M}(\varphi, \dot{\varphi}, \dot{x}, x)$ were discovered automatically. The performance of the compressed rules decreased with respect to the original GA-induced BOXES-like rules due to inaccurate interpretation of the interval labels. As in the case of Table 13.1, the 100% failure rate of the compressed rule indicates that this rule was never able to balance the system for 1 000 000 steps. Since the defining thresholds were learned during Phase 1 to perform well with the original GA-induced rules, these thresholds should be adapted to suit the new compressed rules.

Phase 3: Fine-tuning by optimizing control performance

In Phase 3, the interpretation of symbolic values, *i.e.* interval labels, appearing in the qualitative rule $\mathcal{M}(\varphi, \dot{\varphi}, x, \dot{x})$ found in Phase 2 was adjusted to maximise the control quality. For this purpose, a GA was employed again. This time, each chromosome represented four binary coded thresholds while the rule structure was set to $\mathcal{M}(\varphi, \dot{\varphi}, x, \dot{x})$ and left unchanged throughout the optimisation process.

To calculate a fitness value for each individual, only 15 trials were carried out with maximal duration of a trial set to 2000 steps. Populations of size 50 were evolved for 30 generations. After 30 generations, individuals representing rules better than those obtained during Phase 1 were generated. Through the extensive evaluation, the fine-tuned rules were shown reliable (see results in Table 13.1).

13.4.1   Robustness and adaptation

Additional experiments were carried out. The robustness of learning "from scratch" was tested by performing the experiment twice: first, with force $F \in \{+10\,\text{N}, -10\,\text{N}\}$, and

Table 13.1: (©1993 IEEE) Control performance of GA-induced BOXES-like rule, compressed rule $\mathcal{M}(\varphi, \dot{\varphi}, x, \dot{x})$, fine-tuned rule $\mathcal{M}(\varphi, \dot{\varphi}, x, \dot{x})$, and the original Makarovič's rule $\mathcal{M}(\dot{\varphi}, \varphi, \dot{x}, x)$.

Rule	Failures [%]	Avg. survival time [steps]	Fitness
GA-based	4	978 149	0.9442
Compressed	100	9 290	0.0072
Fine-tuned	0	1 000 000	0.9630
Makarovič's	0	1 000 000	0.8857

second, with asymmetrical force $F \in \{+10\,N, -5\,N\}$. The possibility of adaptation of the qualitative rule $\mathcal{M}(\varphi, \dot{\varphi}, x, \dot{x})$ obtained for symmetrical force $F \in \{+1\,N, -1\,N\}$ to the new conditions, $F \in \{+10\,N, -10\,N\}$ and $F \in \{+10\,N, -5\,N\}$, was examined by performing two further fine-tuning experiments.

Table 13.2 shows the performance of four rules obtained in these experiments. It can be seen that GAs can successfully learn to control the pole-cart system also under modified conditions.

Table 13.2: (©1993 IEEE) Control performance of GA-induced BOXES-like rules for $F \in \{+10\,N, -10\,N\}$ and $F \in \{+10\,N, -5\,N\}$, and rule $\mathcal{M}(\varphi, \dot{\varphi}, x, \dot{x})$ fine-tuned for $F \in \{+10\,N, -10\,N\}$ and $F \in \{+10\,N, -5\,N\}$.

Rule	Failures [%]	Avg. survival time [steps]	Fitness
GA+10–10	0	1 000 000	0.9222
GA+10–5	44	665 772	0.5572
Tuned+10–10	0	1 000 000	0.9505
Tuned+10–5	0	1 000 000	0.9637

To summarise, successful and comprehensible control rules were synthesized automatically in three phases. Here, a remark should be made about the number of performed trials. In this research, it was very high due to the following reasons. First, the emphasis was put on the reliability of learned rules and this, of course, demands much more experimentation in order to ensure good performance on a wide range of initial states. In our recent experiments with a more narrow range of initial states the number of trials was considerably reduced without affecting the reliability. Second, the performance of the rules after the first phase was practically the same as that of the rules after the third phase. Maybe the same controller structure could be obtained in the second phase from less perfect rules. However, it is difficult to know when the learned evidence suffices. To conclude, the exhaustiveness of these experiments was conciously accepted by the authors in order to show that 100% reliable rules can be learned from scratch.

13.5 EXPLOITING PARTIAL EXPLICIT KNOWLEDGE

13.5.1 BOXES with partial knowledge

To see how adding domain knowledge affects speed and results of learning, three series of experiments were done by Urbančič & Bratko (1992). The following variants of learning control rules with program BOXES were explored:

A.   without domain knowledge,

B.   with partial domain knowledge, considered as definitely correct, and

C.   with partial initial domain knowledge, allowed to be changed during learning.

The following rule served as partial domain knowledge:

if $\dot{\varphi} > \dot{\varphi}_{critical}$ then action RIGHT

else if $\dot{\varphi} < -\dot{\varphi}_{critical}$ then action LEFT

Although the rule alone is not effective at all (average survival was 30 steps), it considerably decreased the number of trials needed for achieving 10 000 survival time steps (Table 13.3). At the same time, the reliability (*i.e.* the percentage of trials with the learned state-action table, surviving more than 10 000 simulation steps) increased from 16.5% to 50%. More detailed description of the experiments is available in Urbančič & Bratko (1992).

Table 13.3: Experimental results showing the influence of partial knowledge.

Version	Length of learning [av. num. of trials]	Av. reliability [ratio]	Av. survival [steps]
A.	427	3/20	4894
B.	50	10/20	7069
C.	197	4/20	4679

13.5.2   Exploiting domain knowledge in genetic learning of control

Domain knowledge can be exploited to bypass the costly process of learning a control rule from scratch. Instead of searching for both the structure of a rule and the values of numerical parameters required by the rule, we can start with a known rule structure derived by Bratko (1991) from a qualitative model of pole and cart. Then we employ a GA to tune the parameters p_1, p_2 and p_3 appearing in the rule.

To calculate a fitness value of an individual, 25 trials were carried out with maximal duration of a trial set to 2000 steps, corresponding to 40 seconds of simulated time. Populations of size 30 were evolved for 50 generations. The GA was run 10 times. In all the runs, the parameter settings, that ensured maximal survival of the system for all 25 initial states, were found. Table 13.4 gives the best three obtained parameter settings along with their fitness values.

The parameter tuning and evaluation procedures were repeated identically for two modified versions of the pole-cart system, one being controlled with symmetrical force $F \in \{+10\,\mathrm{N}, -10\,\mathrm{N}\}$, and the other with asymmetrical force $F \in \{+10\,\mathrm{N}, -5\,\mathrm{N}\}$. The problems were found no harder for the GA than the $F \in \{+1\,\mathrm{N}, -1\,\mathrm{N}\}$ case.

It can be noted that in this case, the genetic algorithm is applied just to tune a controller with known structure. In a similar way, other types of controllers can be tuned, for example the classical PID controller (Urbančič *et al.*, 1992).

13.6   EXPLOITING OPERATOR'S SKILL

13.6.1   Learning to pilot a plane

Sammut *et al.* (1992) and Michie & Sammut (1993) describe experiments in extracting, by Machine Learning, the pilot's subcognitive component of the skill of flying a plane. In

Table 13.4: (©1993 IEEE) Control performance of Bratko's control rule (a) with parameter values found by a GA, and (b) with parameter values that make the rule equivalent to the bang-bang variant of the classical control rule.

	Parameters			Failures [%]	Avg. survival time [steps]	Fitness
	p_1	p_2	p_3			
(a)	0.45	0.60	22.40	0	1,000,000	0.9980
	0.30	0.45	19.00	0	1,000,000	0.9977
	0.25	0.40	13.65	0	1,000,000	0.9968

	Parameters			Failures [%]	Avg. survival time [steps]	Fitness
	p_1	p_2	p_3			
(b)	0.147	0.319	3.91	0	1,000,000	0.9781

these experiments, a simulator of the Cessna airplane was used. Human pilots were asked to fly the simulated plane according to a well defined flight plan. This plan consisted of seven stages including manouevres like: take off, flying to a specified point, turning, lining up with the runway, descending to the runway and landing.

The pilots' control actions during flight were recorded as "events". Each event record consisted of the plane's state variables and the control action. The values of state variables belonging to an event were actually taken a little earlier than the pilot's action. The reason for this was that the action was assumed to be the pilot's response, with some delay, to the current state of the plane variables. Sammut *et al.* (1992) stated that it remains debatable what a really appropriate delay is between the state of the plane variables and control action invoked by that state:

> ... the action was performed some time later in response to the stimulus. But how do we know what the stimulus was? Unfortunately there is no way of knowing.

The plane's state variables included elevation, elevation speed, azimuth, azimuth speed, airspeed etc. The possible control actions affected four control variables: rollers, elevator, thrust and flaps. The problem was decomposed into four induction problems, one for each of the four control variables. These four learning problems were assumed independent.

The control rules were induced by the C4.5 induction program (Quinlan, 1987a). The total data set consisted of 90 000 events collected from three pilots and 30 flights by each pilot. The data was segmented into seven stages of the complete flight plan and separate rules were induced for each stage. Separate control rules were induced for each of the three pilots. It was decided that it was best not to mix the data corresponding to different individuals because different pilots carry out their manouevres in different styles.

There was a technical difficulty in using C4.5 in that it requires discrete class values whereas in the flight problem the control variables are mostly continuous. The continuous ranges therefore had to be converted to discrete classes by segmentation into intervals. This segmentation was done manually. A more natural learning tool for this induction task would therefore be one that allows continuous class, such as the techniques of learning regression trees implemented in the programs CART (Breiman *et al.*, 1984) and Retis (Karalič, 1992).

Sammut *et al.* (1992) state that control rules for a complete flight were successfully synthesized resulting in an inductively constructed autopilot. This autopilot flies the Cessna in a manner very similar to that of the human pilot whose data was used to construct the rules. In some cases the autopilot flies more smoothly than the pilot.

We have observed a 'clean-up' effect noted in Michie, Bain and Hayes-Michie (1990). The flight log of any trainer will contain many spurious actions due to human inconsistency and corrections required as a result of inattention. It appears that effects of these examples are pruned away by C4.5, leaving a control rule which flies very smoothly.

It is interesting to note the comments of Sammut *et al.* (1992) regarding the contents of the induced rules:

One of the limitations we have encountered with existing learning algorithms is that they can only use the primitive attributes supplied in the data. This results in control rules that cannot be understood by a human expert. The rules constructed by C4.5 are purely reactive. They make decisions on the basis of the values in a single step of simulation. The induction program has no concept of time and causality. In connection with this, some strange rules can turn up.

13.6.2   Learning to control container cranes

The world market requires container cranes with as high capacity as possible. One way to meet this requirement is to build bigger and faster cranes; however, this approach is limited by construction problems as well as by unpleasant feelings drivers have when moving with high speeds and accelerations. The other solution is to make the best of the cranes of "reasonable" size, meaning in the first place the optimisation of the working cycle and efficient swing damping.

It is known that experienced crane drivers can perform very quickly as long as everything goes as expected, while each subsequent correction considerably affects the time needed for accomplishing the task. Also, it is very difficult to drive for hours and hours with the same attention, not to mention the years of training needed to gain required skill. Consequently, interest for cooperation has been reported by chief designer of Metalna Machine Builders, Steel Fabricators and Erectors, Maribor, which is known world-wide for its large-scale container cranes. They are aware of insufficiency of classical automatic controllers (for example Sakawa & Shinido, 1982), which can be easily disturbed in the presence of wind or other unpredictable factors. This explains their interest in what can be offered by alternative methods.

Impressive results have been obtained by predictive fuzzy control (see Yasunobu & Hasegawa, 1986). Their method involves steps such as describing human operator strategies, defining the meaning of linguistic performance indices, defining the models for predicting operation results, and converting the linguistic human operator strategies into predictive fuzzy control rules.

In general, these tasks can be very time consuming, so our focus of attention was on the automated synthesis of control rules directly from the recorded performance of well-trained operators. In this idea, we are following the work of Michie *et al.* (1990), Sammut *et al.* (1992) and Michie & Camacho (1994) who confirmed the findings of Sammut *et al.* (1992) using the ACM public-domain simulation of an F-16 combat plane. When trying to solve the crane control problem in a manner similar to their autopilot construction, we encountered some difficulties which are to be investigated more systematically if the method is to become general.

To transport a container from shore to a target position on a ship, two operations are to be performed:

- positioning of the trolley, bringing it above the target load position, and
- rope operation, bringing the load to the desired height.

The performance requirements are as follows:

- basic safety: obstacles must be avoided, swinging must be kept within prescribed limits;
- stop-gap accuracy: the gap between the final load position and the target position must be within prescribed limits;
- high capacity: time needed for transportation is to be minimised.

The last requirement forces the two operations to be performed simultaneously. The task parameters specifying stop-gap accuracy, swinging limits and capacity are given by the customer and vary from case to case.

Instead of a real crane, a simulator was used in our experiments. The state of the system is specified by six variables:

- trolley position and its velocity, x and $\dot{x}$;
- rope inclination angle and its angular velocity, φ and $\dot{\varphi}$;
- rope length and the length velocity, l and $\dot{l}$.

Time is measured in steps. At each step, the state of the system is measured and two control forces are applied: F_x is applied to the trolley in the horizontal direction, and F_l in the direction of the rope. (So $F_l cos(\varphi)$ is the force in the vertical direction.) The next state is computed using Runge-Kutta numerical simulation of fourth order, taking into account the dynamic equations of the system. Parameters of the system (lengths, heights, masses etc.) are the same as those of the real container cranes in Port of Koper. Simulation runs on IBM PC compatible computers and is real-time for 386 (33 MHz or faster) with a mathematical co-processor.

When experimenting with the simulator, one can choose

- input mode "record", "play" or "auto",
- output mode "picture" or "instruments".

In the "record" mode, the values of the current control forces are read from the keyboard, where one strike at the $\leftarrow$ or $\rightarrow$ means a decrease or increase of F_x for a certain predefined step. Similarly, arrows $\uparrow$ and $\downarrow$ indicate the change of F_l. A file containing all control actions together with the corresponding times and system states is recorded. In the "play" mode, recorded experiments can be viewed again, using the recorded files as input. When "auto" mode is chosen, the current values of control forces are determined by a procedure representing an automatic controller.

The choice of the output mode enables the graphical representation of the scene ("picture") or the variant where the six state variables and the force values are presented as columns with dynamically changing height, imitating measuring instruments.

Six students volunteered in an experiment where they were asked to learn to control the crane simulator simply by playing with the simulator and trying various control strategies.

They were given just the "instrument" version; in fact, they didn't know which dynamic system underlied the simulator. In spite of that, they succeeded to learn the task, although the differences in time needed for this as well as the quality of control were remarkable. To learn to control the crane reasonably well, it took a subject between about 25 and 200 trials. This amounts to about 1 to 10 hours of real time spent with the simulator.

Our aim was to build automatic controllers from human operators' traces. We applied RETIS - a program for regression tree construction (Karalič, 1992) to the recorded data. The first problem to solve was how to choose an appropriate set of learning examples out of this enormous set of recorded data. After some initial experiments we found, as in Sammut *et al.* (1992), that it was beneficial to use different trials performed by the same student, since it was practically impossible to find trials perfect in all aspects even among the successful cases.

In the preparation of learning data, performance was sampled each 0.1 second. The actions were related to the states with delay which was also 0.1 second. The performance of the best autodriver induced in these initial experiments can be seen in Figure 13.3. It resulted from 798 learning examples for F_x and 1017 examples for F_l. The control strategy it uses is rather conservative, minimising the swinging, but at the cost of time. In further experiments, we will try to build an autodriver which will successfully cope with load swinging, resulting in faster and more robust performance.

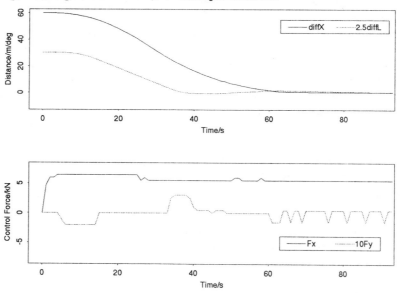

Fig. 13.3: The crane simulator response to the control actions of the autodriver.

These experiments indicate that further work is needed regarding the following questions: what is the actual delay between the system's state and the operator's action; robustness of induced rules with respect to initial states; comprehensibility of induced control rules; inducing higher level conceptual description of control strategies.

13.7 CONCLUSIONS

In this chapter we have treated the problem of controlling a dynamic system mainly as a classification problem. We introduced three modes of learning to control, depending on the information available to the learner. This information included in addition to the usual examples of the behaviour of the controlled system, also explicit symbolic knowledge about the controlled system, and example actions performed by a skilled human operator.

One point that the described experiments emphasise is the importance of (possibly incomplete) partial knowledge about the controlled system. Methods described in this chapter enable natural use of partial symbolic knowledge. Although incomplete, this knowledge may drastically constrain the search for control rules, thereby eliminating in advance large numbers of totally unreasonable rules.

Our choice of the approaches to learning to control in this chapter was subjective. Among a large number of known approaches, we chose for more detailed presentation those that: first, we had personal experimental experience with, and second, that enable the use of (possibly partial) symbolic prior knowledge. In all the approaches described, there was an aspiration to generate comprehensible control rules, sometimes at the cost of an additional learning stage.

An interesting theme, also described, is "behavioural cloning" where a human's behavioural skill is cloned by a learned rule. Behavioural cloning is interesting both from the practical and the research points of view. Much further work is needed before behavioural cloning may become routinely applicable in practice.

Behavioural cloning is essentially the regression of the operator's decision function from examples of his/her decisions. It is relevant in this respect to notice a similarity between this and traditional top-down derivation of control from a detailed model of the system to be controlled. This similarity is illustrated by the fact that such a top-down approach for the pole-and-cart system gives the known linear control rule $F = p_1 x + p_2 \dot{x} + p_3 \varphi + p_4 \dot{\varphi}$ which looks just like regression equation.

As stated in the introduction, there are several criteria for, and goals of, learning to control, and several assumptions regarding the problem. As shown by the experience with various learning approaches, it is important to clarify very precisely what these goals and assumptions really are in the present problem. Correct statement of these may considerably affect the efficiency of the learning process. For example, it is important to consider whether some (partial) symbolic knowledge exists about the domain, and not to assume automatically that it is necessary, or best, to learn everything from scratch. In some approaches reviewed, such incomplete prior knowledge could also result from a previous stage of learning when another learning technique was employed.

Acknowledgements: This work was supported by the Ministry of Science and Technology of Slovenia. The authors would like to thank Donald Michie for comments and suggestions.

Appendices

A DATASET AND SOFTWARE AVAILABILITY

A.1 Datasets

The "public domain" datasets are listed below with an anonymous ftp address. If you do not have access to these, then you can obtain the datasets on diskette from Dr. P. B. Brazdil or J. Gama. University of Porto, Laboratory of AI and Computer Science, R. Campo Alegre 823, 4100 Porto, Potugal. (Fax.: +351 600 3654, email: pbrazdil@ncc.up.pt, jgama@ncc.up.pt). The main source of datasets is **ics.uci.edu (128.195.1.1)** - the UCI Repository of Machine Learning Databases and Domain Theories which is managed by D. W. Aha. The following datasets (amongst many others) are in directory pub/machine-learning-databases (sub-directories are given in brackets):

  australian credit (credit-screening/crx.data statlog/australian)
  diabetes (pima-indian-diabetes)
  dna (molecular-biology/splice-junction-gene-sequences)
  heart disease (heart-disease/ statlog/heart)
  letter recognition
  image segmentation (statlog/segment)
  shuttle control (statlog/shuttle)
  LANDSAT satellite image (statlog/satimage)
  vehicle recognition (statlog/vehicle)

The datasets were often processed, and the processed form can be found in the stat-log subdirectory where mentioned above. In addition, the processed datasets (as used in this book) can also be obtained from **ftp.strath.ac.uk (130.159.248.24)** in directory Stams/statlog. These datasets are *australian, diabetes, dna, german, heart, letter, satimage, segment, shuttle, vehicle,* and there are associated .doc files as well as a split into train and test set (as used in the StatLog project) for the larger datasets. The processed datasets have also been stored at **ftp.ncc.up.pt (192.26.239.52)** in directory /pub/statlog/datasets. This latter site will attempt to maintain a complete list of all (future) results, so users are asked to keep them informed so that a database can be updated regularly.

An anonymous ftp site may be accessed by typing

```
ftp ``site.address''
```

(where "site.address" is either the internet name or number). For example, ftp ftp.ncc.up.pt to connect to the Porto site. Then log with username anonymous, giving your email address as password. You can change directory and list files in the usual way; use the command get filename to copy a file "filename" from the remote site to your current directory.

A.2   Evaluation Assistant

Evaluation Assistant is a software tool developed within the Statlog project - see Section 7.2.3. Its aim is to facilitate testing of statistical, machine learning and neural algorithms on given datasets and provide standardised performance measures. The Evaluation Assistant is oriented towards classification tasks. Two versions of Evaluation Assistant exist: a command version, and an interactive one.

The command version of Evaluation Assistant consists of a set of basic commands that enable the user to test learning algorithms. This version is implemented as a set of Cshell scripts and C programs.

The interactive version of Evaluation Assistant provides an interactive interface that enables the user to set up the basic parameters for testing. The interactive interface is implemented in C and exploits X windows. This version generates a customised version of some scripts which can be examined and modified before execution.

The source code of both versions can be obtained from **ftp.ncc.up.pt (192.26.239.52)**. The command version is stored in the directory /pub/statlog/eac. The source code of the interactive version can be obtained from the directory /pub/statlog/eai. Both versions run on SUN SPARCstation IPC and other compatible workstations.

A.3   Application Assistant

This software prototype can analyse previous test results and generates rules concerning applicability of different machine learning, statistical and neural network algorithms. The rules can be used to provide the user with a recommendation concerning which classification method is appropriate for a given dataset.

The rules referred to earlier are generated on the basis of previous test results and dataset characteristics. The automatic analysis of previous test results is done with the help of one particular ML algorithm (C4.5). The result is transcribed in the form of rules which can be altered or edited by the user. The rules constitute, in effect, a knowledge base of an expert system. The system can be applied to a new dataset to provide the user with a set of recommendations concerning the suitability of different algorithms, graded by a score. More details about the underlying method can be found in Section 10.6.

Application Assistant has been implemented in C, exploits features of X-windows and runs on a SPARCstation IPC and other compatible hardware. The source code can be obtained from **ftp.ncc.up.pt (192.26.239.52)**, directory /pub/statlog/aplas.

B   ALGORITHM SOURCES AND DETAILS

Many of the classical statistical algorithms are available in standard statistical packages. Here we list some public domain versions and sources, and some commercial packages. If a simple rule has been adopted for parameter selection, then we have also described this.

ALLOC80 is a Fortran program available from J. Hermans, Dept. of Medical Statistics, Niels Bohrweg 1, 2333 CA Leiden, University of Leiden, The Netherlands.

SMART is a collection of Fortran subroutines developed by J. H. Friedman, Dept. of Statistics, Sequoia Hall, Stanford University, Stanford, CA 94305, USA.

CASTLE can be obtained from R. Molina, Dept of Computer Science and A.I., Faculty of Science, University of Granada. 18071-Granada, Spain.

IndCART, Bayes Tree and **Naive Bayes**. are part of the IND package which is available from W. Buntine, NASA Ames Research Center, MS 269-2, Moffett Field, CA 94035-1000, USA. (email: wray@kronos.arc.nasa.gov)

DIPOL92 and **CAL5** is available from F. Wysotzki, Fraunhofer-Institute, Kurstrasse 33, D-19117 Berlin, Germany.

For DIPOL92 the number of clusters has to be fixed by the user with some systematic experimentation. All other parameters are determined by the algorithm.

For Cal5 the confidence level for estimation and the threshold for tree pruning were optimised either by hand or a special C - shell. An entropy measure to choose the best discrimination attribute at each current node was used.

Logistic discriminants, Quadratic discriminants and **Logistic discriminants** are FOR-TRAN programs available from R. J. Henery, Department of Statistics and Modelling Science, University of Strathclyde, Glasgow G1 1XH, UK. They are also available by anonymous ftp from **ftp.strath.ac.uk (130.159.248.24)** in directory Stams/statlog/programs.

AC^2 is available from H. Perdrix, ISoft, Chemin de Moulon, 91190 Gif sur Yvette, France. The user must choose between 4 evaluation functions:

```
1- the information gain
2- the gain ratio
3- a measure of distance between partitions introduce by Mantaras
4- an information gain measure taking into account the hierarchy of
objects defined by the user.
```

In the reported results, the fourth option was chosen.

Backprop, Cascade correlation and **Radial Basis Function** are FORTRAN programs available from R. Rohwer, Department of Computer Science and Applied Mathematics, Aston University, Birmingham B4 7ET, UK.

The inputs for all datasets were normalised to zero mean and unit variance. The outputs were converted to a 1-of-n representation; ie., the ith class of an N-class classification problem was represented as an N-dimensional vector with all components equal to 0 except the ith, which is 1.

The Multilayer Perceptron simulations were done with AutoNet on Sun UNIX workstations. AutoNet is commercial software available from Paul Gregory, Recognition Research, 140 Church Lane, Marple, Stockport, SK6 7LA, UK, (+44/0) 61 449-8628.

The settings were:

```
Number of hidden layers = 1.
Hidden and output unit activations : sigmoid.
Weight intialisation +- 1.
```

10 runs were made, with 10% of the training data held out to determine which of the 10 runs was best. Random number seed for each run was = run number (1..10). Having picked the

best net by cross validation within the training set, these nets were then used for supplying the performance figures on the whole training set and on the test set. The figures averaged for cross validation performance measures were also for the best nets found during local cross-validation within the individual training sets.

Training proceeds in four stages, with different stages using different subsets of the training data, larger each time. Training proceeds until no improvement in error is achieved for a run of updates.

The RRNN simulator provided the radial basis function code. This is freely available at the time of writing by anonymous ftp from **uk.ac.aston.cs (134.151.52.106)**. This package also contains MLP code using the conjugate gradient algorithm, as does AutoNet, and several other algorithms. Reports on benchmark exercises are available for some of these MLP programs in Rohwer (1991c).

The centres for the radial basis functions were selected randomly from the training data, except that centres were allocated to each class in proportion to the number of representatives of that class in the dataset, with at least one centre provided to each class in any case. Each Gaussian radius was set to the distance to the nearest neighbouring centre. The linear system was solved by singular value decomposition.

For the small datasets the number of centres and their locations were selected by training with various numbers of centres, using 20 different random number seeds for each number, and evaluating with a cross validation set withheld from the training data, precisely as was done for the MLPs. For the large datasets, time constraints were met by compromising rigour, in that the test set was used for the cross-validation set. Results for these sets should therefore be viewed with some caution. This was the case for all data sets, until those for which cross-validation was explicitly required (australian, diabetes, german, isoft, segment) were repeated with cross-validation to select the number of centres carried out within the training set only.

The rough guideline followed for deciding on numbers of centres to try is that the number should be about 100 times the dimension of the input space, unless that would be more than 10% of the size of the dataset.

LVQ is available from the Laboratory of Computer Science and Information Science, Helsinki University of Technology, Rakentajanaukio 2 C, SF -02150 Espoo, Finland. It can also be obtained by anonymous ftp from **cochlea.hut.fi (130.233.168.48)**.

CART is a licensed product of California Statistical Software Inc., 961 Yorkshire Court, Lafayette, CA 94549, USA.

C4.5 is available from J.R. Quinlan, Dept. of Computer Science, Madsen Building F09, University of Sydney, New South Wales, New South Wales.

The parameters used were the defaults (with the exception of windowing). The heuristic was information gain.

```
Windowing: disabled
Probability threshold: default (10%)
No force subsetting
Verbosity for displaying information: 0
Number of decision trees: 10
Pruning confidence level: 10%
```

Note that two versions were used in the project. An older (1989) version was used on the following datasets: Heart, Dig44, SatIm, Shuttle, Vehicle, Head. However, since the StatLog project was completed, there is a still more recent version of C4.5, so the results contained in this book may not be exactly reproducible.

NewID and **CN2** are available from Robin Boswell and Tim Niblett, respectively at The Turing Institute, George House, 36 North Hanover Street, Glasgow G1 2AD, UK.

For NewID:

```
[Variance termination threshold]: 10.00;
[Threshold for tree pruning]: 10.00\%;
[Format of tree printing]: display.
```

For CN2:

```
1) Rule type: Ordered rules
2) STAR size: 5
3) Maximum class forcing: Set
4) Error estimate: Laplacian function
5) Significance threshold (chisquared) for accepting rules: 10.00
```

ITrule is available from Prof. R. Goodman, California Institute of Technology, Electrical Engineering, Mail code 116-81, Pasadena, CA 91125, USA.

For most of the datasets the parameters used were:

```
maximum order of rules: 2
number of rules: 100
```

although the two "Belgian power" datasets were run with the above parameters set to (3,5000) and 3,2000).

Kohonen was written by J. Paul, Dhamstr. 20, W-5948 Schmallenberg, Germany for a PC with an attached transputer board.

k-NN is still under development. For all datasets, except the satellite image dataset, $k = 1$. Distance was scaled in a class dependent manner, using the standard deviation. Further details can be obtained from C. C. Taylor, Department of Statistics, University of Leeds, Leeds LS2 9JT, UK.

C   CONTRIBUTORS TO THE STATLOG PROJECT

This volume is based on the StatLog project, which involved many workers at over 12 institutions. In this list we try to include those who contributed to the Project and the Institutions at which they were primarily based at that time.

- G. Nakhaeizadeh, U. Kressel, S. Keh, K.P. Huber, A. Merkel, H. Keller, M. Pechowski, B. Weidenmueller, Daimler-Benz, Germany
- R.J. Henery, D. Michie, J.M.O. Mitchell, A.I. Sutherland, R. King, S. Haque, C. Kay, D. Young, W. Buntine, B. D. Ripley, University of Strathclyde, U.K.
- S.H. Muggleton, C. Feng, T. Niblett, R. Boswell, Turing Institute, U.K.
- H. Perdrix, T. Brunet, T. Marre, J-J Cannat, ISoft, France
- J. Stender, P. Ristau, D. Picu, I. Chorbadjiev, C. Kennedy, G. Ruedke, F. Boehme, S. Schulze-Kremer, Brainware GmbH, Germany

- P.B. Brazdil, J. Gama, L. Torgo, University of Porto, Portugal
- R. Molina, N. Pérez de la Blanca, S. Acid, L.M. de Campos, A. Gonzalez, University of Granada, Spain
- F. Wysotzki, W. Mueller, Der, Buhlau, Schmelowski, Funke, Villman, H. Herzheim, B. Schulmeister, Fraunhofer Institute, Germany
- T. Bueckle, C. Ziegler, M. Surauer, Messerschmitt Boelkow Blohm, Germany
- J. Paul, P. von Goldammer, Univeristy of Lübeck, Germany
- C.C. Taylor, X. Feng, University of Leeds, U.K.
- R. Rohwer, M. Wynne-Jones, Aston University, U.K.

References

Acid, S., Campos, L. M. d., González, A., Molina, R., & Pérez de la Blanca, N. (1991a). Bayesian learning algorithms in castle. Report no. 91-4-2 University of Granada.

Acid, S., Campos, L. M. d., González, A., Molina, R., & Pérez de la Blanca, N. (1991b). CASTLE: Causal structures from inductive learning. release 2.0. Report no. 91-4-3 University of Granada.

Agresti, A. (1990). *Categorical Data Analysis*. New York: Wiley.

Aha, D. (1992). Generalising case studies: a case study. In: *9th Int. Conf. on Machine Learning* pp. 1-10, San Mateo, Cal.: Morgan Kaufmann.

Aha, D. W., Kibler, D., & Albert, M. K. (1991). Instance-based learning algorithms. *Machine Learning, 6*, 37-66.

AIRTC92 (1992). *Preprints of the 1992 IFAC/IFIP/IMACS International Symposium on Artificial Intelligence in Real-Time Control*. Delft, The Netherlands, 750 pages.

Aitchison, J. & Aitken, C. G. G. (1976). Multivariate binary discrimination by the kernel method. *Biometrika, 63*, 413-420.

Al-Attar, A. (1991). *Structured Decision Tasks Methodology*. Newlands House, Newlands Road, Leigh, Lancs.: Attar Software Ltd.

Aleksander, I., Thomas, W. V., & Bowden, P. A. (1984). Wisard: A radical step forward in image recognition. *Sensor Review, 4*, 120-124.

Anderson, C. W. (1987). Strategy learning with multilayer connectionist representations. In: *Proceedings of the 4th International Workshop on Machine Learning*, (Lengley, P., ed) pp. 103-114, Morgan Kaufmann.

Anderson, C. W. & Miller, W. T. (1990). Challenging control problems. In: *Neural Networks for Control*, (Miller, W. T., Sutton, R. S., & Werbos, P. J., eds) pp. 475-510, The MIT Press.

Anderson, J. A. (1984). Regression and ordered categorical variables. *J. R. Statist. Soc. B, 46*, 1-30.

Anderson, T. W. (1958). *An introduction to multivariate statistical analysis*. New York: John Wiley.

Andrews, D. F. & Herzberg, A. M. (1985). *Data: a collection of problems from many fields for the student and research worker*. New York: Springer-Verlag.

Arbab, B. & Michie, D. (1988). Generating expert rules from examples in prolog. In: *Machine Intelligence 11*, (Hayes, J. E., Michie, D., & Richards, J., eds) pp. 289–304. Oxford University Press Oxford.

Ash, T. (1989). Dynamic node creation in back-propagation networks. ICS Report 8901 Institute of Cognitive Science, University of California, San Diego La Jolla, California 92093, USA.

Åström, K. J. (1991). Intelligent control. In: *Proceedings of the ECC 91 European Control Conference* pp. 2328–2339. Grenoble.

Atlas, L., Connor, J., & Park, D. *et al.*. (1991). A performance comparison of trained multi-layer perceptrons and trained classification trees. In: *Systems, man and cybernetics: proceedings of the 1989 IEEE international conference* pp. 915–920, Cambridge, Ma: Hyatt Regency.

Bain, M. (1990). Machine-learned rule-based control. In: *Knowledge-Based Systems in Industrial Control*, (Grimble, M., McGhee, J., & Mowforth, P., eds) pp. 222–244, Stevenage: Peter Peregrinus.

Bain, M. (private communication). *Learning Logical Exceptions in Chess*. PhD thesis University of Strathclyde, Glasgow.

Banerji, R. B. (1980). *Artificial Intelligence: A Theoretical Approach*. New York: North Holland.

Barto, A. G., Sutton, R. S., & Anderson, C. W. (1983). Neuronlike adaptive elements that can solve difficult learning control problems. *IEEE Transactions on Systems, Man and Cybernetics*, **SMC-13** (5), 834–846.

Begg, C. B. & Gray, R. (1984). Calculation of polychotomous logistic regression parameters using individualized regressions. *Biometrika*, **71**, 11–18.

Bilbro, G. & den Bout, D. V. (1992). Maximum entropy and learning theory. *Neural Computation*, **4**, 839–853.

Bledsoe, W. W. (1961). Further results on the n-tuple pattern recognition method. *IRE Trans. Comp.* **EC-10**, 96.

Bledsoe, W. W. & Browning, I. (1959). Pattern recognition and reading by machine. In: *Proceedings of the Eastern Joint Computer Conference* pp. 232–255, Boston:.

Blyth, C. R. (1959). Note on estimating information. *Annals of Math. Stats.* **30**, 71–79.

Bonelli, P. & Parodi, A. (1991). An efficient classifier system and its experimental comparisons with two representative learning methods on three medical domains. In: *ICGA-91: genetic algorithms: proceedings of the fourth international conference* pp. 288–295, San Mateo, CA: Morgan Kaufmann.

Booth, T. H., Stein, J. A., Hutchinson, M. F., & Nix, H. A. (1990). Identifying areas within a country climatically suitable for particular tree species: an example using Zimbabwe. *International Tree Crops Journal*, **6**, 1–16.

Bourlard, H. & Wellekens, C. J. (1990). Links between Markov models and multilayer perceptrons. *IEEE Transactions on Pattern Analysis and Machine Intelligence*, **12**, 1–12.

Bratko, I. (1983). Generating human-understandable decision rules. Technical report Ljubljana University, Slovenia.

Bratko, I. (1991). Qualitative modelling: Learning and control. In: *Proceedings of the 6th Czechoslovak Conference on Artificial Intelligence* . Prague.

Bratko, I. (1993). Qualitative reasoning about control. In: *Proceedings of the ETFA '93 Conference* . Cairns, Australia.

Bratko, I. Mozetic, I. & Lavrac, L. (1989). *KARDIO: A Study in Deep and Qualitative Knowledge for Expert Systems*. Cambridge, MA, and London: MIT Press.

Breiman, L. & Friedman, J. H. (1985). Estimating optimal transformations for multiple regression and correlation (with discussion). *Journal of the American Statistical Association, 80, 580–619.*

Breiman, L., Friedman, J. H., Olshen, R. A., & Stone, C. J. (1984). *Classification and Regression Trees*. Monterey, Ca: Wadsworth and Brooks.

Breiman, L., Meisel, W., & Purcell, E. (1977). Variable kernel estimates of multivariate densities. *Technometrics, 19, 135–144.*

Bretzger, T. M. (1991). *Die Anwendung statistischer Verfahren zur Risikofruherkennung bei Dispositionskrediten.* PhD thesis Universitat Hohenheim.

Broomhead, D. S. & Lowe, D. (1988). Multi-variable functional interpolation and adaptive networks. *Complex Systems, 2, 321–355.*

Bruner, J. S., Goodnow, J. J., & Austin, G. A. (1956). *A Study of Thinking.* New York: Wiley.

Buntine, W. (1988). Generalized subsumption and its applications to induction and redundancy. *Artificial Intelligence, 36, 149–176.*

Buntine, W. (1992). Learning classification trees. *Statistics and Computing, 2, 63–73.*

Buntine, W. (a). Ind package of machine learning algorithms ind 1.0. Technical Report MS 244-17 Research Institute for Advanced Computer Science, NASA Ames Research Center Moffett Field, CA 94035.

Camacho, R. & Michie, D. (1992). An engineering model of subcognition. In: *Proceedings of the ISSEK Workshop 1992* . Bled, Slovenia.

Carpenter, B. E. & Doran, R. W., eds (1986). *A. M. Turing's ACE Report and Other Papers.* Cambridge, MA: MIT Press.

Carter, C. & Catlett, J. (1987). Assessing credit card applications using machine learning. *IEEE Expert: intelligent systems and their applications, 2, 71–79.*

Cestnik, B. & Bratko, I. (1991). On estimating probabilities in tree pruning. In: *EWSL '91, Porto, Portugal, 1991* , Berlin: Springer-Verlag.

Cestnik, B., Kononenko, I., & Bratko, I. (1987). Assistant 86: A knowledge-elicitation tool for sophisticated users. In: *Progress in Machine Learning: Proceedings of EWSL-87* pp. 31–45, Bled, Yugoslavia: Sigma Press.

Cherkaoui, O. & Cleroux, R. (1991). Comparative study of six discriminant analysis procedures for mixtures of variables. In: *Proceedings of Interface Conference 1991* , Morgan Kaufmann.

Clark, L. A. & Pregibon, D. (1992). Tree-based models. In: *Statistical Models in S,* (Chambers, J. & Hastie, T., eds). Wadsworth & Brooks Pacific Grove, California.

Clark, P. & Boswell, R. (1991). Rule induction with cn2: some recent improvements. In: *EWSL '91, Porto, Portugal, 1991* pp. 151–163, Berlin: Springer-Verlag.

Clark, P. & Niblett, T. (1988). The CN2 induction algorithm. *Machine Learning, 3, 261–283.*

Clarke, W. R., Lachenbruch, P. A., & Broffitt, B. (1979). How nonnormality affects the quadratic discriminant function. *Comm. Statist. — Theory Meth.* IT-16, 41–46.

Connell, M. E. & Utgoff, P. E. (1987). Learning to control a dynamic physical system. In: *Proceedings of the 6th National Conference on Artificial Intelligence* pp. 456–459, Morgan Kaufmann.

Cooper, G. F. (1984). NESTRO: A computer-based medical diagnostic that integrates causal and probabilistic knowledge. Report no. 4,HPP-84-48 Stanford University, Stanford California.

Cooper, G. F. & Herkovsits, E. (1991). A bayesian method for the induction of probabilistic networks from data. Technical report ksl-91-02 Stanford University.

Cover, T. M. (1965). Geometrical and statistical properties of systems of linear inequalities with applications in pattern recognition. *IEEE Transactions on Electronic Computers*, **14**, 326–334.

Cox, D. R. (1966). Some procedures associated with the logistic qualitative response curve. In: *Research papers on statistics: Festschrift for J. Neyman*, (David, F. N., ed) pp. 55–77. John Wiley New York.

Crawford, S. L. (1989). Extensions to the cart algorithm. *Int. J. Man-Machine Studies*, **31**, 197–217.

Cutsem van, T., Wehenkel, L., Pavella, M., Heilbronn, B., & Goubin, M. (1991). Decision trees for detecting emergency voltage conditions. In: *Second International Workshop on Bulk Power System Voltage Phenomena - Voltage Stability and Security* pp. 229–240, USA: McHenry.

Davies, E. R. (1988). Training sets and a priori probabilities with the nearest neighbour method of pattern recognition. *Pattern Recognition Letters*, **8**, 11–13.

Day, N. E. & Kerridge, D. F. (1967). A general maximum likelihood discriminant. *Biometrics*, **23**, 313–324.

Devijver, P. A. & Kittler, J. V. (1982). *Pattern Recognition. A Statistical Approach.* Englewood Cliffs: Prentice Hall.

Djeroski, S., Cestnik, B., & Petrovski, I. (1983). Using the m-estimate in rule induction. *J. Computing and Inf. Technology*, **1**, 37–46.

Dubes, R. & Jain, A. K. (1976). Clustering techniques: The user's dilemma. *Pattern Recognition*, **8**, 247–260.

Duin, R. P. W. (1976). On the choice of smoothing parameters for Parzen estimators of probability density functions. *IEEE Transactions on Computers,* **C-25**, 1175–1179.

Dvorak, D. L. (1987). Expert systems for monitoring and control. Technical Report Technical Report AI87-55 Artificial Intelligence Laboratory, The University of Texas at Austin.

Džeroski, S. (1989). Control of inverted pendulum. B.Sc. Thesis, Faculty of Electrical Engineering and Computer Science, University of Ljubljana (in Slovenian).

Efron, B. (1983). Estimating the error rate of a prediction rule: improvements on cross-validation. *J. Amer. Stat. Ass.* **78**, 316–331.

Enas, G. G. & Choi, S. C. (1986). Choice of the smoothing parameter and efficiency of the k–nearest neighbour classification. *Comput. Math. Applic.* **12A**, 235–244.

Enterline, L. L. (1988). Strategic requirements for total facility automation. *Control Engineering*, **2**, 9–12.

Ersoy, O. K. & Hong, D. (1991). Parallel, self-organizing, hierarchical neural networks for vision and systems control. In: *Intelligent motion control: proceedings of the IEEE international workshop*, (Kaynak, O., ed) , New York: IEEE.

Fahlman, S. E. (1988a). An empirical study of learning speed in back-propagation. Technical Report CMU-CS-88-162 Carnegie Mellon University, USA.

Fahlman, S. E. (1988b). Faster learning variation on back-propagation: An empirical study. In: *Proccedings of the 1988 Connectionist Models Summer School* , Morgan Kaufmann.

Fahlman, S. E. (1991a). The recurrent cascade-correlation architecture. Technical Report CMU-CS-91-100 Carnegie Mellon University.

Fahlman, S. E. (1991b). The cascade-correlation learning algorithm on the monk's problems. In: *The MONK's problems - a performance comparison of different learning algorithms*, (Thrun, S., Bala, J., Bloedorn, E., & Bratko, I., eds) pp. 107–112, Carnegie Mellon University, Computer Science Department.

Fahlman, S. E. & Lebière, C. (1990). The cascade correlation learning architecture. In: *Advances in Neural Information Processing Systems 2*, (Tourzetsky, D. S., ed) pp. 524–532. Morgan Kaufmann.

Fahrmeir, L., Haussler, W., & Tutz, G. (1984). Diskriminanzanalyse. In: *Multivariate statistische Verfahren*, (Fahrmeir, L. & Hamerle, A., eds). Verlag de Gruyter Berlin.

Fienberg, S. (1980). *The Analysis of Cross-Classified Categorical Data*. Cambridge, Mass: MIT Press.

Fisher, D. H. & McKusick, K. B. (1989a). An empirical comparison of ID3 and back-propagation (vol 1). In: *IJCAI 89* pp. 788–793, San Mateo, CA: Morgan Kaufmann.

Fisher, D. H. & McKusick, K. B. et al.. (1989b). Processing issues in comparisons of symbolic and connectionist learning systems. In: *Proceedings of the sixth international workshop on machine learning, Cornell University, Ithaca, New York*, (SPATZ, B., ed) pp. 169–173, San Mateo, CA: Morgan Kaufmann.

Fisher, R. A. (1936). The use of multiple measurements in taxonomic problems. *Annals of Eugenics, 7*, 179–188.

Fisher, R. A. (1938). The statistical utilisation of multiple measurements. *Ann. Eugen. 8*, 376–386.

Fix, E. & Hodges, J. L. (1951). Discriminatory analysis, nonparametric estimation: consistency properties. Report no. 4, project no. 21-49-004 UASF School of Aviation Medicine, Randolph Field, Texas.

Frean, M. (1990a). The upstart algorithm: A method for constructing and training feed-forward neural networks. *Neural Computation, 2*, 198–209.

Frean, M. (1990b). *Short Paths and Small Nets: Optimizing Neural Computation*. PhD thesis University of Edinburgh UK.

Frey, P. W. & Slate, D. J. (1991). Letter recognition using holland-style adaptive classifiers. *Machine Learning, 6*.

Friedman, J. (1989). Regularized discriminant analysis. *J. Amer. Statist. Assoc. 84*, 165–175.

Friedman, J. H. (1984). Smart user's guide. Tech. report 1. Laboratory of Computational Statistics, Department of Statistics, Stanford University.

Friedman, J. H. (1991). Multivariate adaptive regression splines (with discussion). *Annals of Statistics, 19*, 1–141.

Friedman, J. H. & Stuetzle, W. (1981). Projection pursuit regression. *J. Amer. Statist. Assoc. 76*, 817–823.

Fukunaga, K. (1990). *Introduction to Statistical Pattern Recognition*. Academic Press, 2nd edition.

Fukunaga, K. & Narendra, P. M. (1975). A branch and bound algorithm for computing k—nearest neighbours. *IEEE Trans. Comput.* **C-25**, 917–922.

Funahashi, K. (1989). On the approximate realization of continuous mappings by neural networks. *Neural Networks*, **2**, 183.

Fung, R. M. & Crawford, S. L. (1991). Constructor: A system for the induction of probabilistic models. In: *Proceedings Eighth of the Conference on Artificial Intelligence* pp. 762–769, Boston, Massachussetts:.

Gallant, S. I. (1985). The pocket algorithm for perceptron learning. Technical Report SG-85-20 Northeastern University College of Computer Science USA.

Gates, G. W. (1972). The reduced nearest neighbour rule. *IEEE Transactions on Information Theory*, **IT-18**, 431.

Geva, S. & Sitte, J. (1993a). The cart-pole experiment as a benchmark for trainable controllers. Submitted to IEEE Control Systems Magazine.

Geva, S. & Sitte, J. (1993b). Boxes revisited. In: *Proceedings of the ICANN '93*. Amsterdam.

Gilbert, E. S. (1969). The effect of unequal variance covariance matrices on Fisher's linear discriminant function. *Biometrics*, **25**, 505–515.

Glymour, C., Scheines, R., Spirtes, P., & Kelley, K. (1987). *Discovering causal structures Statistics and Search*. New York: Academic Press.

Goldberg, D. E. (1989). *Genetic Algorithms in Search, Optimization and Machine Learning*. Addison-Wesley.

Good, I. J. (1950). *Probability and the Weighing of Evidence*. London: Griffin.

Goodman, R. M. & Smyth, P. (1989). The induction of probabilistic rule sets - the itrule algorithm. In: *Proceedings of the sixth international workshop on machine learning.*, (Spatz, B., ed) pp. 129–132, San Mateo, CA: Morgan Kaufmann.

Gorman, R. P. & Sejnowski, T. J. (1988). Analysis of hidden units in a layered network trained to classify sonar targets. *Neural networks*, **1**, 75–89.

Habbema, J. D. F., Hermans, J., & Van der Burght, A. T. (1974). Cases of doubt in allocation problems. *Biometrika*, **61**, 313–324.

Hampshire, J. & Pearlmuter, B. (1990). Equivalence proofs for the multilayer perceptron classifier and the bayes discriminant function. In: *Proceedings of the 1988 Connectionist Models Summer School* , San Mateo CA: Morgan Kaufmann.

Hand, D. J. (1981). *Discrimination and Classification*. Chichester: John Wiley.

Hand, D. J. & Batchelor, B. G. (1978). An edited nearest neighbour rule. *Information Sciences*, **14**, 171–180.

Hanson, S. J. (1990). Meiosis networks. In: *Advances in Neural Information Processing Systems 2*, (Tourzetsky, D. S., ed) pp. 533–541, Morgan Kaufmann.

Hart, P. E. (1968). The condensed nearest neighbour rule. *IEEE Transactions on Information Theory*, **IT-14**, 515–516.

Häussler, W. M. (1979). Empirische ergebnisse zur diskriminationsverfahren bei kreditscoringsystemen. *Zeitschrift fur Operations Research. Serie B*, **23**, 191–210.

Häussler, W. M. (1981a). Methoden der punktebewertung fur kreditscoringsysteme. *Zeitschrift fur Operations Research*, **25**, 79–94.

Häussler, W. M. (1981b). *Punktebewertung bei Kreditscoringsystemen*. Frankfurt: Knapp.

Hebb, D. O. (1949). *The Organisation of Behaviour*. John Wiley and Sons.

Hecht-Nielsen, R. (1989). *Neurocomputing*. Reading, Mass.: Addison-Wesley.

Herkovsits, E. & Cooper, G. F. (1990). Kutató: An entropy-driven system for the construction of probabilistic expert systems from databases. Report ksl-90-22 Stanford University.

Hertz, J., Krogh, A., & Palmer, R. (1991). *Introduction to the Theory of Neural Computation*. Addison-Wesley.

Higonnet, R. A. & Grea, R. A. (1958). *Logical Design of Electrical Circuits*. McGraw-Hill Book Co. Ltd.

Hill, M. (1982). Correspondence analysis. In: *Encyclopaedia of Statistical Sciences* volume 2 pp. 204–210. Wiley New York.

Hinton, G. E., Rumelhart, D. E., & Williams, R. J. (1985). Learning internal representations by back-propagating errors. In: *Parallel Distributed Processing: Explorations in the Microstructure of Cognition*, (Rumelhart, D. E., McClelland, J. L., & the PDP Research Group, eds) volume 1 chapter 8. MIT Press Cambridge, MA.

Hinton, G. E., Rumelhart, D. E., & Williams, R. J. (1986). Learning representations by back-propagating errors. *Nature, 323*, 533–536.

Hoehfeld, M. & Fahlman, S. E. (1991). Learning with limited precision using the cascade-correlation algorithm. Technical Report CMU-CS-91-130 Carnegie Mellon University.

Hofmann, H. J. (1990). Die anwendung des cart-verfahrens zur statistischen bonitatsanalyse von konsumentenkrediten. *Zeitschrift fur Betriebswirtschaft, 60*, 941–962.

Højsgaard, S., Skjøth, F., & Thiesson, B. (a). *User's guide to Bifrost*. Aalborg University, Aalborg, Denmark.

Holland, J. H. (1975). *Adaptation in Natural and Artificial Systems*. Ann Arbor, MI: University of Michigan Press.

Huang, H. H., Zhang, C., Lee, S., & Wang, H. P. (1991). Implementation and comparison of neural network learning paradigms: back propagation, simulated annealing and tabu search. In: *Intelligent Engineering Systems Through Artificial Neural Networks: Proceedings of the Artificial Neural Networks in Engineering Conference*, (Dagli, C., Kumara, S., & Shin, Y. C., eds) , New York: American Society of Mechanical Engineers.

Huang, W. Y. & Lippmann, R. P. (1987). Comparisons between neural net and conventional classifiers. In: *Proceedings of the IEEE first international conference on neural networks* pp. 485–494, Piscataway, NJ: IEEE.

Hunt, E. B., Martin, J., & Stone, P. I. (1966). *Experiments in Induction*. New York: Academic Press.

Hunt, K. J., Sbarbaro, D., Żbikovski, R., & Gawthrop, P. J. (1992). Neural networks for control systems – a survey. *Automatica, 28*, 1083–1112.

Jacobs, R. (1988). Increased rates of convergence through learning rate adaptation. *Neural Networks, 1*, 295–307.

Jennet, B., Teasdale, G., Braakman, R., Minderhoud, J., Heiden, J., & Kurzi, T. (1979). Prognosis of patients with severe head injury. *Neurosurgery, 4*, 283–288.

Jones, D. S. (1979). *Elementary Information Theory*. Oxford: Clarendon Press.

Karalič, A. (1992). Employing linear regression in regression tree leaves. In: *Proceedings of the 10th European Conference on Artificial Intelligence* pp. 440–441, Wiley & Sons.

Wien, Austria.

Karalič, A. & Gams, M. (1989). Implementation of the gynesis pc inductive learning system. In: *Proceedings of the 33rd ETAN Conference* pp. XIII.83–90. Novi Sad, (in Slovenian).

Kass, G. V. (1980). An exploratory technique for investigating large quantities of categorical data. *Appl. Statist.* **29**, 119–127.

Kendall, M. G., Stuart, A., & Ord, J. K. (1983). *The advanced Theory of Statistics, Vol 3, Design and Analysis and Time Series.*. London: Griffin, fourth edition.

King, R. D., Lewis, R. A., Muggleton, S. H., & Sternberg, M. J. E. (1992). Drug design by machine learning: the use of inductive logic programming to model the structure-activity relationship of trimethoprim analogues binding to dihydrofolate reductase. *Proceedings of the National Academy Science,* **89**.

Kirkwood, C., Andrews, B., & Mowforth, P. (1989). Automatic detection of gait events: a case study using inductive learning techniques. *Journal of Biomedical Engineering,* **11**, 511–516.

Knoll, U. (1993). *Kostenoptimiertes Prunen in Entscheidungsbaumen.* Ulm: Daimler-Benz, Forschung und Technik.

Kohonen, T. (1984). *Self-Organization and Associative Memory.* Berlin: Springer Verlag.

Kohonen, T. (1989). *Self-Organization and Associative Memory.* Berlin: Springer-Verlag, 3rd edition.

Kohonen, T., Barna, G., & Chrisley, R. (1988). Statistical pattern recognition with neural networks: Benchmarking studies. In: *IEEE International Conference on Neural Networks* volume 1 pp. 61–68, (San Diego 1988) New York: IEEE.

Kononenko, I. & Bratko, I. (1991). Information-based evaluation criterion for classifier's performance. *Machine Learning,* **6**.

Kressel, U. (1991). The impact of the learning set size in handwritten digits recognition. In: *Proceedings of the International Conference on Artifical Neural Networks* , Helsinki, Finland:.

Krishnaiah, P. & Kanal, L., eds (1982). *Classification, Pattern Recognition, and Reduction of Dimensionality,* volume 2 of *Handbook of Statistics.* Amsterdam: North Holland.

Kwakernaak, H. & Sivan, R. (1972). *Linear Optimal Control Systems.* John Wiley.

Lachenbruch, P. & Mickey, R. (1968). Estimation of error rates in discriminant analysis. *Technometrics,* **10**, 1–11.

Lachenbruch, P. A. & Mickey, M. R. (1975). *Discriminant Analysis.* New York: Hafner Press.

Lang, K. J., Waibel, A. H., & Hinton, G. E. (1990). A time-delay neural network architecture for isolated word recognition. *Neural Networks,* **3**, 23–44.

Lauritzen, S. L. & Spiegelhalter, D. J. (1988). Local computations with probabilities on graphical structures and their application to expert systems (with discussion). *J. Royal Statist. Soc., Series B,* **50**, 157–224.

Lawrence, E. C. & Smith, L. D. (1992). An analysis of default risk in mobile home credit. *J. Banking and Finance,* **16**, 299–312.

Le Cun, Y., Boser, B., Denker, J. S., Henderson, D., Howard, R. E., Hubbard, W., & D., J. L. (1989). Backpropagation applied to handwritten zip code recognition. *Neural Computation,* **1**, 541–551.

Lee, C. (1990). Fuzzy logic in control systems: Fuzzy logic controller – part 1, part 2. *IEEE Transactions on Systems, Man and Cybernetics,* **20,** 404–435.

Leech, W. J. (1986). A rule based process control method with feedback. *Advances in Instrumentation,* **41.**

Leitch, R. (1992). Knowledge based control: selecting the right tool for the job. In: *Preprints of the 1992 IFAC/IFIP/IMACS International Symposium on Artificial Intelligence in Real-Time Control* pp. 26–33. Delft, The Netherlands.

Leitch, R. R. & Francis, J. C. (1986). Towards intelligent control systems. In: *Expert Systems and Optimisation in Process Control,* (Mamdani, A. & Efstathiou, J., eds) pp. 62–73, Aldershot, England: Gower Technical Press.

Luttrell, S. P. (1990). Derivation of a class of training algorithms. *IEEE Transactions on Neural Networks,* **1,** 229–232.

Luttrell, S. P. (1993). A bayesian analysis of vector quantization algorithms. *Submitted to Neural Computation.*

Machado, S. G. (1983). Two statistics for testing for multivariate normality. *Biometrika,* **70,** 713–718.

MacKay, D. (1992a). A practical bayesian framework for backpropagation networks. *Neural Computation,* **4,** 448–472.

MacKay, D. (1992b). The evidence framework applied to classification networks. *Neural Computation,* **4,** 720–736.

Makarovič, A. (1988). A qualitative way of solving the pole balancing problem. Technical Report Memorandum Inf-88-44 University of Twente. Also in: Machine Intelligence 12, J.Hayes, D.Michie, E.Tyugu (eds.), Oxford University Press, pp. 241–258.

Mardia, K. V. (1974). Applications of some measures of multivariate skewness and kurtosis in testing normality and robustness studies. *Sankhya B,* **36,** 115–128.

Mardia, K. V., Kent, J. T., & Bibby, J. M. (1979). *Multivariate Analysis.* London: Academic Press.

Marks, S. & Dunn, O. J. (1974). Discriminant functions when covariance matrices are unequal. *J. Amer. Statist. Assoc.* **69,** 555–559.

McCarthy, J. & Hayes, P. J. (1969). Some philosophical problems from the standpoint of artificial intelligence. In: *Machine Intelligence 4,* (Meltzer, B. & Michie, D., eds) pp. 463–502. EUP Edinburgh.

McCullagh, P. & Nelder, J. A. (1989). *Generalized Linear Models.* London: Chapman and Hall, 2nd edition.

McCulloch, W. S. & Pitts, W. (1943). A logical calculus of the ideas immanent in nervous activity forms. *Bulletin of Methematical Biophysics,* **9,** 127–147.

McLachlan, G. J. (1992). *Discriminant Analysis and Statistical Pattern Recognition.* New York: John Wiley.

Meyer-Brötz, G. & Schürmann, J. (1970). *Methoden der automatischen Zeichenerkennung.* Berlin: Akademie-Verlag.

Mézard, M. & Nadal, J. P. (1989). Learning in feed-forward layered networks: The tiling algorithm. *Journal of Physics A: Mathematics, General,* **22,** 2191–2203.

Michalski, R. S. (1969). On the quasi-minimal solution of the general covering problem. In: *Proc. of the Fifth Internat. Symp. on Inform. Processing* pp. 125–128, Bled, Slovenia:.

Michalski, R. S. (1973). Discovering classification rules using variable valued logic system

VL1. In: *Third International Joint Conference on Artificial Intelligence* pp. 162–172.

Michalski, R. S. (1983). A theory and methodology of inductive learning. In: *Machine Learning: An Artificial Intelligence Approach*, (R. S. Michalski, J. G. C. & Mitchell, T. M., eds). Tioga Palo Alto.

Michalski, R. S. & Chilauski, R. L. (1980). Knowledge acquisition by encoding expert rules versus computer induction from examples: a case study involving soybean pathology. *Int. J. Man-Machine Studies*, **12**, 63–87.

Michalski, R. S. & Larson, J. B. (1978). Selection of the most representative training examples and incremental generation of vl1 hypothesis: the underlying methodology and the description of programs esel and aq11. Technical Report 877 Dept. of Computer Sciencence, U. of Illinois, Urbana.

Michie, D. (1990). Personal models of rationality. *J. Statist. Planning and Inference*, **25**, 381–399.

Michie, D. (1991). Methodologies from machine learning in data analysis and software. *Computer Journal*, **34**, 559–565.

Michie, D. & Al Attar, A. (1991). Use of sequential bayes with class probability trees. In: *Machine Intelligence 12*, (Hayes, J., Michie, D., & Tyugu, E., eds) pp. 187–202. Oxford University Press.

Michie, D. & Bain, M. (1992). Machine acquisition of concepts from sample data. In: *Artificial Intelligence and Intelligent Tutoring Systems*, (Kopec, D. & Thompson, R. B., eds) pp. 5–23. Ellis Horwood Ltd. Chichester.

Michie, D., Bain, M., & Hayes-Michie, J. (1990). Cognitive models from subcognitive skills. In: *Knowledge-Based Systems in Industrial Control*, (Grimble, M., McGhee, J., & Mowforth, P., eds) pp. 71–90, Stevenage: Peter Peregrinus.

Michie, D. & Camacho, R. (1994). Building symbolic representations of intuitive real-time skills from performance data. To appear in Machine Intelligence and Inductive Learning, Vol. 1 (eds. Furukawa, K. and Muggleton, S. H., new series of Machine Intelligence, ed. in chief D. Michie), Oxford: Oxford University Press.

Michie, D. & Chambers, R. A. (1968). Boxes: an experiment in adaptive control. In: *Machine Intelligence 2*, (Dale, E. & Michie, D., eds) pp. 137–152, Edinburgh University Press.

Michie, D. & Sammut, C. (1993). Machine learning from real-time input-output behaviour. In: *Proceedings of the International Conference Design to Manufacture in Modern Industry* pp. 363–369.

Miller, W. T., Sutton, R. S., & Werbos, P. J., eds (1990). *Neural Networks for Control*. The MIT Press.

Minsky, M. C. & Papert, S. (1969). *Perceptrons*. Cambridge, MA, USA: MIT Press.

Møller, M. (1993). A scaled conjugate gradient algorithm for fast supervised learning. *Neural Networks*, **4**, 525–534.

Mooney, R., Shavlik, J., Towell, G., & Gove, A. (1989). An experimental comparison of symbolic and connectionist learning algorithms (vol 1). In: *IJCAI 89: proceedings of the eleventh international joint conference on artificial intelligence, Detroit, MI* pp. 775–780, San Mateo, CA: Morgan Kaufmann for International Joint Conferences on Artificial Intelligence.

Muggleton, S. H. (1993). Logic and learning: Turing's legacy. In: *Machine Intelligence*

13, (Muggleton, S. H. & Michie, D. Furukaw, K., eds). Oxford University Press Oxford.

Muggleton, S. H., Bain, M., Hayes-Michie, J. E., & Michie, D. (1989). An experimental comparison of learning formalisms. In: *Sixth Internat. Workshop on Mach. Learning* pp. 113–118, San Mateo, CA: Morgan Kaufmann.

Muggleton, S. H. & Buntine, W. (1988). Machine invention of first-order predicates by inverting resolution. In: *Proceedings of the Fifth International Machine. Learning Conference*, (R. S. Michalski, T. M. M. & Carbonell, J. G., eds) pp. 339–352. Morgan Kaufmann, Ann Arbor, Michigan.

Muggleton, S. H. & Feng, C. (1990). Efficient induction of logic programs. In: *First International Conference on Algorithmic Learning Theory* pp. 369–381, Tokyo, Japan: Japanese Society for Artificial Intellligence.

Neapolitan, E. (1990). *Probabilistic reasoning in expert systems.* John Wiley.

Nowlan, S. & Hinton, G. (1992). Simplifying neural networks by soft weight-sharing. *Neural Computation*, **4**, 473–493.

Odetayo, M. O. (1988). Balancing a pole-cart system using genetic algorithms. Master's thesis Department of Computer Science, University of Strathclyde.

Odetayo, M. O. & McGregor, D. R. (1989). Genetic algorithm for inducing control rules for a dynamic system. In: *Proceedings of the 3rd International Conference on Genetic Algorithms* pp. 177–182, Morgan Kaufmann.

Ozturk, A. & Romeu, J. L. (1992). A new method for assessing multivariate normality with graphical applications. *Communications in Statistics - Simulation*, **21**, 15–34.

Pagallo, G. & Haussler, D. (1990). Boolean feature discovery in empirical learning. *Machine Learning*, **5**, 71–100.

Pearce, D. (1989). The induction of fault diagnosis systems from qualitative models. In: *Proc. Seventh Nat. Conf. on Art. Intell. (AAAI-88)* pp. 353 –357, St. Paul, Minnesota:.

Pearl, J. (1988). *Probabilistic Reasoning in Intelligent Systems: Networks of Plausible Inference.* San Mateo: Morgan Kaufmann.

Piper, J. & Granum, E. (1989). On fully automatic feature measurement for banded chromosome classification. *Cytometry*, **10**, 242–255.

Plotkin, G. D. (1970). A note on inductive generalization. In: *Machine Intelligence 5*, (Meltzer, B. & Michie, D., eds) pp. 153–163. Edinburgh University Press.

Poggio, T. & Girosi, F. (1990). Networks for approximation and learning. *Proceedings of the IEEE*, **78**, 1481–1497.

Pomerleau, D. A. (1989). Alvinn: An autonomous land vehicle in a neural network. In: *Advances in Neural Information Processing Systems*, (Touretzky, D. S., ed). Morgan Kaufmann Publishers San Mateo, CA.

Prager, R. W. & Fallside, F. (1989). The modified Kanerva model for automatic speech recognition. *Computer Speech and Language*, **3**, 61–82.

Press, W. H., Flannery, B. P., Teukolsky, S. A., & Vettering, W. T. (1988). *Numerical Recipes in C: The Art of Scientific Computing.* Cambridge: Cambridge University Press.

Quinlan, J. R. (1986). Induction of decision trees. *Machine Learning*, **1**, 81–106.

Quinlan, J. R. (1987a). Simplifying decision trees. *Int J Man-Machine Studies*, **27**, 221–234.

Quinlan, J. R. (1987b). Generating production rules from decision trees. In: *Proceedings of the Tenth International Joint Conference on Artificial Intelligence* pp. 304–307. Morgan Kaufmann San Mateo, CA.

Quinlan, J. R. (1988). Simplifying decision trees. In: *Knowledge Acquisition for Knowledge-Based Systems*, (Gaines, B. & Boose, J., eds) pp. 239–252. Academic Press London.

Quinlan, J. R. (1990). Learning logical definitions from relations. *Machine Learning*, 5, 239–266.

Quinlan, J. R. (1992). C4.5. In: *Programs for Machine Learning*. Morgan Kaufmann San Mateo, CA.

Quinlan, J. R. (1993). *C4.5: Programs for Machine Learning*. San Mateo, CA: Morgan Kaufmann.

Quinlan, J. R., Compton, P. J., Horn, K. A., & Lazarus, L. (1986). Inductive knowledge acquisition: a case study. In: *Proceedings of the Second Australian Conference on applications of expert systems* pp. 83–204, Sydney: New South Wales Institute of Technology.

Reaven, G. M. & Miller, R. G. (1979). An attempt to define the nature of chemical diabetes using a multidimensional analysis. *Diabetologia*, 16, 17–24.

Refenes, A. N. & Vithlani, S. (1991). Constructive learning by specialisation. In: *Proceedings of the International Conference on Artificial Neural Networks*, Helsinki, Finland:.

Remme, J., Habbema, J. D. F., & Hermans, J. (1980). A simulative comparison of linear, quadratic and kernel discrimination. *J. Statist. Comput. Simul.* 11, 87–106.

Renals, S. & Rohwer, R. (1989). Phoneme classification experiments using radial basis functions. In: *Proceedings of the International Joint Conference on Neural Networks* volume I pp. 461–468, Washington DC:.

Renders, J. M. & Nordvik, J. P. (1992). Genetic algorithms for process control: A survey. In: *Preprints of the 1992 IFAC/IFIP/IMACS International Symposium on Artificial Intelligence in Real-Time Control* pp. 579–584. Delft, The Netherlands.

Reynolds, J. C. (1970). Transformational systems and the algebraic structure of atomic formulas. In: *Machine Intelligence 5*, (Meltzer, B. & Michie, D., eds) pp. 153–163. Edinburgh University Press.

Ripley, B. (1993). Statistical aspects of neural networks. In: *Chaos and Networks - Statistical and Probabilistic Aspects*, (Barndorff-Nielsen, O., Cox, D., Jensen, J., & Kendall, W., eds). Chapman and Hall.

Robinson, J. A. (1965). A machine oriented logic based on the resolution principle. *Journal of the ACM*, 12, 23–41.

Rohwer, R. (1991a). Description and training of neural network dynamics. In: *Neurodynamics, Proceedings of the 9th Summer Workshop, Clausthal, Germany*, (Pasemann, F. & Doebner, H., eds), World Scientific.

Rohwer, R. (1991b). Neural networks for time-varying data. In: *Neural Networks for Statistical and Economic Data*, (Murtagh, F., ed) pp. 59–70. Statistical Office of the European Communities Luxembourg.

Rohwer, R. (1991c). Time trials on second-order and variable-learning-rate algorithms. In: *Advances in Neural Information Processing Systems*, (Lippmann, R., Moody, J., & Touretzky, D., eds) volume 3 pp. 977–983, San Mateo CA: Morgan Kaufmann.

Rohwer, R. (1992). A representation of representation applied to a discussion of variable binding. Technical report Dept. of Computer Science and Applied Maths., Aston University.

Rohwer, R. & Cressy, D. (1989). Phoneme classification by boolean networks. In: *Proceedings of the European Conference on Speech Communication and Technology* pp. 557–560, Paris:.

Rohwer, R., Grant, B., & Limb, P. R. (1992). Towards a connectionist reasoning system. *British Telecom Technology Journal,* **10,** 103–109.

Rohwer, R. & Renals, S. (1988). Training recurrent networks. In: *Neural networks from models to applications,* (Personnaz, L. & Dreyfus, G., eds) pp. 207–216. I. D. S. E. T. Paris.

Rosenblatt, F. (1958). *Psychological Review,* **65,** 368–408.

Rosenblatt, F. (1962). *Principles of Neurodynamics.* New York: Spartan Books.

Rumelhart, D. E., Hinton, G. E., & J., W. R. (1986). Learning internal representations by error propagation. In: *Parallel Distributed Processing,* (Rumelhart, D. E. & McClelland, J. L., eds) volume 1 pp. 318–362. MIT Press Cambridge MA.

Sakawa, Y. & Shinido, Y. (1982). Optimal control of container crane. *Automatica,* **18,** 257–266.

Sammut, C. (1988). Experimental results from an evaluation of algorithms that learn to control dynamic systems. In: *Proceedings of the fifth international conference on machine learning. Ann Arbor, Michigan,* (LAIRD, J., ed) pp. 437–443, San Mateo, CA: Morgan Kaufmann.

Sammut, C. (1994). Recent progress with boxes. To appear in Machine Intelligence and Inductive Learning, Vol. 1 (eds. Furukawa, K. and Muggleton, S. H., new series of Machine Intelligence, ed. in chief D. Michie), Oxford: Oxford University Press.

Sammut, C. & Cribb, J. (1990). Is learning rate a good performance criterion of learning? In: *Proceedings of the Seventh International Machine Learning Conference* pp. 170–178, Austin, Texas: Morgan Kaufmann.

Sammut, C., Hurst, S., Kedzier, D., & Michie, D. (1992). Learning to fly. In: *Proceedings of the Ninth International Workshop on Machine Learning,* (Sleeman, D. & Edwards, P., eds) pp. 385–393, Morgan Kaufmann.

Sammut, C. & Michie, D. (1991). Controlling a "black box" simulation of a space craft. *AI Magazine,* **12,** 56–63.

Sammut, C. A. & Banerji, R. B. (1986). Learning concepts by asking questions. In: *Machine Learning: An Artificial Intelligence Approach, Vol 2,* (R. S. Michalski, J. C. & Mitchell, T., eds) pp. 167–192. Morgan Kaufmann Los Altos, California.

Scalero, R. & Tepedelenlioglu, N. (1992). A fast new algorithm for training feedforward neural networks. *IEEE Transactions on Signal Processing,* **40,** 202–210.

Schoppers, M. (1991). Real-time knowledge-based control systems. *Communications of the ACM,* **34,** 27–30.

Schumann, M., Lehrbach, T., & Bahrs, P. (1992). *Versuche zur Kreditwurdigkeitsprognose mit kunstlichen Neuronalen Netzen.* Universitat Gottingen.

Scott, D. W. (1992). *Multivariate Density Estimation: Theory, Practice, and Visualization.* New York: John Wiley.

Sethi, I. K. & Otten, M. (1990). Comparison between entropy net and decision tree classifiers. In: *IJCNN-90: proceedings of the international joint conference on neural networks* pp. 63–68, Ann Arbor, MI: IEEE Neural Networks Council.

Shadmehr, R. & D'Argenio, Z. (1990). A comparison of a neural network based estimator and two statistical estimators in a sparse and noisy environment. In: *IJCNN-90: proceedings of the international joint conference on neural networks* pp. 289–292, Ann Arbor, MI: IEEE Neural Networks Council.

Shapiro, A. D. (1987). *Structured Induction in Expert Systems*. London: Addison Wesley.

Shapiro, A. D. & Michie, D. (1986). A self-commenting facility for inductively synthesized end-game expertise. In: *Advances in Computer Chess 5*, (Beal, D. F., ed). Pergamon Oxford.

Shapiro, A. D. & Niblett, T. (1982). Automatic induction of classification rules for a chess endgame. In: *Advances in Computer Chess 3*, (Clarke, M. R. B., ed). Pergamon Oxford.

Shastri, L. & Ajjangadde, V. (a). From simple associations to systematic reasoning: A connectionist representation of rules, variables, and dynamic bindings using temporal synchrony. *Behavioral and Brain Sciences.* to appear.

Shavlik, J., Mooney, R., & Towell, G. (1991). Symbolic and neural learning algorithms: an experimental comparison. *Machine learning,* **6**, 111–143.

Siebert, J. P. (1987). Vehicle recognition using rule based methods. Tirm-87-018 Turing Institute.

Silva, F. M. & Almeida, L. B. (1990). Acceleration techniques for the backpropagation algorithm. In: *Lecture Notes in Computer Science 412, Neural Networks*, (Almeida, L. B. & Wellekens, C. J., eds) pp. 110–119. Springer-Verlag Berlin.

Silverman, B. W. (1986). *Density estimation for Statistics and Data Analysis*. London: Chapman and Hall.

Smith, J. W., Everhart, J. E., Dickson, W. C., Knowler, W. C., & Johannes, R. S. (1988). Using the adap learning algorithm to forecast the onset of diabetes mellitus. In: *Proceedings of the Symposium on Computer Applications and Medical Care* pp. 261–265, IEEE Computer Society Press.

Smith, P. L. (1982). Curve fitting and modeling with splines using statistical variable selection techniques. Technical Report NASA 166034 Langley Research Center Hampton, Va.

Snedecor, W. & Cochran, W. G. (1980). *Statistical Methods (7th edition)*. Iowa, U.S.A: Iowa State University Press.

Spikovska, L. & Reid, M. B. (1990). An empirical comparison of id3 and honns for distortion invariant object recognition. In: *TAI-90: tools for artificial intelligence: proceedings of the 2nd international IEEE conference* , Los Alamitos, CA: IEEE Computer Society Press.

Spirtes, P., Scheines, R., Glymour, C., & Meek, C. (1992). *TETRAD II, Tools for discovery*.

Srinivisan, V. & Kim, Y. H. (1987). Credit granting: A comparative analysis of classification procedures. *The Journal of Finance,* **42**, 665–681.

StatSci (1991). S-plus user's manual. Technical report StatSci Europe Oxford. U.K.

Stein von, J. H. & Ziegler, W. (1984). The prognosis and surveillance of risks from commercial credit borrowers. *Journal of Banking and Finance,* **8**, 249–268.

Stone, M. (1974). Cross-validatory choice and assessment of statistical predictions. *J. Roy. Statist. Soc.* **36**, 111–147 (including discussion).

Switzer, P. (1980). Extensions of linear discriminant analysis for statistical classification of remotely sensed satellite imagery. *J. Int. Assoc. for Mathematical Geology,* **23**, 367–376.

Switzer, P. (1983). Some spatial statistics for the interpretation of satellite data. *Bull. Int. Stat. Inst.* **50**, 962–971.

Thrun, S. B., Mitchell, T., & Cheng, J. (1991). The monk's comparison of learning algorithms - introduction and survey. In: *The MONK's problems - a performance comparison of different learning algorithms,* (Thrun, S., Bala, J., Bloedorn, E., & Bratko, I., eds) pp. 1–6. Carnegie Mellon University, Computer Science Department.

Titterington, D. M., Murray, G. D., Murray, L. S., Spiegelhalter, D. J., Skene, A. M., Habbema, J. D. F., & Gelpke, G. J. (1981). Comparison of discrimination techniques applied to a complex data set of head injured patients (with discussion). *J. Royal Statist. Soc. A,* **144**, 145–175.

Todeschini, R. (1989). k-nearest neighbour method: the influence of data transformations and metrics. *Chemometrics Intell. Labor. Syst.* **6**, 213–220.

Toolenaere, T. (1990). Supersab: Fast adaptive back propagation with good scaling properties. *Neural Networks,* **3**, 561–574.

Tsaptsinos, D., Mirzai, A., & Jervis, B. (1990). Comparison of machine learning paradigms in a classification task. In: *Applications of artificial intelligence in engineering V: proceedings of the fifth international conference,* (Rzevski, G., ed) , Berlin: Springer-Verlag.

Turing, A. M. (1986). Lecture to the London Mathematical Society on 20 February 1947. In: *A. M. Turing's ACE Report and Other Papers,* (Carpenter, B. E. & Doran, R. W., eds). MIT Press Cambridge, MA.

Unger, S. & Wysotzki, F. (1981). *Lernfähige Klassifizierungssysteme.* Berlin: Akademie-Verlag.

Urbančič, T. & Bratko, I. (1992). Knowledge acquisition for dynamic system control. In: *Dynamic, Genetic, and Chaotic Programming,* (Souček, B., ed) pp. 65–83, Wiley & Sons.

Urbančič, T., Juričić, D., Filipič, B., & Bratko, I. (1992). Automated synthesis of control for non-linear dynamic systems. In: *Preprints of the 1992 IFAC/IFIP/IMACS International Symposium on Artificial Intelligence in Real-Time Control* pp. 605–610. Delft, The Netherlands.

Varšek, A., Urbančič, T., & Filipič, B. (1993). Genetic algorithms in controller design and tuning. *IEEE Transactions on Systems, Man and Cybernetics.*

Verbruggen, H. B. & Åström, K. J. (1989). Artificial intelligence and feedback control. In: *Proceedings of the Second IFAC Workshop on Artificial Intelligence in Real-Time Control* pp. 115–125. Shenyang, PRC.

Wald, A. (1947). *Sequential Analysis.* London: Chapman & Hall.

Wasserman, P. D. (1989). *Neural Computing, Theory and Practice.* Van Nostrand Reinhold.

Watkins, C. J. C. H. (1987). Combining cross-validation and search. In: *Progress in Machine Learning,* (Bratko, I. & Lavrac, N., eds) pp. 79–87, Wimslow: Sigma Books.

Wehenkel, L., Pavella, M., Euxibie, E., & Heilbronn, B. (1993). Decision tree based transient stability assessment - a case study. volume Proceedings of IEEE/PES 1993 Winter Meeting, Columbus, OH, Jan/Feb. 5. Paper # 93 WM 235–2 PWRS.

Weiss, S. M. & Kapouleas, I. (1989). An empirical comparison of pattern recognition, neural nets and machine learning classification methods (vol 1). In: *IJCAI 89: proceedings of the eleventh international joint conference on artificial intelligence, Detroit, MI* pp. 781–787, San Mateo, CA: Morgan Kaufmann.

Weiss, S. M. & Kulikowski, C. A. (1991). *Computer systems that learn: classification and prediction methods from statistics, neural networks, machine learning and expert systems.* San Mateo, CA: Morgan Kaufmann.

Werbos, P. (1975). *Beyond Regression: New Tools for prediction and analysis in the behavioural sciences.* PhD thesis Harvard University. Also printed as a report of the Harvard / MIT Cambridge Project.

Whittaker, J. (1990). *Graphical models in applied multivariate analysis.* Chichester: John Wiley.

Widrow, B. (1962). Generalization and information in networks of adaline neurons. In: *Self-Organizing Systems,* (Yovits, J. & Goldstein, eds) , Washington: Spartan Books.

Wolpert, D. H. (1992). A rigorous investigation of "evidence" and "occam factors" in bayesian reasoning. Technical report The Sante Fe Institute 1660 Old Pecos Trail, Suite A, Sante Fe, NM, 87501, USA.

Wu, J. X. & Chan, C. (1991). A three layer adaptive network for pattern density estimation and classification. *International Journal of Neural Systems,* **2**, 211–220.

Wynne-Jones, M. (1991). Constructive algorithms and pruning: Improving the multi layer perceptron. In: *Proceedings of IMACS '91, the 13th World Congress on Computation and Applied Mathematics, Dublin* volume 2 pp. 747–750.

Wynne-Jones, M. (1992). Node splitting: A constructive algorithm for feed-forard neural networks. In: *Advances in Neural Information Processing Systems 4,* (Moody, J. E., Hanson, S. J., & Lippmann, R. P., eds) pp. 1072–1079, Morgan Kaufmann.

Wynne-Jones, M. (1993). Node splitting: A constructive algorithm for feed-forward neural networks. *Neural Computing and Applications,* **1**, 17–22.

Xu, L., Krzyzak, A., & Oja, E. (1991). Neural nets for dual subspace pattern recognition method. *International Journal of Neural Systems,* **2**, 169–184.

Yang, J. & Honavar, V. (1991). Experiments with the cascade-correlation algorithm. Technical Report 91-16 Department of Computer Science, Iowa State University Ames, IA 50011-1040, USA.

Yasunobu, S. & Hasegawa, T. (1986). Evaluation of an automatic container crane operation system based on predictive fuzzy control. *Control-Theory and Advanced Technology,* **2**, 419–432.

Index